das   81569

SCIENCE: U.S.A.

Also by William Gilman

The Language of Science:
A Guide to Effective Writing

Our Hidden Front

SCIENCE: U.S.A.

by William Gilman

NEW YORK · THE VIKING PRESS

First published in 1965 by The Viking Press, Inc.
625 Madison Avenue, New York, N.Y. 10022

Published simultaneously in Canada by
The Macmillan Company of Canada Limited

Library of Congress catalog card number: 65-23995
Printed in U.S.A.

Contents

v

Preface

The reader will see for himself that this is a frank book about science and technology. He will also note its unconventionally broad scope. It therefore requires some explanation about how and for whom it was written.

For one thing, though my subject spanned the physical and life sciences, I was dissatisfied with a theme limited to describing their goals and accomplishments. The research is fruitful, often dramatic, but I could not overlook the increasing charges that our science is losing its integrity, and genuine creativity too. Moreover, outside the laboratory is society's problem—how to direct the scientific revolution in an enlightened, democratic way? I pictured technical folk and laymen alike who want clarification of the economics and politics, the growing wealth and power, the social responsibilities and failings of today's science. Without reporting these intruding and often dominating elements, the worries and controversies they breed within science, education, and government, the book would be incomplete. Accordingly, I blended this strong fare with the rest, seeking the realism that is neither partisan glorification nor damnation of science, and supplying facts with the interpretation they require. My objective was science in context, in the context of our times.

But in this blend, what of the technical portion? At what level should it be written? This required practicing what I have taught writers who deal with science or engineering. Before writing, even before assembling the material, I decided on the kind of reader I was working for—the person who seriously wants to be better informed about what modern research and development have already accomplished and what they seek at new frontiers. The reader might be still a student; he could be the otherwise knowledgeable layman who is abashed by science; with equal likelihood he could be the scientist or engineer oppressed by the confines of his specialty. So I tried to treat readers accordingly: supplying necessary background; keeping theory and predictions within bounds; favoring facts over ornamented prose; subjecting readers neither to baby talk, on the one hand, nor to obfuscating jargon, on the other; assuming that they would want genuine clarity, which does not compromise with accuracy.

Something else concerning technical content. For such readers it should encompass the various fields of science and engineering. Hence the book's scope is multidisciplinary. And interdisciplinary too —the chapter dealing with a specific field also brings in the relevant and useful from elsewhere. A quick example: understanding the human brain helps explain the electronic computer, and vice versa. Less obvious, the future for desalinated seawater is related both to the increased enthusiasm for nuclear power and the reduced confidence in manmade rain.

And what about the "tone" of this book that both praises and condemns science? Possibly, adapting a maxim applied to religion long ago, "Science being the best of things, its corruptions are likely to be the worst." I mistrust such superlatives, and I cite many examples of science practiced by those who remain young at heart. Nevertheless, some readers will undoubtedly think parts of my report overbold. My rejoinder is that frankness about the failings of today's science is overdue. In this, I confess to a fondness for science: my love affair with it goes back to school days, when, like many others, I was fortunate to have inspiring teachers. Because of this fondness I hope to see science face up to its responsibilities—and plain talk about them is the first step.

Other readers may wonder about my "connections." There was only the mutual-faith contract between author and reputable publisher. So, wanting nothing but information from people in science, government, industry, universities, and the like, I could do the book without fret or fear about conflict of interest, heeding only the truth-seeking standards professed by the two vocations with which I have been associated: science and journalism.

There was another link between them. The same background, first as a young chemist, then as newspaperman, science writer, and engineering editor, went into the two and a half years of continuous labor on this book. It required weaving material from my already voluminous files; from the inpour of research papers, government reports, and the like; from technical journals, reference books, and the better newspapers; from the ever-rising and often contradictory flood of statistics; and, most enlightening, from what I saw for myself at representative laboratories and heard for myself from Nobel laureates and administrators, and down through the ranks.

For this phase of the project, most of my time was spent in the nation's five leading areas of research and development: three in the East, two in the West. I was at science conferences, congressional hearings, etc., but the bulk of my notes came from interviewing policymakers and visiting 126 R & D facilities of various kinds. These notes, which in wordage exceeded that of the final book, served several purposes. They supplied me with fresh, firsthand information from real people doing real things. They filled in technical details. They caught contradictory claims. As important as anything else, they provided viewpoints that I could appraise and compare for documented interpretation.

From all my sources, facts and opinions were then distilled for the book, and account for its semi-documentary approach. Technical exposition is interwoven with narrative, politics, economics, personality profile, laboratory-at-work, the expert speaking—whatever is needed to carry the information economically and effectively. This also explains why I do not ascribe all the material used: a typical section is built out of information from too many sources; and it is no solution to torture the reader with footnotes. He will see the source mentioned in the text whenever this seemed useful or necessary.

Such are the ingredients. Very likely, again because of the book's scope, the reader might like a short guide to the content and sequence of the fifteen chapters.

The first four, accounting for a little over one-third of the total text, comprise the section titled "State of the Establishment." These chapters are not assigned to specific divisions of the laboratory world. Rather, their science and technology serve as backdrop for a detailed picture of the new elite's power, prosperity, and consequent problems. Thus, Chapter I introduces the challenges that confront science and laymen. Next is the story of how this situation arose. Chapter III is principally a firsthand report on representative laboratories, then Chapter IV focuses on the establishment's members, leaders, organization.

The second section, "State of the Art," moves on to specific fields and their significant research projects; it is now the science-and-society theme that provides background—although, where appropriate, it comes very much to the front. For example, "The Big Experiment" of Chapter X refers to both laboratory work that bred the atomic bomb, and the resulting program to give society control over nuclear research so fraught with good and ill.

Introducing this section is an informal version of a textbook chapter. Starting with the atom, it reviews what the reader will find useful to know about today's research concepts, methods, and tools, and ends with the role played by statisticians in the wars against cancer and cholesterol. This leads to "Of Life and Drugs" and on to genetic manipulation. A third life-science chapter deals with the brain, so is a natural bridge to the physical sciences—the chapter on computers and automation. Then come three Nuclear Age chapters about the atom, followed by one on the new physics and another that brings once-glamorous chemistry up-to-date. The last chapter sums up with evolutionary man now invading Space.

Concerning acknowledgments, I thank the many I interviewed who spoke freely about their own work and their field. Their frankness lightened my labor with the material. My thanks also to those who called attention to faults in the resulting manuscript: to Viking's editors; to my former editor-associate, Douglas C. Greenwood; and to Eleanor—who not only supplied the devil's advocacy of a professional editor but shouldered the more familiar burdens that come to an author's wife.

I

State of the Establishment

I: *Science and Layman*

"January 10, 1610: Galileo abolishes Heaven."
—Bertolt Brecht's play *Galileo*

"There is something unnatural about these fellows."
—The Devil, in G. B. Shaw's play *Man and Superman*

Man has faced other important adventures but none like the big scientific ones of today. They are massively organized and intended to take him much farther from the "natural condition" of the dumb beasts who are his fellow mammals. He is now ready to become truly a Space traveler; this heralds environmental changes that the imagination can only glimpse. Simultaneously, science now knows enough about the life processes to begin manipulating them seriously. This portends changing a human's heredity, again with results that only the future can reveal.

Not everybody is overjoyed by these and other prospects. Even disregarding the possibility of nuclear war, there are laymen—and disillusioned scientists too—who fear that science is ruining the world. Not many years ago, people believed with equal fervor that science was saving the world. These are emotional extremes, and reason warns against both. Reason suggests that the only answer to dangerous knowledge, which cannot be unlearned anyway, is more knowledge; specifically, that we must now learn how to govern this revolution in the making. For there is more to all this than engineers launching their missiles and rockets, biologists twisting and untwisting strands of genetic material. They and their fellows add up to a science establishment that has become a potent force in itself.

So, before a closer look at the projects of science, its people, and its laboratories, let us see in this chapter what chances the scientist and layman have of getting on with each other rather than on each other's nerves.

For here is a mushrooming new profession characterized by two things. One is obvious. Science and its technology are changing our way of life faster than ever before. The other, not so apparent, reveals that nowhere is the change more dramatic than within science itself.

The lonely laboratory scholar and equally lonely basement inventor became antique years ago. Today the tightly knit little research team—and its equally tight little budget—faces a similar fate. We are in the era of task force and crash program. America's starveling science has vanished. In its place is an elite which is two things in one. It is an aristocracy composed of a new type of intellectuals. It is also a booming new industry, whose goals are scientific knowledge and material products of that knowledge.

This industry has no sharp boundaries. It reaches into other industries, into education, into government. However, it is quickly recognizable by its outstanding activity. The federal government, which pays three-fourths of the bill, calls it Research and Development—usually abbreviated to R & D (and often simply called science). It is a term that recognizes the marriage of engineering and other physical sciences; it also encompasses activities of the biologist, mathematician, psychologist, and other such non-producers of "hardware," including the press agents for R & D.

This federal R & D is ubiquitous. It supports over half of the New York Botanical Garden's budget. It studies old fossils and newly born stars. It theorizes about gravitation and the weather. It seeks new antibiotics and new nuclear bombs. It breeds leaner hogs and tastier turkeys. Its physicists seek faster computers and its chemists build better plastics. It mothers monorails and spaceships.

The factories for its white-collar people are a complex of laboratories—some operated by universities and the like, some by private industry, some by government's own agencies. The labor in these think-factories is performed on a mass scale that has made R & D the biggest and fastest-growing of America's new industries.

The rate of growth has inevitably slowed down. Extrapolators no longer toy with the thought that R & D could equal the entire federal budget by 1980. Nevertheless, the nation's R & D spending did pass the $20-billion mark in 1964, after tripling in twelve years; and in 1965 the government's portion, over $15 billion, had become one-sixth of the federal budget. Government's long and luxurious honeymoon with R & D was settling into an established marriage.

Funds of such magnitude promise financial security for the scientist and engineer, and a growing political power too. Science has not only invented robots of a sort; it seems also to have invented the indispensable man. He made his first appearance, with his radar and atomic bomb, in the hot war with Fascism. Soon, too soon, the emergency call sounded again, this time for the panicky years of cool war with Communism. As a result, some spokesmen for science now sit alongside statesmen and military men at the council table; others serve as administrators of multibillion-dollar research programs for both peace and war.

Down in the ranks it is much the same with the working scientist or engineer, especially when a manpower shortage looms. Private industry seduces him. His university tempts him with opportunity to double his salary as an outside consultant. The government waves the flag at him and, if that isn't enough, offers him work in the tax-exempt "nonprofit" auxiliaries set up for researchers who want less red tape and more pay than Civil Service regulations will allow.

All this has given America something more than a thriving new industry. It has also created a unique social problem. The people of science are badly needed. They belong to an elite profession. They are equally important in university, industry, and government, and circulate constantly among all three. The bonds linking them are further strengthened by an esoteric language that warns the easily awed layman against trespass.

Add these together. The sum is an apartheid; potentially the most powerful minority in American history, the more so when we include the large number of scientists and engineers who do not work directly in R & D but share the same background and professional outlook. The total for what a leader of the establishment calls this "privileged minority group" was about 1.5 million in 1965 and optimists estimate 2 million by 1970. Extrapolators swell the figure to over 10 million by including family members and technical assistants, but that strays too far. It is also exaggeration to expect all scientists and engineers to begin thinking and voting alike. And there is still too much competition, even open brawling, among various groups for larger slices of the federal R & D pie.

Equally important is the lack of fraternization among the many specialties and subspecialties. The layman can be excused for not understanding the different sciences and their languages; science groups themselves complain they cannot understand each other. Then there are the different banners: "pure science," "basic research," "applied research." Formal distinctions are made between "scientists interested in the how and why" and "engineers interested in the how and when." This, of course, is artificiality. All three serve their purpose: Maxwell, who mathematically postulated radio waves; Hertz, who discovered them; Marconi, who put them to use.

Efforts are being made to break the various barriers. For example, scientists are urged to come under the "interdisciplinary" banner. As a summons to a tempting way of life this has been no more successful than attempts to buy creativity or cajole scientists to write more clearly. As a necessity, however, it has forced a few changes. Here, government is the prime mover. In exchange for its money, it exacts a price. The R & D project must be "mission-oriented." In Space, for instance, a mission may need cooperation of the pure and the applied, and of such disciplines as rocketry, astronomy, biology, chemistry, geology, and physics.

Meanwhile, efforts have increased to weld the various families of scientists and engineers into an all-embracing organization that will speak for the profession. This, too, is a slow process. It has been easier for individual scientists to wield power indirectly. Affiliation with the university provides prestige; consultant work for industry increases income; special assignments with the government give influence without need to court the public. This is a neat balancing act but the situation is new and in a state of flux.

If and when science does compromise its internal differences, it will be potent indeed. Then how much power shall it wield? Humbly or arrogantly? For what goals?

Already, we see outlines of a technocracy. Not the kind composed of frustrated engineers who talked a rebellious power-grabbing unionism back in the relatively simple days of the great Depression. Today's science is too proudly professional to be much concerned with unions. At its top are the big-name spokesmen and administrators. At bottom are the warm bodies puttering at "research"—the so-called "fellowship bums" shifting from campus to campus, the job-hoppers skipping from employer to employer. At intermediate levels is the bulk of the science population. Here are the productive workers. Here, too, are the professional students, busily filling out forms that move them along from master's degree to doctorate to postdoctorate to post-postdoctorate and so on through the wide sea of grants-in-aid.

This adds up to a varied but potent elite. And thoughtful scientists worry over how to give the public a better image of their profession. Our science, as we shall see, has been torn too abruptly out of its age of innocence. Despite its prosperity, it lives with many fears.

The Researchers

When a biologist asked his secretary for the "Sears Catalog" he meant the Research Grants Index issued by the United States Public Health Service. The volume had 1450 pages, weighed 7 pounds, listed the programs that PHS was supporting at 1552 research institutions.

Or consider the discovery of the "omega minus," which added its mite to the confusion about atomic particles. The announcement was authored by 33 researchers who worked with 100,000 photographs taken with the aid of a $30-million atom-smasher.

Now bigness is not necessarily bad in itself; ambitiously big programs may even be inevitable in today's science setup. But it does raise questions of control, of which program, of what happens to the creative individual. The solitary busy bumblebee is replaced by the ant colony, and the traditions of science are such that not all of the ants are contented. Even an employer of ants wistfully wonders if there isn't a better way. From a Xerox Corporation ad in *Physics Today* and the Sunday *New York Times*: "How can we spot the creative, responsible, nonconformist at this stage of the game? . . . Send us a creative, responsible, nonconformist resume." This confesses that the task forces have not yet been truly creative. They are still sprouting seed that the Einsteins, Rutherfords, Darwins, and Pasteurs supplied fifty and a hundred years ago.

To be sure, science does have its many rebels. Furthermore, researchers are as varied as nature and nurture make them. Nuclear warfare has been advanced by men so different as unceremonious Edward Teller, "father" of the hydrogen bomb, and Princeton's polite Eugene Wigner. One day, this theoretician finally lost his argument with a campus traffic cop, said "Go to hell!" but remembered to add "please." There are slangy men like John Stack, the aeronautical engineer twitching with anger at Washington's "cast in concrete" lack of imagination in developing the airplanes he designed to fly at three times the speed of sound. There are also the scholars who used dainty pastel colors for the experimental area of the synchrotron at Harvard and named the giant magnets after Greek gods and six wives of Henry the Eighth. There is the laboratory for advanced electronics where a young woman complained, "My husband is a microbiologist and I am a theoretical physicist, and sometimes I wonder if we mutually exist." But there is also the husband-and-wife team at Langley Flight Research Center. They liked to fly kites as a hobby. This gave them an idea for a parachute-glider with which to land a spacecraft. For the invention they received a record award of $35,000 from the government's space agency.

But this is only a sampling of individuals, of the human instruments used by today's science. It is the total establishment that explains what F. Joachim Weyl, chief scientist at the Office of Naval Research, offered me as the biggest discovery we need in the next twenty years—"how to integrate science with society."

First, however, science needs to do a psychiatric job of research upon itself. On the one hand, it appreciates the vast funds placed at its disposal and enjoys the influence it wields. On the other, it has been transplanted too roughly from the old-fashioned laboratory; it still cherishes the concept of the independent creative man, as opposed to the plug-in module assigned to a crash program; it wants to be asked "What are you doing?" instead of "Who are you with?" This duality underlies the discontents of science.

Even its humor is mostly self-satire. For example, from a parable written by astronomer B. T. Lynds of the University of Arizona:

"Once upon a time there were three astronomers who lived on top of a mountain. . . . One day the littlest astronomer looked out the window and said, 'My, it looks as if we will have a clear night tonight. Who would like to use the telescope?'

" 'Not I,' said the biggest astronomer. 'I have to write applications in sextuplet for money to hire assistants.'

" 'Not I,' said the middle-sized astronomer. 'I have to prepare my television interview for tomorrow.'

" 'Very well,' said the littlest astronomer, 'I will use it myself.' And he did. . . ."

Of course, that little story also illustrates the other side of the picture. There is still basic research to be done, and there are people who eagerly plunge into it, even under the troubled conditions of the 1960s. Here are three examples showing the thrust of curiosity in action:

. . . At Brookhaven National Laboratory in Long Island a researcher was running down the hall in sneakers. He was carrying a sample that had just been hit by a spurt of atomic particles from the cyclotron. The sample had been converted to a radioactive isotope and the biologist was taking it to his workroom for his experiment. Now the cyclotron is a busy machine. You must take your turn, schedule it in advance, and no dawdling. But why race in sneakers— and away from the cyclotron? The answer is that time was running out for this isotope. Unlike iodine-131 in the "iodine cocktails" used for diagnosing thyroid ailments, this one had a half-life of only 20 seconds instead of 8 days. Hence, in 20 seconds one-half of the original material and the radioactivity would be gone; in 40 seconds only one-fourth would remain, and so on. Consequently, though any project of bringing mankind closer to immortality might seem endless, this modern Faust was in a hurry. Every split second counted.

. . . At General Electric Research Laboratory, near Schenectady but removed in both distance and function from GE's mass production of toasters and electric light bulbs, a modern Siegfried was trying to steal the Nibelung secret of our sun: the stupendous energy it gives by changing four atoms of hydrogen into one of helium. He was one of the adventurers in the technique called "controlled thermonuclear reaction," or simply CTR. It seeks to harness the wild explosion of the H-bomb, to convert it into peaceful electrical power. So, patiently, every three minutes or so, the physicist switched a massive jolt of electricity to a gas tube that enclosed his fuel, a special form of hydrogen. Several feet way, safe in the heavily shielded control room, he read his neutron counter for the result. Yes, there was fusion. Thanks to the sudden magnetic squeeze he was giving the fuel, and the temperature of 30 million degrees centigrade, he was getting as many as a billion individual reactions per blast. True, this gave only negligible power compared to the millions of kilowatts he was using. But, more important right now, the blast lasted only a few millionths of a second. He could stretch it longer if he lowered either the high pressure or high temperature—and he needed both. In fact, he knew that he would eventually need 200 million degrees or more for a self-sustaining reaction with this kind of fusion fuel. Such were the stern limitations as he continued trying for something better, day after day, month after month.

. . . At Green Bank, in Pocahontas County, West Virginia, a modern Columbus was exploring the heavens. He was an astronomer of the new kind. Instead of looking, he was listening in an electronic way, doing it with an 85-foot antenna shaped like a dish to intensify the radio waves it received, much as an optical lens focuses light waves. Until science reaches a peak only dreamed of today, we cannot plan to set foot on any planet outside our solar system. Even at the speed of light it is over 4 light-years to Alpha Centauri, the nearest sun to our own. But remember that light and radio are kin— different wavelengths, but both are electromagnetic energy traveling at 186,000 miles per second. So why not radio communication? The astronomer was aiming at two likely spots—Epsilon Eridani and Tau Ceti, solar systems respectively 11 and 12 light-years away. His radiometer was busily processing a hissing whisper—the sound of primordial hydrogen dancing out in Space—and translating it into a tape record he could read. This was background noise. What he wanted to catch was some sort of signaling on approximately that same universal wavelength. Certain of success? Of course not; this was named Project Ozma, after the queen of the Land of Oz. And if he did detect signals they might defy decoding. And they would be a dozen years old after the long journey. And yet, and yet . . . maybe intelligent creatures out there have been signaling for thousands of years in hope of discovering a companionable planet. They could therefore be advanced creatures who would open wondrous secrets to us. For example, how, after you have eradicated tigers and tuberculosis, do you conquer yourself?

Because of the very nature of his work, each of those three researchers could not be certain of the outcome. That can be taken for granted. The trouble is that the outcome would also be governed by something beyond his scientific problem.

The Ozma astronomer, for example, was using time on an expensive instrument. His project was not, to put it mildly, very "mission-oriented"—hardly the kind to guarantee either quick or practical results. And he was hardly working in an ivory tower. Above him was the director of the observatory, who, in turn, had to satisfy a consortium of ten universities that ran the family of telescopes at Green Bank. This organization, in turn, did not own the observatory, but was a contractor operating it for the National Science Foundation, officially the government's patron of basic research. But NSF was coming under fire for inefficiency. So Project Ozma paid for blunders committed elsewhere. It lasted three months; then the astronomer and telescope were assigned other work.

That illustrates one of the frustrations that our science lives with today. In exchange for R & D funds it has surrendered the independence it cherishes. Linked with this is the embarrassing realization that science has become an instrument of war to an extent never seen before. Missiles and rockets, computers, nuclear power, even antibiotics, started as war babies, and the Cold War required leaders of science to go on serving as a military priesthood. The rank and file feel less committed. Moreover, I constantly found among them a trauma dating from Hiroshima. Sometimes it is combined with rebellion against "Big Science." At an Ivy League university, for instance, was the professor who had fled from one of our nuclear-bomb plants. Why? "I prefer small, cute experiments—working with students, rather than behind fifteen feet of concrete. I hated to think that my epitaph would be: 'This man made five tons of TNT-equivalent for every man, woman, and child in the world. R.I.P.'"

But flight to the campus does not turn out to be an easy answer, because the bigger schools today are heavily indebted to military R & D in one form or another. Furthermore, military or not, the university man is embarrassed by something else. Too few of his colleagues consider that teaching the traditional college student, the undergraduate, remains a noble calling. To keep up with the times the instructor must think in terms of research and the crew of graduate students that goes with it. Science has done more dramatic harm but none so unthinkingly as in the part it has played luring the campus away from education to research.

Two comments indicate the nature of this situation, as odd as it is malign. Congresswoman Edith Green: "We believe in free education through the twelfth grade; then if someone can make it by pluck or luck from the twelfth through the sixteenth years, support becomes available again." Senator John Pastore: "What does the graduate student give society that he doesn't as an undergraduate? Why support him in one instance and not in another: Does he eat more?"

Now this is much bigger than a scramble for bigger pieces of government R & D pie, or a tactic to evade bans on federal aid to education. It is simple arithmetic on a vast scale. Research, most of it government-sponsored, is crowding the campus. The emphasis is upon massive programs for graduates. "They are being bought," says a dean, "and the better prospects go to the highest bidders." Another sighs. "We will still need some undergraduates, though, to have a football team." In any case, fewer than half of the scientists and engineers at the larger schools now do any teaching. The subsidized research programs are seductive; they also carry the implied warning: "Produce—or remain a teacher of undergraduates the rest of your life."

Who, then, in this high-pressure atmosphere of grantsmanship and contract research will prepare the growing number of young laymen who should have some competently taught science? By 1970, we expect a war-baby crop of seven million heading for college. Also, and ironically, who in this self-defeating system will process worthwhile graduates for worthwhile research? Evidence from everywhere is that the mass programs are producing low-quality researchers and that many use graduate school simply as a device to postpone a meeting with real life. The plain fact is that science today attracts a swarm of incompetents: beatniks, with or without beard; "scholars" who learned that philanthropic foundations are a soft touch and find today's government grants even softer; sons and daughters sometimes bullied, sometimes wheedled, into comfortable science by parents who formerly favored the other three comfortable professions: law, medicine, dentistry. The student need only solve the problem of getting the four-year degree somehow; the rest is easy enough because "all graduate students should be supported, all graduate students need to be supported."

How far beyond financing the support can go I did not realize until, at a leading university, I strayed into its service laboratory, complete with $26,000 ultracentrifuge and the like. Why "service"? The graduate students bring their "research" experiments here and leave them. The work is done for them. After that, the results are calculated for them. In some astonishment I asked who does all this. A chap in the corner was pointed out. "Who are you?" I asked. "Oh, I'm just a technician."

This is more than overfeeding the young. It provides a better, though less respectful, term than Big Science. What we have here is Corpulent Science. This refers not only to overnourishment and overweight but to a heaviness that can oppress others. At the campuses, reports the Carnegie Foundation for the Advancement of Teaching, "students are just impediments in the headlong search for more and better grants, fatter fees, higher salaries, higher rank." The graduate school becomes the invading cowbird whose young crowd out the smaller young for whom the nest was built. And further wrecking education is the fact that the graduate students are themselves oppressed by something bigger—the multimillion-dollar contracts with which government attracts the campuses to do industrial-type R & D that lacks even a nodding acquaintance with education.

To all this, of course, there are exceptions. Columbia University, one of the first to become a factory for turning out Ph.D.s, and more recently getting half of its $97-million budget from Washington, does remember to honor the inspired teacher of undergraduates with a small Great Teacher Award. Colorado College insists on being small, selective, dedicated to teaching undergraduates. It is reassuring, too, to know that some smaller schools still find the money to provide undergraduates with superior facilities. For example, St. Peter, Minnesota (population: 8400) was agog to find 26 Nobel laureates in town one day. They had come to help Gustavus Adolphus College (student body: 1200) dedicate its new $1.5-million science building named after Alfred Nobel, the Swedish engineer who invented dynamite and later left a fortune to establish lasting peace. Edgar Carlson, president of the college, informed me that one-third of the building

fund came from the Lutheran Church, one-third from alumni and
other well-wishers, the rest from a bank loan.

More typical, however, is the financial arrangement between
Corpulent Education and Corpulent Science, as in Harvard's $100-
million budgets; or in Princeton's receiving 95 per cent of its $30-
million sponsored-research funds from Washington, or in University of
Michigan's advertising that it is in the market for bigger grants; or
in the goodwill gesture by which the National Science Foundation
may give an undergraduate $200 while his college gets $500.

Or take California Institute of Technology. Ironically, it was
founded as a training school for teachers. Later, it moved into research. But no matter—Caltech won fame with the quality of its
instructors, the caliber of its undergraduates and graduates alike, the
attention it gave the humanities as well as sciences. It was small and
truly elite. Today, it still has only 250 teachers. But it also has a
separate force of 4000 people handling over $200 million worth of
space work yearly for the government at a sprawling complex where
a faculty member is hired like any other consultant and students do
not exist. And, like a private contractor, Caltech has to answer to
the government for price-gouging, mismanagement, and the like.

Thus the universities, which once proclaimed, accurately or not,
that they were "free," are now caught up in the R & D industry and
its mixed loyalties. A full-page ad in Scientific American reminds
readers: "The scientist today is one-half business executive—are you
neglecting your business half?" Even the professional organizations,
with such few exceptions as the American Chemical Society, are
deep in the easy-money game. With so many billions available to
and often forced upon R & D, in line with the task-force theory that
nine pregnant women can produce a baby in one month, and with
too few science-minded government inspectors to scan the bills
sharply, one would expect profiteering to attract sharpies to the
feast. It does. In industry there is the rocketry man who received
overtime on overtime, and double overtime on double overtime,
totaling $250 an hour. In the universities there is the department
head who said helplessly, "So many of the research proposals are
dishonest—it will give all science a black eye." Throughout have
been exorbitant contracts that were later canceled when the spending
became too flagrant.

Lightning flashes have already presaged the headlines we can expect when it becomes politically expedient to probe the mess. Meanwhile there is preparation for that day. In cubbyhole offices at the ancient George Washington Inn, a stucco building near the Capitol, Congress has had its committee investigators checking transcripts of much testimony. A few blocks away, in their modern new building, the Comptroller General's staff, who are the nonpartisan servants of Congress, have built up dossiers on favoritism, extravagance, profiteering, and megabuck swindle sheets.

Meanwhile, understandably enough, the easy money is not always gratefully received. A stock complaint is that the government pays most of the R & D bill and thereby calls the tune. Moreover, the Pentagon provides the biggest share of this federal money, a situation worrisome in itself. Industry, for example, likes receiving more R & D money from the government than it supplies itself, but complains that it is being diverted from civilian needs, that its scientists gripe about war work and its secrecy, that "we may become a second-class power in the arts of peace." Furthermore, defense dollars are insecure. The contract maneuvered this week may be canceled next month when an alluring new project appears. A Pentagon official described this to me somewhat rhapsodically: "The history of our past fifteen years is bleached with the skulls of Navaho, Saint, Skybolt, B-70, and so on." In return, of course, the defense industries have their own ways of evening the score.

As with industry, so with educational institutions, which receive around 15 per cent of the government's R & D distribution. They extol academic freedom but cannot resist the megabuck contracts for contract research and the cut they get on grants for graduate programs. This amounts to over $2 billion yearly. Some of the schools do worry over their virginity—their commitment to genuine education. But even these end, as in Shakespeare's lean verse, with their "maiden virtue rudely strumpeted"—as if proud Harvard or MIT were a trusting little milkmaid of a college. In return, the schools cuckold the government by diverting some of the funds to other purposes. Today, Washington's investigators hunt less for campus Communism than for financial juggling.

But there is considerably less such unhappiness than there might be, thanks to the emergence of a new, sophisticated minority that

President Eisenhower worriedly called the "scientific-technological elite." As we shall see, it exerts powerful influence over the nation in many ways. It can operate flagrantly enough to explain why Washington is called an "insider's town." It can also be subtly genteel. England calls the method "closed politics"; American justice calls the result "conflict of interest" and is perennially puzzled over what to do about it. When an industrialist becomes a member of the President's cabinet, it is easy enough to require that he give up direct financial control of his company. But when a company head doubles as a consultant, which of the two hats does he wear when he advises the government on vast R & D programs? . . . what of the government bureau chief who received over $200,000 directly and indirectly from R & D companies he was paid to regulate? . . . what of a government chief who also presides over a "nonprofit" organization that receives research grants from his agency? . . . and so on and on. Some of these situations will enter the R & D picture in later chapters. For the moment, consider the person heading a research foundation that receives over $5 million from a government agency that uses him to evaluate grant proposals. He is enjoined not to judge his organization's requests for funds, yet the facts of life are such that he would be on good terms with his fellow experts. Such chummy relations, however innocent in the absence of pro-hibitive law, do offend our sense of smell. A top official who became involved in conflict-of-interest controversy put it this way: "I am aware that public confidence in our public processes demands not only impartiality but also the appearance of impartiality." There is also the bizarre suggestion by Chief Justice Earl Warren of the United States Supreme Court that we develop a profession of "ethics counselors" to guide people who "wish to discern the right."

The Layman

Through sheer money-power we have built the largest research organization in the world. Its chief patron is the government, which means that the layman public pays most of the bills. Oddly, it does so quite willingly, yet has frequent doubts about what its money is buying.

There is always, of course, dread of the Bomb and all that it connotes. This is understandable. Moviegoers have grown up under the conditioning of *Hiroshima, Mon Amour* and *On the Beach* and *Fail-Safe*. Meanwhile, fiction readers remember the futilities of Aldous Huxley's *Brave New World* (in the year 632 A.F.—"After Ford"—approximately 2500 A.D.) and the savage hopelessness of nearby *1984*, George Orwell's "strongest possible wish that the future should not exist." Others have been influenced by bug-eyed monsters in today's Penny Dreadfuls. Through the educated and un-educated alike run latent terrors descended through the centuries: mistrust of Dr. Faustus's black magic, Professor Frankenstein's care-lessness, Professor Moriarty's mistreatment of hero Sherlock Holmes.

It is to avoid stampeding the layman's sensitivities that science tries bowdlerisms. It has begun using the word Overkill less brashly. At first, proponents of the space program promised a "fallout" of beneficial new products for us here on earth; later they switched to the less connotative words "spinout" and "spillover." When the Weather Bureau seeds a hurricane, in an effort to break it up, it does so by dropping a bomb of silver iodide into it. "That's what it is, a bomb," I was told, "but we prefer to call it a canister."

Justifiable or not, such delicacy is explainable. Sometimes the "technological cynicism" described by Sir Charles Snow becomes too cocky. Two professors in clinical psychology, dismissed by Harvard because they had tested the hallucination drug LSD-25 on undergraduates, retorted in *Harvard Review* that bold research is coming: "The game is about to be changed, ladies and gentlemen. Head for the hills or prepare your intellectual craft to flow with the current."

This, of course, was science at its worst, a mixture of ignorance, insolence, insouciance. But even reputable Sloan-Kettering research-ers turned reckless. They injected live cancer cells into hospital patients. The defense was that the experiment did not endanger the patients. The point, however, was that this was in no sense whatever for their benefit, and that they were not told what was being done to them. At any rate, there was public uproar resulting from an un-comfortable remembrance of things past, the Nazi experiments on humans. Others brought up a contrast with researcher Albert Sabin, who had been the first to swallow his polio vaccine; and with re-searcher Jonas Salk, who injected himself, his wife, and his three sons with his rival vaccine.

Again, then, what path for science? Will this elite keep its house clean? Will government have to control it completely? And if neither of these, will the public rise against it as, in the past, when ordinary checks and balances have failed, it has humbled Big Labor and Big Business? It can do so again. And here would be a need for informed laymen, to prevent the reaction from becoming runaway anti-intellectualism and a burning of the books.

For example, man is notoriously touchy about his breeding habits. At present, biology cannot even dream seriously of creating manikins. But it is busily experimenting with mutation methods to alter genetic material that already exists. The desire to suppress hereditary defects is laudable. But what about biologists eager for this new opportunity to provide a "better class" of humans? Are they qualified judges of what is "better"? Is an anthropologist oversimplifying when he can see only "a choice between genetic twilight and moral twilight"? What will the results be, in view of our vast remaining ignorance about body processes? Is this why Arne Tiselius, head of the Nobel Foundation and himself a pioneer whose laboratory techniques made today's sophisticated biology possible, proposed an international moral code for researchers? He warned that today's science could lead to "tampering with life and will mean an even greater responsibility than we now have with atomic energy."

Combine such "tampering" with other frustrations and fears blamed on science: it is no scare picture to see Everyman responding to a latent nihilism and swept along by rabble-rousers. Argument could not stop the radicals. Moreover, science has its listless pessimisms, its disappointment with theory and disgust with the empiric. The reaction would be nourished by quotations direct from the scientists themselves. Thus, from Robert Oppenheimer, while director of the Institute for Advanced Study: "We need new knowledge like we need a hole in the head."

This all-is-vanity theme runs counter to what the courageous and the young at heart have always believed. Also, it does not get the chores of education done. And one of these chores very much involves the layman. If he claims intelligence, he can hardly remain illiterate about the science revolution bursting around his ears. Its potential dangers are manifest. It is also a builder. How, then, to decide intelligently what kind of tomorrow's world to buy?

Some change, of course, depends mainly on our degree of affluence. There is a long list of things we want, ranging from automobiles and detergents we can control better; to innovations such as electro-luminescent walls and looky-talky telephones; to gadgets like automatic bedmakers, and golf balls that can be found with a Geiger counter. But there is also a very personal collection of questions that the public asks the experts. Wherever I went, for example, I found that the biggest ashtrays, and best filled with cigarette butts, were most likely to be in laboratories of the medical researchers. This is an interesting anomaly, but it does not answer the immediate questions. Shall we give up cigarettes to save our lungs; DDT, to save our livers; butter and eggs, to save our hearts? And what about manmade radiation, from fallout or from X-ray equipment—how harmful is it to us, and to our progeny? Another example is the specter of automation. Can we join comedian Jackie Gleason, who said that if he is thrown out of work by pushbuttons he will get a job making the pushbuttons? And if the answers to such questions are yes-and-no, then how much yes, how much no?

Then comes the procession of staggering financial questions. What big new jobs shall we give science? To begin with, any evaluation should recognize what capable researchers do. Science cannot "break through" to everything its heart desires. Money can be had, by turning the printing presses; brainpower is not inflatable. The National Institutes of Health, for example, has not known where to find enough researchers—capable ones—to match the vast funds it has been ordered to spend on breakthroughs against disease. The dollar figure for any proposal must therefore be translated into how much equipment and creativity can be allotted to it. The rest should then be easy—an informed appraisal of what we want.

. . . Shall the shopping list start with mundane things? Hailstones ruin $50 million worth of crops yearly. Shall we research to stop that? Animal ticks spread a disease costing the cattlemen $50 million yearly. Let's stop that too. But it is easier to count gigabucks, and we do have challenges that need billions of dollars. One is our chronic nuisance, corrosion, costing between five and ten billions yearly. Wouldn't it be worth a few gigabucks to stop that?

. . . Or shall we listen to economists who need stimulants for the stagnant economy? Very well, we could work harder to become our

planet's leading spacefaring nation. The race will cost us perhaps
$50 billion this decade. Why not enlarge it into a crash program to
be first on Mars? That could mean $100 billion. But then, the same
amount could develop an elaborate harness for the nation's streams,
a system to end our water-shortage troubles for a few decades. And
twice that sum might be more than enough to buy fallout-proof,
blast-proof shelter for every American.

. . . Shall we assign slices of the research pie? Even the government's favorites are dissatisfied: physicists campaign for an $8-
billion atom-smasher program; space men sadly postpone an
experiment to learn whether Mars has some form of life. The experiment could be done for perhaps one-fourth of what the physicists
ask or, if you prefer, one-fourth of the $8 billion in obsolescence
that missiles cost us in 1964. All these are large figures, but some
superhighways cost $20 million per mile, and an expressway across
lower Manhattan may cost much more.

. . . What about the tyranny of the flesh? Would we gain more by
spending the moon billions to fulfill all our hopes that "the crooked
shall be made straight" and that the straight live longer? But without
breeding a population explosion, and also overlooking the fact that
medical research already receives more billions than it is able to
spend fruitfully.

And so on, and on. The array of possibilities overpowers laymen
and makes scientists forget their good manners in squabbles for
money. In the past when science was younger, smaller—and more
sure of itself—the objectives were simpler. For less than the price of
one of today's sophisticated spectrometers, geneticists produced corn
hybrids that eventually enriched America's agricultural output by
$40 billion. In Depression days, when an agronomist was asked what
he could do with the price of a battleship, he glowed. "I could heal
the Dust Bowl—every one of its fifty million acres." Today, with
surpluses, agricultural science is embarrassed.

Then shall we go really "far out"? Maybe spending ten times the
$50 billion of space money would be worth it. Like those modern
Arabs, the summer campers who leave their beer cans and drift
away, we might discard this as the worst of all possible worlds and
sink all our treasure into finding a pristine planet for our new home.

But in all this, who is to choose among the many projects? Thomas

Jefferson's answer to the would-be elite of his day was that of a wise, worldly man, "And true it is that the people, especially when moderately instructed, are the only safe, because the only honest, depositories of public rights."

The public operates as an electorate, of course. It reciprocated Jefferson's confidence. In that era before science became a remote province, the philosopher-statesman-scientist was elected President. Then a century passed before the nation tried another chief executive with science background. He was Herbert Hoover, originally a mining engineer. It was his fate, however, to coincide with the Great Depression, and "Hoover the Great Engineer" became a taunt of that era. Since then, in the era of Big Science, America has contentedly chosen among presidential candidates who have all been indisputably laymen.

This has produced shuddery moments for the republic but no outright disaster; and, in truth, an overconfident or overimaginative scientist might have been worse. It has, however, brought oddities. Dwight D. Eisenhower had not the slightest idea of how a computer works, yet computers were building the invisible government that worried and frustrated him. His election opponent, Adlai E. Stevenson, was illiterate about nuclear weapons but busily sounded alarms against fallout and earth's being knocked off axis.

Not that science is powerless in Washington. On the contrary, it contributes many movers and shakers, the experts, advisers, and consultants whom an electorate hasn't chosen and whom it therefore has not scrutinized. These modern wizards serve as influentials rather than topmost decision-makers, but their influence is strong, pervasive, and often, transducer-like, it changes with pressure. For example, when the White House needed public support for a test ban on nuclear weapons, some of these wise men obligingly saw danger from fallout. A year earlier, when testing was desirable, they advised that fallout was not dangerous. But of what value is the tribe's wise man who sways? Or, to put it another way, isn't it disturbing that congressional committee abandoned the idea of hiring scientific consultants?—it could find no unbiased ones in that field.

Apparently, then, the layman cannot leave everything to an expert. He can read selectively, avoiding both the jargonists and the propagandists. Common sense can be useful too. For one thing, it

agreement with truly great men of science. They reassure us that the difficulties in probing nature's mysteries lie in the awesome overburden of details that hide the inner simplicity, a simplicity comparable to that of the computer talking to itself as it makes speedy choices, "yes or no," "yes or no"; the rest is merely engineering details that make the computer decide even faster, store more in its memory, handle more of the instructions itself.

One of the layman's disadvantages is his being overawed by numbers, much as the usual scientist and engineer shies from even medium-high mathematics. But need numbers be so frightening? Light travels 186,000 miles per second. Very well, in 1 hour it will travel 3600 times that far and in a year the necklace of zeros will be that much more impressive. Good science doesn't goggle at 100 million smell sensors in a rabbit's nose; it hopes the estimate is partly correct and would be happy to know exactly how even one of the cells works. Radio astronomers have put together their concept of our galaxy by studying incoming hydrogen radiation that totals less than one erg of energy—your finger expends more than that when it flicks the ash off a cigarette. Our sun is but one of a billion trillion stars within the range of our largest telescopes. Again, why let this become oh-my-gosh statistics? The scientist can reach for his slide rule and computer. The layman need only hope the micro-times and pico-distances are correct, realize that many of them are "subject to change," and remember that too many others—like statistics brandished in the quarrels over danger from nuclear fallout—are subject to the intense radiation of propaganda.

Another trouble is with the words of science, but here the expert outside his specialty, and even within it, also becomes a victim. The villain is needless jargon—not the precise label-words that science needs but the fog built around such words, therefore not the blameless understander but the blameworthy explainer. Physicist Jerrold Zacharias of MIT has this rule of thumb: "If you can't put it into English, it means you don't understand it yourself." Even that is too gentle. True, some jargon is the effort by junior specialists to sound like wizards, but much is infatuation with complication for its own sake, no different from jargoneering by the overspecialized bibliophile or baseball statistician. And too much is the squid's deliberate squirt of inky verbiage to conceal ignorance or outright

faking. Anyway, the defense against the jargonist is to find a better explainer, especially the one willing to indulge sometimes in "I don't know the answer." Another defense is to heed common sense occasionally.

Common sense should have ridiculed the cholesterol panic and the resulting polyunsaturated purge conducted against milk, eggs, and butter. Even the National Institutes of Health, government sponsor of most of the cholesterol research, has begun having self-doubts, though unofficially. At its headquarters I found in circulation an intramural mimeographed sheet that spoofed cholesterol's rise, fall, and rise over two decades:

THE MARCH OF SCIENCE: HEADLINE DEPARTMENT

Pre-1946: Cholesterol is a good guy
1947: Cholesterol found to be associated with atherosclerosis
1948: Cholesterol seen causally related to heart disease
1950: Cholesterol is killing you
1954: Cholesterol is killing you, but it has help
1958: Cholesterol, stress, and lack of exercise are killing you
1959: Cholesterol may not be killing you, but it isn't saving you either
1960: Cholesterol probably isn't killing you
1962: Cholesterol isn't even helping other things kill you—much
1963: Anything that helps make sex hormones can't be all bad
1965: Cholesterol has been much maligned
1966: Cholesterol is a good guy

The Expert Laymen

Ignoring the intellectual excitement that science offers, let us agree that the layman with common sense can better cope with the experts if he also knows some science. But how much science does he need? And how far can his interests wander? As Robert S. McNamara reminded me, "We can't all be Leonardo da Vincis."

He said it wistfully. Here was an alert face, alert brain, the man heading history's mightiest war machine, with mammoth R & D to match. He was a liberal-arts Phi Beta Kappa who went on to teach at Harvard Business School, who rose to the presidency of Ford Motor Company, then moved to the $50-billion-a-year Pentagon, becoming its eighth Secretary of Defense and the most successful in administering military R & D. An efficient man obviously, in his shirtsleeves, merely tolerating the ceremonial expanses of his office, working with papers easily within reach beside and behind him. He was surprising. Some image-makers had prepared me for a computerized human of some sort. Others had apparently confused McNamara's calm steel with cold steel. At his desk, he could grin, and his alert understanding made him delightful to interview.

What other civilians had tried, McNamara had done. He had tamed the Pentagon. No one doubted his courage, but his readiness to overrule military and scientific advisers where multibillion-dollar defense projects were concerned had provoked a storm against his judgment. One of the mildest charges: "his enthusiasm for proving he is 100 per cent right 110 per cent of the time."

So, before bringing up specific subjects, I asked: ". . . Don't you sometimes wish your own science background was stronger?" That brought the reference to Leonardo, and McNamara continued: "We have to expand one facet at the cost of another. . . . Yes, I find my education is acceptable. I would not have shifted the emphasis I put on liberal arts. But, of course, we are dealing more and more with technical subjects."

This layman left no doubt about his method of handling experts. "I have to make my own judgments. No policy-maker should accept the statement of a technical expert just because it is allegedly accurate. Rather, he should evaluate it in terms of advice from other experts, and then form his own judgment. Furthermore, the expert must give not only his conclusion but the reasoning that supports it. This, any true expert is able to do. It becomes input to the decision-maker."

Later, I brought up the subject with Harold Brown, the Pentagon's R & D director, and therefore one of McNamara's chief advisers. Brown, of course, had the problem of dealing with *his* advisers. He replied: "People overemphasize the difficulties of science. There are two ways the experts can be kept honest enough: by learning something about the subject, and by deciding which scientist to trust—not by his standing, but by what experience he has."

These are eye-opening opinions about experts. However, Brown had been a nuclear physicist, and McNamara a specialist in statistical control, which involves computers and makes loud claims to being scientific. To certify the genuine layman's right to judge the experts, let us visit a congressman—California's Chet Holifield, who had been a haberdasher. It is good to come to Capitol Hill anyway, to see again the values in our governmental system of checks and balances.

Now Congress is no more perfect than the electorate that chooses its members. Furthermore, unlike the White House, it cannot easily retreat into fog; it blares its imperfections. Yet it is authentic America, and its committee method—listening to differing interests and quizzing the experts so that a decision can then be hammered out—has been preferable to that of an aristocracy and, in our troubled century, far superior to the method of dictators.

Congress's only qualification for handling matters of science is that it is Washington's most truly representative agent of the public will; of special qualifications it has none. Its makeup is even less scientific than that of the nation as a whole. The usual scientist doesn't run for Congress. More characteristic of its handful of "scientists" have been Senator Ernest Gruening, who studied medicine, and Senator Hubert Humphrey, who came from pharmacy. Then how does a layman Congress cope with science? Partly with the work of diligent, unpublicized staff members of the committees. Partly with the aid of those consultants whom Congress can trust. And increasingly through "homework," which helps Congress question the judgment of the experts and even catches them in technical errors.

The best example is provided by the Joint Committee on Atomic Energy, which has guarded our atomic future for war and peace and done remarkably well. It also symbolizes effective democracy in action. To those seduced by the "wave of the future" and who yearn for the strong man, committees are a waste of time. Very well, this committee should be inefficient. It has eighteen members, and they are from both the Senate and House. It should also be stupid indeed, because its domain is the inmost part of the enigmatic atom, and these are certified laymen. Its outstanding members include Representatives Craig Hosmer and Melvin Price, lawyer and sports editor respectively; Senators Pastore and George Aiken, lawyer and farmer. Yet it came to pass that Chairman Glenn T. Seaborg of the United States Atomic Energy Commission, a Nobelist, told an American Chemical Society symposium: "When I first met its members I was pleased to find them so well acquainted with the subject matter—in fact, in many areas their competence certainly exceeded my own."

Two of its leaders in recent years have been Senator Clinton Anderson, ex-insurance man, and Representative Holifield, who went directly from high school into a men's clothing shop, and from there to Congress in 1942. After the war he was assigned to the new Joint Committee, where he moved on to the chairmanship as well as acquiring a reputation for being the "best brain" in Congress on nuclear matters.

In his office late one Friday afternoon I found him easy to question, as all clear thinkers are. His appearance—a bit chubby, with a wisp of white mustache and with keen white eyebrows—made him a family-doctor sort of man. Two hours later, we continued chatting out at the street corner a block from the Capitol while he waited for his wife to pick him up. As usual, he would return to the office Saturday and lock himself in for undisturbed work. But right now the Holifields had noisy neighbors and had to find time to change apartments this weekend.

Meanwhile, in his office we had talked nuclear war and peace, then gone on to discuss the need for better science and for a better-informed public. In Holifield, manifestly, I could find no better example of a layman.

"I didn't go to college. Like Harry Truman I ran a haberdashery shop." He chuckled. "I suppose the difference is that he moved on, but I still own my clothing store back home."

The rest, he said, was simple enough. He had picked up his science by homework—by reading. This in turn enabled him to question, and learn from, the experts. Here, I knew, was another contrast with layman Truman, who knew no science and apparently had not tried to learn any. His decision in 1950 to manufacture the H-bomb came from advice, as had his decision in 1945 to fire the A-bomb. But there was a difference. In 1950 the fateful decision was easier. A group from the young Joint Committee was advising him on which experts to believe. Leading the group was Holifield, neither militarist nor pacifist, neither scientist nor ignorant layman.

Lest we forget, this committee was born in bitter days. Immediately after the war, scientists flocked to Washington. Some were conscience-stricken about Hiroshima, others feared military control or big-business control of the Nuclear Age. At Capitol Hill they found men who would listen: men like Brien McMahon, the Connecticut lawyer, in the Senate; and Holifield in the House. Out of the resulting hearings and debate was forged the Atomic Energy Commission and its duenna, the Joint Committee. No political arrangement in American science has worked better than this fortunate liaison between the experts and the people's agents.

The formula isn't magic. It works because of a capable committee staff, aided by the Legislative Reference Service of the Library of Congress. And basically it works because the Joint Committee brings the expert down to a human level. He is considered an instrument responsive to stresses, prejudices, disappointments. Or put it another way: he fits neatly, like any other human, into the broadest and most tantalizing of sciences—ecology—which studies the mutual relations between organisms and their environment. The lemmings of the north, driven to mass suicide when they breed beyond capacity of the land to feed them, are a relatively simple example. More sophisticated is man. He can change his environment in many and vital ways. But he remains as responsive as a thermometer or barometer to influences. Like the piezoelectric crystal, which gives electricity when you squeeze it, he glows when you applaud him. Wound his ego, and the reaction is different. Concerning a book he had written, veteran anthropologist Carleton S. Coon challenged veteran zoologist Theodosius Dobzhansky, who had reviewed the book: "I shall ignore his dislike of my style and his godlike strictures—unbecoming to a scientist—about the immorality of telling the truth. . . . I consider his rejection of my criteria . . . as being professionally incompetent."

Accordingly, the Joint Committee has little awe of experts. Holifield explained its success this way: "A congressional committee can be a wonderful and fearsome thing—a method simply evolved; the framers of the Constitution never dreamed of it. What we do on our committee is sort out opinions of the scientists, and make them then justify their opinions—after all, they are parties in interest. This means that the expert is pitting his mind against the minds of eighteen men representing a wide variety of experience. By the time he is past the committee he knows that he has indeed been through the wringer."

But the Joint Committee is outstanding. And voters do not always elect a Holifield to Congress—or keep him there. In apathetic times the voice of the public is complacent; even in exciting times it can swell to a chorus dominated by Peter Pans who refuse to grow up. Either way, such is a public that has not been "moderately instructed," if we are to believe Jefferson and others with confidence in educable man.

So the science-and-layman theme is new only in context of the scientific revolution. A healthy democracy needs a sufficient number of informed people who will judge issues intelligently enough to recognize trustworthy politicians, scientists, or any other surrogates. But this requires the usual precautions concerning what one hears and reads.

For instance, there are scientists aware that the new elite must recognize its responsibilities or face ever-increasing governmental control. To fulfill one responsibility some have returned to a British tradition—lectures that inform their fellow citizens about science. But even when this is "pure" science it is modern science, involved deeply, often controversially, in government, war, education, and so forth. The layman must therefore judge whom to trust, as he should a conventional speechmaking politician, business spokesman, or any other communicator for that matter; it is ever astonishing how many otherwise alert people accept the lecturer, author, even the political commentator, without sufficient knowledge of his credentials. Here the scientific expert is no different from anybody else who enters the public arena, quietly or otherwise. What is his record of achievement? And his role in the establishment? Is he part of an organized campaign for or against pesticides, for or against a nuclear test ban? Though unquestionably sincere, is an astronomer painting his lily and a physicist gilding his gold because the one wants more telescopes and his rival wants more atom-smashers? And how qualified are such experts to speak outside their specialty?

These are hardly abstract questions. Ordinary awareness and common sense are sufficient to answer them. The rest is "moderate instruction"—choosing the communicator, specialist or not, who neither flounders in jargon nor insults the intelligence with amateurish popularization.

II: *The Roots of Science*

" 'Tis magic, magic that hath ravished me."
—Christopher Marlowe,
*The Tragical History
of Doctor Faustus*

"A government contract becomes virtually
a substitute for intellectual curiosity."
—Dwight D. Eisenhower

At first glance, science in both the USA and USSR seems a mammoth defense reaction. Even our educational programs are influenced by scares that Russia's booming production of Ph.D.s in science and engineering will doom us. Meanwhile, of course, our biggest R & D programs have been answering Russia's missiles and rockets, just as Russia's were in response to our atomic bomb—and so on, back to original sin. And each nation's fears will continue to catalyze the other's science. But seeing only the military connections oversimplifies as much as calling all this no more than friendly rivalry between Russian and American scientists. Broader perspective is needed to reveal what our science is now doing and to anticipate where it is going, war threats or no.

This chapter, accordingly, will show how our science of today came to be. There is no need to dwell on all the begats. We will concentrate on the years that saw the R & D industry replace a helter-skelter of scholars and inventors; years of crisis science and breakthrough science that began around 1940 and proceeded under one layman President after another, each handling the puzzling new responsibility in his distinctive way, each learning science to this extent: learning that its people, though cast in today's mold of formula science, go on polishing the image of freedom that science once had, or that they think it still has.

That word "freedom" illustrates another need for perspective. Like all freedom, of course, it is freedom for whom? The bursts of creativity that were the glory of Greece and the Renaissance weren't for slave and peasant. Then comes the question: freedom for what kind of science? This requires a look at the fairy tale called scientific method.

It is fiction because it overlooks the difference in skills, personality, and motive between this human instrument and that one. Consequently, it overlooks the difference in "method." There is a difference between classifier and experimenter; also between theorist and investigator—a gap that did not exist for Darwin and Mendel but has grown so wide that only a precious few modern scientists can cross it, or try. It is easier to be either the speculative biologist pondering why slight molecular variations distinguish one baby from another, or the practical biologist seeking a better contraceptive pill. But only fiction would guarantee that this difference is between "idealist" and "realist." Rather, it distinguishes between theory and empiricism, meditating and investigating, lecture hall and laboratory, just as it formerly was a line drawn between university and industry.

As with the lay world, then, or the arts, science sees a difference between what might be called its sayers and doers. It prefers to overlook an occasional Irving Langmuir, who starred in all three—theory, "basic science," and "applied science"—and remain formally class-conscious. It likes to feel that it advances by balancing observation with explanation. For this it assumes that some people are experimenters, handy with their hands; others are theorists, handy with their heads. And, as theory, this works fairly well—if nobody asks which came first, chicken or egg; or whether in olden days the prophet and singer of songs was more or less valuable to the tribe than the huntsman and carver of tools.

Furthermore, the nicely balanced script requires players who will come in at their cues. Without interpretation, the new facts of biology or physics become doodling; without facts, theory becomes intellectual foppery, which is as bad as relying on the dogma of "Aristotle says . . ." This situation is not the result of open hostilities between the two players. They ridicule each other more than they fight. After all, it is another experimenter that the experimenter wants to scoop; it is another theorist that the theorist wants to overwhelm. The main trouble is imbalance. This wrecks the teamwork script as surely as actual warfare would. Physics today, for instance, awaits an Albert Einstein willing to seek meaning, and able to find it, in the staggering output of automated data from atom-smashing machines operating in the remote world of subatomic particles. The Einstein does not appear and physics chokes on the overexuberance of its experimenters.

Whose fault is this? Experimenters complain that theorists have lost the courage to be heretics, are satisfied to practice an abstract art form. Theorists complain that it is impossible to dig through the mountains of new data, that they have been overwhelmed. By the challenging data, perhaps; not, the evidence shows, because they are an oppressed minority. Hardly that. Whatever the reason, a plain fact is that theory has mushroomed in most fields, even in so-called "materialistic" America, and despite blasts such as that by Aldous Huxley against "substituting false abstractions for the living complexities of reality." He might have saved his breath. From the arts and sciences, theory has gone on to invade other areas. For example, the pseudosciences of operations research, motivation research, and market research now have their own dialectics on "minimax" strategy, on how to overkill a nation or polysaturate the better-than-butter market.

And education has swiftly joined this wave of the future, even at MIT, according to its president, J. A. Stratton. His view is valuable because of his allegiance to both camps. He was a theoretical physicist; on the other hand, MIT was founded to give "learning by doing." Stratton's appraisal is this:

"An almost arrogant intellectualism seems to affect a wide domain of American scholarship. My concern is a curious dichotomy in our American culture. On the one hand, there is our familiar obsession with gadgets and devices. On the other, as if in protest, our scholarship reveals increasingly this trend toward the analytical and abstract. When abstraction becomes an end to itself, science and art will invite sterility. Philosophy at this moment shows greater interest in the processes of mathematical logic than in the problems of human existence."

The imbalance does not add to man's comfort. A symmetrical creature, he apparently prefers equilibrium between abstract and real, as he does between the two legs that carry him forward. Nor has the imbalance been fruitful. While the sayers debate at the outer shell of nature's basic secrets, doers neglect an almost limitless list of R & D jobs that both rich and poor want performed—toward a healthier, longer life, for example. Along the edges of science, too, are fields that await tilling: enough physicians to apply science capably and, at least as important, enough capable teachers to give the future layman—and future scientist too—sufficient knowledge with which to make decisions that make sense, whether they concern nuclear test bans, monorail versus hydrofoil, birth-control method A versus B, which career to choose in an increasingly automated age, and so on through all the puzzles of a civilization that has lost its simplicity.

And yet . . . practical science is not enough. It is true, too true, that we have been drawing on the savings account called seed knowledge. To be something more than tinkering, science sorely needs new roadmaps that only a fruitful balance between doer and sayer can restore. But both have lost freedom to be truly creative. They are dominated by an R & D industry in which the talented are submerged by the rest and all are programed, whether the grant, salary, or fee comes from government, private company, or university. This is one of the predicaments facing science today: how to satisfy its multibillion-dollar appetite and yet feel free to probe the tantalizing mysteries.

Somewhere in the Einstein story may be an allegory. He was a daydreamer who was given a compass as a gift when he was five and immediately explored its mysteries. At twelve, he fell in love with geometry. Otherwise, he was unpromising. He was a drop-out from school who later earned a degree in his own way. He could not have qualified for a modern research grant. There was no need; he was content with a job as a patent examiner. Later, he called it "a kind of salvation." It earned his living; it left his mind free after work for riddles of the universe. And he changed the world. In contrast, the alchemists were highly "motivated" by their pursuit of homemade gold. And they got nowhere.

From Athens to Washington

The Greeks called him philosopher—lover of wisdom. We call him the ancestor of today's scientist. This overlooks other and older lines of descent: from toolmaker, magician, and so on. But the beginnings of history elude us. Just how and when prehistoric man discovered that he had a brain, tamed fire to be his slave, transformed wild forage into crops, engineered the wheel and the lever—all this we can only conjecture. Then came historic man, and eventually his bookkeepers, soothsayers, herbalists. They, too, were prototypes. We of Western civilization usually find it convenient to skip over these crude mathematicians, astronomers, and physicians to rulers of the ancient Asian empires. But they did exist, and it is worth noting that they were not free. They were beholden to government.

And then? The Greeks, of course. Athens, for example, was famed for its triad: the sculptor's son Socrates, who taught the nobleman's son Plato, who taught the physician's son Aristotle. By definition, they loved wisdom. And to this the gadfly Socrates added an insistence upon intellectual freedom, for which he was willing to pay his life.

By now wisdom was already an overgrown mistress. Philosophy examined morals, politics, the stars and gods, the reason for dew in the morning and hailstones in hot weather. So there came a vague cleavage. Some wisdom-lovers shut themselves within the metaphysical. Others observed the real world. But this was not a formal clash between sayers and doers. Theory was dominant. Experiment as we know it was in its infancy. Aristotle, for instance, was the great "natural philosopher"—in modern terms, a scientist. But his science went no farther than classifying and trying to explain. He was the encyclopedist, not experimenter. Even the inventive Archimedes, a century later, was far more interested in the serenity of mathematics. It remained for the Egyptians, Arabs, Chinese—and those get-rich-quick optimists, the alchemists—to keep experiments going. Scholars of the West were content to repeat, "Aristotle says . . ."

Eventually, the freshness of the Renaissance brought its new thrust of curiosity. Now came the model Renaissance man Leonardo da Vinci—painter, sculptor, architect, musician, engineer, scientist. Soon, in England's brilliant early 1600s, Shakespeare was writing superb psychological analyses, though he didn't call them that, and Francis Bacon turned from his disgraceful career in court politics to write out the requirements of scientific method. His point was simply: don't theorize until you have facts. Already, a few others were practicing what he preached. England's William Harvey was discovering the pumping circuits of the blood; Italy's Galileo was founding modern physics. Soon enough, later that century, came Isaac Newton to ponder on the data and write down the laws of gravitation and motion. Science was now on a plateau far above Aristotle's. In a history of revolutions, this one in the seventeenth century would be called the first in science.

The next century's Age of Reason did more than produce the American and French political revolutions. It stimulated science immensely. Real chemists, like Scheele and Lavoisier, supplanted the alchemists. Engineers began moving in with practical applications of physics—railroad, steamship, power loom. And so a new surge, the Industrial Revolution of the early nineteenth century. But now, in obedience to Newton's third law, an action produced a reaction. Science had already seemed in league with the Devil; it was soon to challenge the Bible's version of Genesis. But the Industrial Revolution was more materialistic than all that, and not everybody welcomed the sensationally powerful mechanical slaves. English mobs destroyed weaving machines. John Ruskin took time off from teaching good taste in art and architecture to chastise the railroads and other defilers of beauty. A rash of utopian colonies were formed in England and America "to get away from it all," and Thoreau wrote his prescription on how to do it. In 1848 Karl Marx issued the Communist Manifesto and foresaw workers literally "chained to their machines."

It was industry rather than science, however, that was still the major villain. Research was allowed to bloom and it now thrust its curiosity into something nonmechanical—what we call the life sciences. In midcentury, the gentle Charles Darwin was turning data from his voyage on the *Beagle* into his theory of evolution, which aggressive men soon interpreted as a fang-and-claw "survival of the fittest." The Austrian priest Gregor Mendel was hybridizing peas in his monastery garden to demonstrate how hereditary characteristics pass from generation to generation. Louis Pasteur was crossing biology with chemistry to produce biochemistry, and also demonstrating that pure and applied science are not easily separated. His fermentation research for the brewers and winemakers of France led to pasteurization, then to vaccination; along the way he proved that maggots grow in spoiled meat only because flies have laid their eggs there, that "all life comes from life." For all practical purposes he had killed off the belief in spontaneous generation.

And what of that underdeveloped nation, the United States? The young better-class American who wanted recognition in polite science was advised to get his degree in Europe. America was too busy growing to spend much time with such science; it preferred the inventive Yankee kind of science that was speeding its growth. Later, the twentieth century looked patronizingly upon the "snuff-colored little man" Benjamin Franklin, the printer who captured lightning with a kite and taught Revolutionary colonists how to convert barnyard materials into gunpowder. But he belonged to his times and his country.

This was the America of Eli Whitney's cotton gin and of mass-produced muskets, of telegraphy and reapers. And of two Vermont blacksmiths: one, John Deere, invented the steel plow; the other, Thomas Davenport, applying physicist Joseph Henry's experimental contributions to electromagnetism, built, patented, and demonstrated the first serviceable electric motor. Even young Abraham Lincoln took out a patent, on a riverboat that could crawl past rocks. A nineteenth-century American's imagination had to be practical: James Whistler lost his job with the Coast and Geodetic Survey when his fondness for painting seduced him into adding beautiful whales to the sober harbor chart assigned to him. And so on, through Alexander Graham Bell to the horseless carriage, flying machine, and all the rest. Thomas Edison's only claim to being a scientist—his "Edison effect," which led to the electronic vacuum tube—was dismissed as an experimental discovery in technology, not "science." Even the cyclotron later, and the radio telescope, were given as evidence that American science is "hardware."

However, toward the end of the nineteenth century, America did begin showing active signs of more talent for genteel science and, particularly, theory. Its Josiah Willard Gibbs, father of physical chemistry, used the second law of thermodynamics to explain the kinship of chemistry, electricity, and thermal energy. This won him England's Copley Prize, and Anglophile Henry Adams thereupon admitted him to the company of the "three or four greatest minds of his century." Another luminary was our first winner of a Nobel Prize in science: physicist Albert Michelson, of the famed Michelson-Morley experiment. Though performed in a Cleveland basement, it was respectable enough. If Galileo abolished heaven, it was Michelson who unintentionally but seriously wrecked the ancient concept, again in vogue in the nineteenth century, of a universal ether that permeates all space. This was destructive science in a sense, but pleasant too. Theory could resume guessing on how light and other radiation, unable to ride an ether, do move from stars to earth. And one theorist, Einstein, had a pillar for his coming theory—he could count on a constant speed for light.

Looking back at the opening of the twentieth century, it is too easy to see only a quaint, peaceful costume play. The period was hot with revolution—and not only by the Schoenbergs and Stravinskys of music, the cubists of painting, and, in America, the Populists of politics and muckrakers of literature. In its genteel way, science was fighting tradition too. And thanks to the discovery by sayers and doers that they could help each other immensely, it was blazing trails in seemingly all directions.

In this period science grew modern. Thomas Hunt Morgan at Columbia and others elsewhere were rediscovering the forgotten Mendel experiments and carrying them farther, with dependable help from the little fruit fly, to establish today's gene explanation of human characteristics. Abroad, Sigmund Freud was studying himself and his medical patients and evolving a new set of explanations for human behavior. Abroad too, Einstein with his relativity, and Max Planck with his energy packet called the quantum, were changing the entire structure of physics in their bold attempts to explain what the Michelsons, Roentgens, Curies, and others were finding experimentally. Soon, chemists joined physicists in discarding the comfortable "billiard ball" atom in favor of the Rutherford-Bohr planetary one. It pictured negatively charged, almost weightless electrons surrounding a positively charged, relatively heavy nucleus. The next steps were now predestined: to break atoms apart, to create atoms never found on earth.

For all this and more, in basic research and in industrial research too, science needed tools and working space. This problem was being solved too.

Originally, Europe's universities were mainly assemblages of lecture halls. But in the latter half of the nineteenth century they started adding laboratories, and American universities did likewise. Morgan was Columbia, Gibbs was Yale, and America's inland was not yet a "science desert": Michelson and Morley were at Case Institute of Technology and Western Reserve University respectively; and also in Ohio was their young contemporary, student Charles Hall of Oberlin. His electrolytic process was a practical way to get aluminum metal from its stubborn oxide. The labs at such places were mainly for leisurely "pure research" by scholars. For practical research, the scientist was best equipped if he happened to be working for farmers. Since Civil War days the federal government had supported laboratories at land-grant colleges and the like for Department of Agriculture programs aimed at finding better foods and fibers.

At the turn of the century, however, the choice opened widely. Now, for one thing, industry seriously began courting men of science. There was already a precedent of a sort—Arthur D. Little, Inc., set up in 1886 by a young chemist whose main asset was his crisp new diploma from nearby MIT. His objective was "the improvement of processes and perfection of products," and he would accept any worthwhile client. One day a prospect rebuffed Little with the old saw, "You can't make a silk purse out of a sow's ear." Whereupon chemist Little ordered 100 pounds of certified sows' ears from a Chicago meatpacker, converted them chemically into soft, glossy threads, and wove the purse. His lab went on to prosper, pioneering in fields as diverse as cryogenics and motivation research. Eventually, one of its contracts was to show General Motors how to set up its own central research lab.

Arthur D. Little offered a precedent, but this company worked mainly as a consultant. Not until 1901 did a manufacturer organize a corps of its own people for basic research. This was General Electric's lab at Schenectady, where Willis Whitney from MIT directed a team including such luminaries as Charles Steinmetz and William D. Coolidge. Irving Langmuir was another. At first, he wouldn't join because he felt his research was too esoteric to be carried on at company expense. Whitney replied, "You'll let the boss worry about practical matters." Chemist Langmuir became one of the few from industry to win a Nobel Prize.

Du Pont followed suit in 1902 and the parade of industrial labs had started. The same year saw still another trend begin, with the birth of Carnegie Institution of Washington, America's first philanthropic setup entirely for scholarly research. There were no income-tax inducements then, and there had been philanthropists before: Conscience money from Ezra Cornell's telegraph fortune endowed Cornell; and Cornell was himself inspired by Peter Cooper, the glue-maker and steelmaker who founded Cooper Union. But the Carnegie labs were unique. Nothing but science! No humanities, no teaching, just probing deeper into physics, biology, astronomy.

Others followed Andrew Carnegie's lead. Later came a branching off as newer institutions, rather than set up their own labs, began simply to write out checks for research grants. One result is the trio that plagues today's foundations and their "clients": growthmanship, brochuremanship, grantsmanship. Another is the problem that the private foundations privately call "competitive philanthropy": too many foundations able to find too few glamour projects.

All this, of course, portended pressures for the sincere scientist and lonely inventor. It also meant that R & D would lose the flamboyance that titillated the science-excited public of the nineteenth century. There would no longer be personal war between an inventor-manager Thomas Edison and his company, and an inventor-manager George Westinghouse and his company, over whose kind of electric current—d.c. or a.c.—was better. Westinghouse's name might go on in the company name after the founder died, but the company would now be run by professional management that bought its technical talent. And long before Edison's death, his electric company was merged to become General Electric.

Meanwhile, the twentieth century saw the federal government begin expansion of its "in-house" capabilities. In 1901 the Commerce Department opened its National Bureau of Standards, which is never glamorous but always vital in basic research. It became the expert to whom everybody—industry, government, university—could bring the most delicate testing and measurement problems. Not that it can solve everything. It is too much to expect that man will find a dependable formula for international peace until his technical folk can persuade governments and industries to agree to something so much simpler as the metric system of measurements. This complaint by a foreign-born chemist shows the double-talk that scientists must use: "I grew up under the old Russian system, which was a little crazier than the English one. Then I studied under the metric system in Germany. Then I had to learn for the third time, the English system, and I can assure you the metric system is the only one that makes any sense."

There also began the enlistment of science for war. By World War I, each of the two defense departments had its own strengthened technical branches. Army, of course, was proud of its Corps of Engineers and Signal Corps; and the latter became our first Air Force just as it had been our first Weather Bureau back in an era when navigators needed its advice more than farmers did. Navy, however, considered itself more truly scientific. It had been a crony of the National Academy of Sciences ever since the academy's birth in the Civil War. One of its ensigns, Michelson, had even gone on to become the ether-discrediting Nobelist. Yet Navy's interest in science is intensely practical. So is Air Force interest, but it is expressed in a totally different way. Air Force resembles the modern foundation that hires its research done. Navy buys outside R & D but also has its own lineup of facilities, led by world-renowned United States Naval Research Laboratory. This explains the high caliber of Navy science. An NRL official told me frankly, "We're in competition with the universities. We have to make a research proposal just like anybody else."

Why Navy's "scientific method"? Because a navy afloat is a navy vulnerable; its technology must not be business as usual. Navy ticks off these needs for reliability: first, its transports must get "there"; then its hardware must be dependable enough, far from drydock, to keep it there; meanwhile, without land wires, it must remain linked dependably to home base; then, in the athletics of actual battle, its gunnery and bombing must be under complicated control, the more so in an electronics age; and all this self-reliance on a rolling sea, not firm land. Hence Navy's R & D policies, and a good record—as long as it doesn't face radically different situations. For instance, it might have changed history had its policy-makers supported the atomic-energy enthusiasm of its scientific people. Before anyone else in government, the latter saw the possibilities in a bit of uranium. Substituted for bulky fuel, it would give submarines an entirely new future. But they couldn't sell the idea for such research. Even after uranium went into nuclear bombs instead, even after victory, Navy's brass was ready to miss the boat again. It had to be bludgeoned into supporting the Rickover program for nuclear-propelled submarines.

What, then, about the world wars?

The first, though it killed 8.5 million and wounded 21 million more, was quite conventional. Its aviation was high-spirited adventure but laughably crude. Its electronics barely hinted at things to come. It conscripted mass armies but science remained free. Its only scientific sensation came from a German. This was Fritz Haber's second historic achievement. The first, which was more or less for peace and won him the Nobel Prize in chemistry, was his practical way to convert the air's inert nitrogen into ammonia. With this, an artificial-fertilizer industry became possible and man now scorned Malthus's prophecy of a world doomed by lack of food.

The same synthetic ammonia, converted into explosives, enabled the Kaiser's Germany to fight on when she could no longer get saltpeter from Chile. Haber's other contribution to this war was more direct. Influenced by the slaughter that he saw at the front, he was swayed by a tempting idea: a humane war is the one ended quickly. The idea became a project, the project became Haber's poison-gas warfare. Such was "end justifies the means" and such was Haber, destined to die a lonely, wandering exile's death when the Nazis came to power and made their own contribution to our perspective: the concept of a "Nordic National-Socialist science."

Inevitably came another, bigger war; and the first in which science was as active as soldier, sailor, and airman. How well did America's scientists perform in competition with the regimented ones of Fascism? Very well, in the seemingly inefficient way of democracy. They were fraternal enough and smart enough to welcome Europe's refugee scientists. Taking upon themselves intelligence duties that the Pentagon couldn't yet comprehend, they began censoring their research reports about nuclear fission experiments. Then, when they got only a polite thank-you from Navy brass, they maneuvered the famous message through Einstein to the White House, alerting Franklin Roosevelt to the possibility that Germany might turn uranium into an unprecedented explosive that would truly justify an adjective such as "stupendous."

In retrospect, mild Einstein seems other-worldly to an amazing degree. The man did not demand government funds! Like an old-fashioned clergyman, or scientist, he scrounged humbly. He suggested that Roosevelt might care to name somebody who might unofficially help the researchers past red tape and help them live within their slim university budgets by providing funds, "if such funds be required, through his contacts with private persons willing to make contributions, and perhaps also by obtaining the cooperation of industrial laboratories which have the necessary equipment."

Like most highly political presidents, Roosevelt stood in awe of great scholars. Einstein's plea started government interest, government money, and government participation in the form of a National Defense Research Committee. Directing this adventure into the unknown were the best men Roosevelt could find. From his presidency of Carnegie Institution came Vannevar Bush, ex-dean of engineering at MIT. And from his presidency of MIT's neighbor came ex-chemist James B. Conant (another leading wartime scientist recalls with a grin: "Conant had many talents. He also could help science because Roosevelt worshiped him as a kind of oracle. It was a case of the former undergraduate's reverence for a Harvard prexy.") Then, as the bomb program progressed, all was wrapped into the Office of Scientific Research and Development and its highly secret Manhattan project, directed by Army engineers and with Du Pont doing the biggest share of the practical work.

Thus had war brought changes. A few years earlier, the Du Ponts adorned Roosevelt's list of "economic royalists," and congressional investigators were pillorying their company as the leading munitions profiteer ("merchant of death") of the First World War. But the company was now more civic-minded, and public-relations-minded; and the nation needed Du Pont's chemical engineering. It had to be cajoled into this bomb project; it accepted on condition that it receive only accident insurance, costs, and a fee of $1. It even abjured patent rights. On the other hand, the scientists, of whom many had scorned this same Du Pont for merchandising death, and Germany for its use of poison gases, now were urging as well as building the deadliest mass killer in history. The difference, of course, was attributed to motive. This was slaughter not for profit but an ideal, and self-preservation. This was like the old-fashioned holy war. And most of the scientists sincerely felt that they were racing with Nazi researchers for first crack with the A-bomb.

In every sense, the A-bomb was a spectacular. But, lest we forget, there was also radar. By war's end the two projects had taken 40 per cent of the nation's physicists.

Unlike the A-bomb, radar was indeed a race: the Germans and Japanese had it too. But theirs was always a few steps behind that of the "decadent" Anglo-Americans. Radar had started in America. Thereafter, many others worked on the idea. Send radio pulses through the air. Those that bounce back to the sender's screen through fog, darkness, distance—they have struck something. The challenge was to refine the method. The best radar was that which could identify the "bogie" accurately as a German plane, Japanese cruiser, or, mayhap, a flock of birds.

Many worked on radar in the 1930s but nobody as hard as England's Sir Robert Watson-Watt, spurred by dread of the day when Nazi bombers would come. And when they did, when such Americans as Charles Lindbergh and Ambassador Joseph P. Kennedy were appraising England as a lost cause, in her September 1940 month of agony, England passed the ball back to America. She sent what may have been the most precious cargo to reach our shores—the black leather suitcase carried by scientist-politician Henry Tizard.

"Black box" has become the quick term for an assembly of clever electronic equipment. The "black box" sent here by England contained, among other secret devices, her new cavity magnetron. It made superior radar—the microwave kind, with a sharper beam and smaller antenna, with which even an airplane could pinpoint its target— practical for the first time.

So radar, discovered accidentally in 1922 by a pair of our Navy's civilian scientists, carried forward by the Carnegie Institution three years later, then enriched by desperate England, was now back in America. It was in the hands of the brand-new Radiation Laboratory set up at MIT, which was quickly becoming the largest research organization in world history. Here gathered physicists who would be heard from constantly through the war and postwar years—I. I. Rabi, L. N. Ridenour, J. A. Pierce, J. R. Zacharias, I. A. Getting, L. J. Haworth.

Let us make a quick comparison. Both the A-bomb and radar projects were necessary. The former cost roughly $2 billion—for the research and the two production bombs dropped on Japan. America's radar cost $2.5 billion in equipment produced, plus the $80 million in R & D at Radiation Laboratory that amounted to almost twice MIT's total endowment. Both projects therefore cost roughly the same. Which was the greater weapon can best be argued in barrooms. Certainly radar was more versatile and did more work. It was England's savior in defense against bomber and submarine; our guiding eye in offense, effective on land, sea, and in the air. The A-bomb made its splash only at the war's very end, after Germany's collapse, when Japan was already debating terms of surrender.

At any rate, the two projects demonstrated the same thing. In time of emergency, for defense of the dignity of man, our scientists knew how to respond, and did. But something else. Those war projects carried in them the seed of the politics and power of today's science. Laboratory men had demonstrated for the blindest to see that they were indispensable men. They had come out of seclusion. Their penury was gone. So was their voicelessness; and immediately after peace they were heard from again. Partly because of their Hiroshima memories, partly because they equated war with "militarism," they joined in lobbying for passage of an Atomic Energy Act that would place the future of nuclear power under civilian control, not military.

But they were not through with international rivalry yet. Somewhere along the line, their simple cause-and-effect had gone wrong. Victory had not brought peace. The Soviet Union was becoming our new nightmare.

Decade of Tremors

Under its Stalin dictatorship our wartime ally, never cordial, was now behaving abominably. Enough so to arouse suspicions that the war was not won—despite our postwar aid to friend and foe, despite the erection of a great building for an international parliament called the United Nations, despite the peaceful-atom promises with which we hoped to make mankind forget the horrors called Hiroshima and Nagasaki.

And despite our A-bomb. The superweapon was an albatross around our neck. It had led us to disarm with jubilant haste, confident that the mere fact of our monopoly would suffice to make any nation behave. That implied threat seemed hollow now. Eager for friends, desperate for peace, we lacked the will to kill any more cities. We now realized also that superbombs weren't really practical for civil disobedience, "brush wars," and similar nastiness. And soon enough we didn't dare use them anyway. Russia had them too, and the threat was now mutual. So we remembered Pearl Harbor more vividly than ever, and President Eisenhower urged his cabinet not to expect wonders from retaliation: "It is cold comfort to be assured that someone still alive will drop a bomb on the Kremlin."

Consequently, the USA had to endure a decade of tremors somehow, while the USSR subjugated neighbors, blockaded Berlin, and helped Red China bleed us in the Korean War. Then a successor to Stalin banged his shoe on a desk at the UN and promised that Russia would dance on America's grave. To prove it, Nikita Khrushchev brandished missiles. Eventually, the impudence of his Sputnik shattered the confidence of American laymen and many others in our science—and our security.

Much of this, of course, was for public display. Neither our security nor military science was that dismal. But the American transition had been too rude from pleasure-loving Sybaris to dwelling under a Stalin thundercloud. The foe in the Kremlin became twelve feet tall. This wasn't common sense. Neither was it sensible to reduce him to dwarf size. The nuclear threat was too real.

As far as science was concerned, the decade of terrors was officially opened by a mysterious blast in August 1949. It did not go unnoticed, thanks to a detection system proposed by scientists Bush and Conant, who knew better than to think only America would explode the atom. Accordingly, planes were equipped with air filters that continued sampling the atmosphere. And one of them eventually found telltale radioactivity. The fallout was then traced back to an area in the Soviet hinterland. So Russia had done it!

The implications of that test blast shook Washington. How now to live with the Kremlin and its unpleasant Stalin? Layman President Truman, though courageous enough, knew that, as far as nuclear weaponry was concerned, he was an illiterate. So were most of his Pentagon people. Here was a problem for the wise men of science.

Specifically, should we use the one-step-ahead strategy? As with radar in the war against the Axis, should our researchers now try to keep our nuclear bomb always better than Russia's? In other words, when Russia reached the stage of actually producing A-bombs, suppose we had something far superior, an "H-bomb"? Such a weapon had been discussed, off and on. Instead of blowing up plutonium atoms by nuclear fission, it would blow special hydrogen atoms together. It would be a fusion weapon, immensely more lethal. But this was theory. Despite assurances by physicists like Edward Teller, would fusion work? And could such a thermonuclear bomb be ready soon enough? Stalin was pushing hard and confidently; we had just been through the frightful tension of the Berlin airlift.

Or should we react less drastically and with possibly greater security? Should we simply step up the production of A-bombs for our stockpile? This would mean risking no time, money, and materials on a dream weapon that might not work. Meanwhile, Russia's blast was a portent, not yet an acute threat. Our scientists felt that her first bombs would be little better than the Hiroshima one. Meanwhile, ours had improved. They were smaller, yet more powerful. The Hiroshima bomb was equivalent to almost 20,000 tons of TNT. The figure could now reach a half-million tons.

Here, then, was a technical decision. Opinions differed. Here arose the controversy, which still exists, between exponents of strategic weapons for mass warfare and smaller, tactical weapons for battlefields.

But the decision couldn't be purely technical. Another crucial question was this: would scientists cooperate? It was not an idle question. There was too much Hiroshima and Nagasaki in the air. Everything that touched on those Japanese cities seemed to carry a curse anyway. And probably with good reason. They were victims of evil in the same Old Testament sense of the word that the Nazi extermination camps were evil. Hiroshima was obliterated by a hideous new weapon without warning or ultimatum—after Germany, for whom the A-bomb was built, was out of the war, and when Japan was ready for peace. In other words, because of fears that Germany was doing so, the scientists could argue it was not immoral to build those first A-bombs. But the use to which they were put was something else again. With elaborate "atoms-for-peace" programs, America tried in following years to make itself and the world forget. An honest admission of guilt and some kind of day of atonement might have been as fruitful.

At any rate, many of the scientists who now declined to work on the H-bomb—those who had protested killing the Japanese cities and the majority who had expressed no opinion—were washing their hands of all nuclear bombs, whatever the type and whoever the target might be. Others lacked motivation now that the Nazis were gone. Still others felt that the "Super," as the H-bomb was called, would only take the world to hell faster.

The opposing camp had leading scientists too. Whatever their feelings about Hiroshima, or war in general, or that unique form of perpetual motion called an arms race, they saw no choice but self-defense and limited their doubts to whether the Super was possible. For example, Nobelist Harold Urey: "I am very unhappy . . . but I do not think we should unintentionally lose the armaments race."

This was the situation that layman members of Congress walked into boldly. Chairman Brien McMahon of the Joint Committee on Atomic Energy authorized Representative Holifield to tour the nation with a special subcommittee. It listened to the experts, put the opinions through its mental computer, reported back in clear language: the thermonuclear weapon was a good gamble technically, and strategically we had no choice. We could not risk Russia's building such a weapon ahead of us. The full committee voted 16 to 2 for this recommendation. When it reached President Truman, he sought additional advice. Agreement came, surprisingly, from even his political foe, former Vice President Henry A. Wallace, an idealistic hater of war.

But these were laymen dealing with military science. And agreement was not yet forthcoming from the special agency that would handle the crash program. This was the United States Atomic Energy Commission. Among the checks and balances set up for the atom after the war, Congress had created the AEC and commissioned it to carry our nuclear R & D on its shoulders—"war atom" in one bucket, "peace atom" in the other. The AEC's five commissioners, four of them laymen, were now sorely troubled because of that split among scientists, which was serious. With Teller, for example, was Norris Bradbury, head of Los Alamos Laboratory. So was John von Neumann. Everybody was fond of this truly great mathematical physicist, and he had won considerable support for Congressman Holifield's proposal. But against the Super were luminaries too. The opposition rallied around Robert Oppenheimer, von Neumann's friend and first director of Los Alamos, where he supervised construction of the first A-bombs. Though now an academician again, he had not entirely retired from the materialistic world. He headed the AEC's special coterie of experts called the General Advisory Committee, a fact that made his opposition to the H-bomb all the more potent. Not surprisingly, therefore, only one AEC commissioner, Lewis L. Strauss, discarded Oppenheimer's recommendation. Eventually, Gordon Dean was argued into aligning himself with Strauss.

But time was fleeing. Evidence had been accumulating since the war that spies had given Russia A-bomb information; there was now growing suspicion that she also had data on what we knew about fusion. So, though AEC was still 3-to-2 against the program, President Truman, on January 30, 1950, ordered it to proceed with the R & D. This blunt action might seem in agreement with AEC Chairman David Lilienthal's frequent declaration, "Scientists should be on tap, not on top." But this time two laymen were disagreeing. Lilienthal resigned.

It was now up to the bomb-makers to prove they could produce. The more so because five months later came another shuddering tremor. It was the Korean War, bad enough in itself, and with new proof that, for one reason or another, our stockpile of A-bombs was no more effective than the UN in guaranteeing peace. Did this mean Russia was already well advanced toward an H-bomb? Von Neumann hurried the elaborate computer he had designed for the research program. The laboratories worked on and in May 1951, sixteen months after Truman's directive, came proof that the fusion idea would work. Another eighteen months, and in the South Pacific came our first test shot. But nine months after that—a new tremor. In August 1953 Russia joined the H-club with her own first test shot. We had gotten the bomb more easily than expected, and apparently in the nick of time, but this hardly presaged utopia. Apparently, the cursed atom would not let us be. Now, for the first time, we had the awkward feeling of looking up the mouth end of the nuclear gun. Nuclear physics was no longer only the foreigner's problem. A leading bomb physicist expressed it glumly: "That test marked our entry into a very disagreeable type of world." If Russia was a bear, so were we; and each had the other by the tail. Sane men in Washington, and presumably Moscow, had to plan using a weapon that nobody but a maniac would use.

The American public, busily overtaking prosperity and the postwar pleasure it had promised itself, was slow to grasp the meaning of all this. But there was little cheer among policy-makers. The new president, Dwight Eisenhower, had inherited an H-bomb which was a blessing only in the sense that having no H-bomb would be worse. The Korean war dragged on miserably. McCarthyism was in full flower. And in the Pentagon, guerrilla war. There the unification that wasn't unification had led our first Secretary of Defense, Truman's James Forrestal, to kill himself. The difference was that Eisenhower's Charles E. ("Engine Charlie") Wilson, ex-president of General Motors, didn't fling himself out of a window. But though he used meat-ax methods to bring interservice peace and parsimony, the target always seemed to shift and the ax met thin air. The rest wasn't peaceful either. For one thing, there was the continuing argument—superbombs dropped by strategic bombers versus smaller nuclear weapons for ground battle. The argument had gone past mere theory. General James M. Gavin, chief of Army's R & D, urged that tactical weapons be used against "a number of well worthwhile nuclear targets in North Korea." Across the Pacific, General Douglas MacArthur had thought likewise and offered a postscript: to end the Korean War, he wanted to "sanitize" the Korean ground with radioactive cobalt. But there was no need. Eventually, according to Sherman Adams, who was Eisenhower's chief assistant, reports were leaked to Red China that the United States was ready to use nuclear weapons if the fighting didn't stop. An armistice followed.

But all such troubles combined were dwarfed by a unique legacy of Hiroshima. Overreliance on the nuclear bomb had made our military science flabby. Just as the British, because they were vulnerable to Nazi bombers, had developed radar, so the Russians, while still without an A-bomb, and without a world-wide system of bomber bases such as ours, were concentrating on rocketry. Yes, America also showed some interest in the prospect of shooting warheads rather than dropping gravity bombs. For instance, Army's ballistic-missiles program led by our German import, the V-2 expert Wernher von Braun. But our military rocketry was still puny—and seemed a rivalry among Army, Navy, and Air Force rather than rivalry with Russia. Once, airpower had been the small boy, bullied in Billy Mitchell days by Army. Now, Air Force was the big fellow, and its heart was primarily with bigger, faster bombers, secondarily with an unmanned bomber like Navaho, a project that consumed $700 million before it was mercifully killed. Meanwhile, to protect its bombers, manned or not, Air Force staked out and fought for its claim to be in charge of their rival—ballistic missiles. Eventually, for instance, came the Pentagon's memorable order that forbade Army to develop any missile with a range of over 200 miles.

Now Eisenhower, unlike both his predecessor and successor, had small zest for congressional politics; and in his preferred role as a unifying Cincinnatus home from the wars he also steered away from Pentagon politics. He preferred to do no more about the wrangling than occasionally lose his temper. But a ballistic-missile decision faced him soon. Like Truman's decision on the H-bomb, it would write history. And as with Truman, he was a layman in need of wise counsel. For despite his war record, Eisenhower could hardly know the complicated R & D of nuclear airpower.

The changed missile situation was this. Russia had just exploded her test H-bomb. Very well, we had done so nine months earlier. But the bomb was meaningless without a way to deliver it. We had intercontinental bombers, of course, just as we had smaller missiles fired by planes and at planes.

But there had been still another tremor, the fearsome reports that Russia was far ahead with ICBMs—intercontinental ballistic missiles. Understandably so. The budget for our R & D of ballistic missiles in the year Eisenhower took office was $1 million—less, he noted, than what we spent to support the price of peanuts.

The problem for experts, then, was this. Granted that we wanted to survive, granted that Russia still had considerable R & D to do, what was our best hope for checkmate?

Accordingly, Defense Secretary Wilson had an Air Force Strategic Missiles Evaluation Committee assembled under chairmanship of von Neumann, the mathematician extraordinary who had been in both the A-bomb and H-bomb projects. Others on the committee were experts in rocketry, electronics, aeronautics, and the like. Among them were George Kistiakowsky, the Harvard chemist who later became Eisenhower's chief science adviser, and Jerome B. Wiesner, the MIT electrical engineering professor who succeeded him in the Kennedy administration.

The committee recommendation, which became the decision in 1954, was to make haste. How? By benefiting from our fusion warhead. Its high power but small size would allow designing light, less complicated ICBMs—missiles that consequently could be ready for production sooner: by 1960 or so. This could keep us abreast of the Russians.

A purely military decision, of course. It disregarded—in fact, it overlooked—the possibility that these missiles would lack enough thrust to launch spaceships. That oversight would have to be remedied later. But because a "satellite lag," which did exist, was confused later with "missile lag," which terrified the nation needlessly, the reason for the decision makes interesting reading. Here is how two of the advisory scientists recall it:

1. "You must look at the start of the program. The Russians didn't have an atomic bomb then. They had to have a 6000-pound warhead. You sit down and calculate what you need for 6000 pounds. It comes out 800,000 pounds of thrust. Later, they had an atomic bomb; they already had a missile built for a nonatomic warhead, so they were in beautiful shape. Actually it was our advance in nuclear energy which caused us to cut this thing down."

2. "Development time would be very much longer if we stayed with the proposal to create ICBMs in the class of 750,000 pounds of thrust, whereas if the thrust were cut to something like 300,000 pounds, then a development time of 5 to 7 years appeared reasonable. If the program were to take beyond that, a serious threat to the United States would exist."

Such, then, was to be the grand strategy. And Air Force was told to begin with the Atlas missile, which it had only toyed with since 1951. Until Atlas and other missiles were ready, America would sweat through somehow: with its radar warnings against invading bombers, and its own bomber fleet for massive retaliation; with a Civil Defense shelter program, if it could arouse enough interest; with nuclear-propelled submarines, a field where we were probably far ahead (our first, the *Nautilus*, had just been launched and would be on patrol in a year); with shorter-range missiles (for instance, they could use some of Atlas's components and be ready sooner); with a foreign policy that tried to exude confidence, even unto State Department brinksmanship.

More complicated than rocket science itself are the ramifications of how the rocketry program progressed. However, one phase tells much, and also illustrates what Eisenhower eventually wrapped into his warning against a "military-industrial complex."

At the outset, the von Neumann committee saw a management problem. The Air Force had not tilled the science field very well; it obviously couldn't direct the R & D part of a program so interdisciplinary—computers, rocketry, nuclear warheads, inertial guidance, radar. Neither could the usual aerospace company. Moreover, this military program would run into billions of dollars, dwarfing any that the nation had ever tried. Financially and technically, therefore, it would be too risky for the conventional method: a prime contractor trying to govern subcontractors.

Eisenhower was tempted at first to take the entire plan away from the regular military and set up a government-administered independent crash program like the Manhattan project, which had produced the A-bomb. But this, he wrote later, might waste work already done and cost precious time. Another idea was to persuade a brainy center like Caltech or MIT to be technical director of the program. These, however, shied away. Already embarrassed with a surfeit of government R & D contracts, each saw that this might erase whatever remained of its image as an educational institution. MIT was an outstanding example. Its radar had come to the nation's defense. After the war it happily tore down the temporary Radiation Laboratory. But following Russia's first nuclear test, MIT was drafted again. Combining its latest computers with its latest radar, it developed SAGE, the emergency system to guide our home defense against enemy bombers; then, farther north, the DEW line, to warn against aircraft approaching from over the North Pole. Those were guards against air-breathers—conventional bombers. But the missile threat brought the need for additional defense, so MIT took on the BMEWS (Ballistic Missile Early Warning System). With such projects, and much else, MIT felt it was doing its duty sufficiently.

What about missiles of our own? Wouldn't anybody, help manage those billions of dollars? History's fascination is that it springs surprises. Or, as Wiesner explained later, the solution "was an accident of the time and the situation."

Also on the eleven-man committee were two active forty-year-olds who had earned *cum laude* Ph.D.s at Caltech: Simon Ramo, in electrical engineering and physics; Dean Wooldridge, in physics. They knew the Air Force well. Both had been executives in Hughes Aircraft Company; both had wearied of serving the moody Howard Hughes. And it happened that in September 1953, a month before the committee had its first meeting, they had set up their own little company in Los Angeles. Backing them financially was Thompson Products, an elderly company that made precision parts for the automotive and aircraft industries. This was the start of the Ramo-Wooldridge Corporation, which sought contracts in defense and electronics. Its interests were broad. It would do anything from consultant work to manufacturing.

When the committee met, it felt the need for a technical staff. Along with being committee members, Drs. Ramo and Wooldridge had a company that could provide such services. Accordingly, their company was hired to do the necessary studies; then it roughed out the committee report. This report stressed the need for something new in the way of managing such an immense "systems engineering" program. All R & D should be coordinated and supervised by a special technical management agency. A few months later, Ramo-Wooldridge was awarded the Air Force contract; thus "they became in a sense the beneficiaries of their own handiwork."

From here, the story becomes even more complicated, partly because, the General Accounting Office later complained to Congress, its investigators were hampered by Air Force refusal to supply all the records. However, the missile program progressed and with it the prosperity of R-W. This was only partly because R-W began work at a fee of 14.3 per cent, which later stabilized at around 10 per cent. Also, the magnitude of the program was increasing. It had started with high-priority Atlas. Soon, for a choice if one or the other failed, the more powerful Titan was added, and then the second-generation ICBM called Minuteman—smaller, cheaper, and promising to obsolete both. Work also moved ahead with the medium-range Thor, which, in turn, was duplicated by Army's Jupiter. In five years the ICBM program and Thor brought $100 million in management contracts to R-W, which was riding herd on thirty major contractors, two hundred major subcontractors, and a veritable army of scientists, engineers, and technicians. The assets of R-W rose from $248,000 to $40 million. But this prosperity had still another source. Though, in its management capacity, R-W was forbidden to sell hardware to that program, it was free to manufacture and sell elsewhere. Its market eventually included hardware for satellites as well as a variety of other missiles.

Inevitably, this wearing of two hats brought complications (Wiesner: "There arose a growing concern about the conflict between what they were doing for the Air Force and what they were doing for themselves"). The oldest of the Air Force "not-for-profit" auxiliaries, the Rand Corporation, sniped continually at its "for-profit rival." Also, rival manufacturers were complaining that R-W, in its management role, had access to their engineering and trade secrets. Consequently, Congress was becoming highly aware, and critical, of an arrangement that had been evolving through years of necessary military secrecy.

So, in 1958, with a share of its original $2 stock now worth $831, R-W reshuffled itself. It merged with its original financial backer to form Thompson Ramo Wooldridge Inc., and set up Space Technology Laboratories to do the missile supervision for Air Force. This subsidiary had its own board of directors, with retired General James Doolittle as chairman. But the shift really solved nothing. Stating "we have a firmly established profit objective realistically related to the facts of life of our business," the subsidiary tried to charge Air Force, therefore the taxpayer, a 14.8-per-cent fee for its services.

At any time this might seem overly ambitious. In a state of cold war, with the nation confronting nuclear holocaust, it sounded as if the company had allowed indispensability to smother its good sense. Congress, complaining that Air Force had "shifted the fate of the nation to a private contractor," demanded an end to the arrangement. So Air Force complied with a task force that found an answer: Air Force created the private "nonprofit" Aerospace Corporation to take over the controversial work. Its president was Ivan Getting, recruited from Raytheon Corporation, the electronics company, where he had been vice president for R & D. Chairman of its board was Roswell Gilpatric, a corporation lawyer who had been Undersecretary of the Air Force (and later moved back to the Pentagon as Undersecretary of Defense). Others on the board were likewise leaders in the military-industry-university world of science.

This solution was no serious blow to the R-W complex. The big thrust of R & D for the ICBM program had now passed its peak anyway. The R-W complex, with a fund of inside knowledge about the defense program that was of incalculable value, was now unhampered in its competition for other business, from Air Force as well as Army, Navy, NASA. It could manufacture hardware, without embarrassment, for such projects as Pershing, Bomarc, Polaris, Samos, Tiros, Transit, Courier, Advent, Relay, OGO, Nike-Zeus, Able-Star, Tartar, Terrier, and Minuteman too. And not only aerospace projects. As Ramo put it, "Batteries, bugs, or what you will— we're in it."

While Ramo was the more ebullient of the two, Wooldridge was restive in his own way. In 1962, though the company's annual sales had passed $400 million, he resigned his $100,000-a-year presidency so that he could return to research and do some writing. But he couldn't resist national affairs altogether. Soon he was heading a White House study of the health-research program, which, among other problems, needed a decision about consultants who both award research grants and receive them.

There had also been growing mistrust of the tax-exempt "nonprofits," of which, ironically, R-W's successor, Aerospace, was one example. Industry detested what it called their unfair competition. It was no secret in Congress or elsewhere that not all government "fees" paid them went for salaries and research. They were building up their plants, and some were salting away surplus in "kitties." Meanwhile, their tax-exempt status enabled them to shop for the cream of scientific talent. Simultaneously, they undermined the government's own Civil Service. Everybody knew they were simply a quasi-governmental device to attract the talent with more money than government could legally pay. In ex-AEC Chairman David Lilienthal's words: "Super civil servants who perform governmental functions, yet who are independent of government obligations; men recruited for and paid and supervised as if they were in private employment, virtually immune from the tough, essential, distinguishing characteristic of democratic processes of public life, the essence of which is direct accountability, in the open air, to public lay scrutiny."

Modern science was apparently getting into situations too complex —policy-making as well as financial—for normal government supervision. It had long been lectured to participate in the nation's life. Now, in these Eisenhower years of a war just this side of suicidal shooting war, it was doing so. But not healthily. Not only were its leaders growing powerful; their influence was a bit too pervasive. It mattered little whether the man's start was in industry, in government, at a university. Soon enough, he would appear elsewhere. He bobbed up continually—consultant, chairman, panelist, academician, lobbyist . . . awarding contracts, winning contracts . . . advising a nonprofit, directing a government program, heading a university department, running an industrial laboratory. In this jungle of conflicting interests, whether they were successive or simultaneous, to whom did his allegiance belong at any frozen moment?

For the time being, however, military protection was paramount. As early as Geneva's "Summit Conference" in 1955 it was apparent that a nuclear stalemate was approaching or had already come; the rest would be R & D by each side to keep the other from springing a technological surprise. But at what cost, in scientific manpower drained from other things that America needed; in the growing power of a military-science establishment; and, of course, in money? The total bill for cold war was enormous.

What began as emergency programs became entrenched. Atlas and Titan went on backstopping each other until both ICBMs were eventually phased out by Minuteman. Among medium-range missiles, Thor and Jupiter went on too, without cancellation of either $1-billion project, and both were operational by 1959. Meanwhile, there had been the short-lived treaty between Army and Navy to develop Jupiter jointly. But Jupiter burned liquid fuel; for its needs, Navy preferred solid fuel. So, in 1956, delighted with its nuclear-powered submarine, excited over the hope for using it as a missile-launcher, Navy was allowed to go off on its own. Thus was born remarkable Polaris, which at once made both Jupiter and Thor obsolete and even rivaled the ICBMs.

Obviously, then, all was not waste. Each missile offered a chance to develop the art. But much of it, as investigation showed later, was rich opportunity for gouging the customer. There were the pork-barrel lobbies demanding aerospace projects for the needy workers back home. There were the special pressure groups; though self-propelled missiles were decreed the weapon of the future, R & D continued for newer bombers. And, to justify these, there was Sky-bolt, the nuclear-tipped missile they would launch; this $2.3-billion program was not abandoned until the $500-million mark. There were the undecided experts and the billion dollars they dropped on the program to develop a nuclear-powered plane. There was the technology that spent $300 million on Army's guided missile called LaCrosse, which won a reputation of being unable to hit any target but the Treasury. And so on and on.

Through it all ran a disturbing pattern of profiteering. There was clear-cut bribery or collusion. More pervasive were the respectable ways. There were the cost-plus contracts whereby a project could eventually cost ten times the amount budgeted. There was a variety of "negotiation" methods whereby the Pentagon could legally side-track competitive bidding and award to the company whose services it preferred; two-thirds of the contracts fell into this category. Bidding, too, could be outmaneuvered. With "liar's poker," for instance, a company bid very low, even taking a loss, on the initial research; this made it indispensable and it could fatten its follow-up contracts on that project. Also, of course, there was pyramiding. An example is the $1.5-billion program to provide Army with Nike missile pro-tection against enemy bombers. Here, a Senate committee found that the prime contractor, Western Electric, earned $112.5 million, a 31-per-cent profit on its $359-million share of the program, by also levying the allowed 7.9 per cent on the work done by sub-contractors, who delivered their products directly to Army. Similarly, its chief subcontractor, Douglas Aircraft, was charged with having taken $63.8 million profit, of which $37 million was markups on work done by *its* subcontractors.

The defense industry was not without rejoinders: This was national emergency; the government was buying the best special technical skills available; the companies were being begged to interrupt normal business and produce things that only one customer, the Pentagon, would buy—with the risk of a government program being changed and even canceled. Therefore, said Senator Sam Ervin, they should "receive profits substantially in excess of those who produce stable goods for sale to the general public."

This much was clear. Science had become indispensable. Science was fully aware of its indispensability. And, in military science anyway, the normal processes of democratic government were undergoing change. Science, government, and industry were working out a special relationship.

Eisenhower saw some of this. What he saw was a complex he didn't like. So? History will have to wade through the paper mountain and make the decision about this war hero taunted for not being heroic in the White House. He compromised: with the Russians; with the Pentagon; with the Democrats, who controlled Congress during the last six of his eight presidential years. Was he, then, a "do-nothing President," or a compromising Hamlet, who was plainly mad—or was he? Or was Eisenhower plainly simple, or was he? Maybe he was sincere in disliking the role of a general cracking the whip over a civilian Congress. Certainly he hated war. He also hated what the arms race was doing to his budgets, and what that might mean. In *The Ordeal of Power* his speechwriter Emmett J. Hughes recalls an Ike-like outburst: "If we let defense spending run wild, you get inflation, then controls, then a garrison state . . . and then we've lost the very values we were trying to defend."

Yet he held his fire. Was he simply putting first things first in his uncomplicated fashion? Through "atoms-for-peace" programs and the like, he tried to prove America's sincerity. With equal directness, through rearming, he warned the Kremlin that another war would be mutually senseless suicide. Meanwhile, he worried about this complex new power called science.

Then, on October 4, 1957, with the nation as serene as cold war could allow, came the decade's worst tremor. It struck with all the impact of another Pearl Harbor. Not a devastating surprise attack this time. Nor even the report of some new enemy bomb or death ray. But certainly novel—the impudent beeping over our heads of an orbiting thing called *Sputnik*, earth's first artificial satellite. The USSR had launched this contribution to IGY—the International Geophysical Year. It was a crude affair carrying simple scientific instruments, but it weighed 184 pounds. A month later came *Sputnik II*, a half-ton this time, even carrying a passenger, the dog Laika.

And America the powerful? For its contribution to IGY it was still pathetically trying to hoist a little satellite that Russia's Khrushchev tauntingly, and accurately, called grapefruit-size. While we focused on matching his missiles he had taken a new lead. He now splashed happily in the new ocean called Space, showing his muscle, playing with a scientific toy that had potential. It could eventually make ballistic missiles even more obsolete than they had made bombers.

The enemy was again twelve feet tall. Eisenhower's first reaction was to reassure the nation that its satellite program was strictly scientific, not part of the missile program. This didn't work. Our ego was in tatters; our fears were of the unfathomable. The monstrous Martian had become a Russian. Scientists trooped to Washington again with their advice. A skeptical Congress demanded something to fill the "vacuum" of executive leadership.

The situation was bad enough without that oversimplification:

1. Our science, concentrating on military hardware, had neglected Space. Even in theory it had fallen behind. Only after scouring the nation, for example, did Vanguard, our first satellite project, find a professor who knew celestial mechanics well enough to calculate orbits reliably. This kind of mathematics, once fashionable among astronomers, had virtually vanished.

2. Our satellite work needed a strong boost from the military, but didn't get it because Buck Rogers could not compete with the missiles race. Not that a satellite need be a pacifist. It might spy. It might be a space platform for launching weapons. It might destroy an enemy satellite. And it would be boosted missile-fashion, the essential difference being that it wasn't a warhead. But satellite weapons were still far out, and warheads were needed now. Even Navy, hospitable

to "pure" science, glad to build and launch Vanguard for the National Academy of Sciences and the National Science Foundation, could hardly give top priority to the IGY project.

3. Our propaganda instinct failed us. Despite our Madison Avenue, our CIA, our Voice of America, and the like, we overlooked what Russia saw: the tangible value of prestige. So Russia, working harder on satellites, reaped her reward. Like Americans, people throughout the world confused satellites with missiles. Ergo, our missile program was a failure; America was a paper tiger.

4. Our internal communications broke down. Somehow, our batteries of computers, information specialists, and "think tanks" ground out the esoteric and missed the obvious. The Sputniks need not have been so startling. All through 1957 Russia was boasting of satellite progress and announcing her timetable. In this, at least, she was neither deceptive nor secretive.

The sum total was a sorry testimonial for technocracy. Apparently no expert had given our layman policy-makers—Congress, the President, or anybody else—a crisp, understandable, unbiased, accurate memo that wrapped up the situation and stressed the need for something more than letting snafu take its course.

Fortunately for world peace, however, the Kremlin didn't believe its own taunts about America's puny power. In this same Sputnik year, while Russia still tested her ICBMs, our Air Force began testing its first one, the Atlas. Medium-range Thor and Jupiter were ordered into production. Polaris was ready for its first launching test.

Our missile program seemed on schedule and was now being accelerated. Eventually there was suspicion that we had been hoaxed by Khrushchev, that Russia's missile-rattling had been to give *her* time to arm. Eventually, too, the Pentagon had to be reminded that it had overconcentrated on Overkill, that there weren't enemy targets enough for all our missile power, that it was no longer in a seller's market, that it could demand quality from the aerospace industry's salesmen rather than quantity, that it was time for such refinements as a truly aimed missile.

But what to do about Space? The satellite uproar brought Army to Navy's rescue: Three months after the first Sputnik, a Jupiter launched our first IGY contribution, *Explorer I*. Two months later,

Navy finally hoisted its first Vanguard. The satellite promptly began demonstrating that nice things can come in small, even grapefruit-size, packages. Not until 1964, long after its beeping had outlasted signals from all other orbiters, did *Vanguard I* finally go silent. In that six years it taught science much. For their radio, the Sputniks used chemical batteries. Making a virtue of necessity, tiny Vanguard resorted to wafer-like solar cells that converted power from sunlight. And it demonstrated something surprising—its orbit could be changed merely by the pressure of sunlight. Science began dreaming of sailships in Space some day—their sails moved by sunlight.

But Explorer and Vanguard were emergency measures. Anybody could see that the space program could no longer drift. And now, with the missile pressure relaxing, the chance had come to help nonmilitary science. One thing was obvious. Russia could boost massive payloads because she was using those same brute-thrust rockets designed before she had the lightweight nuclear warheads. We had not needed them—for warheads. For spaceships we did. Thus began the planning of rockets packing 1,000,000, 5,000,000, even 20,000,000 pounds of thrust; Vanguard's booster had only 37,000 and even then had given trouble.

But who was to do all this?

Four days after the second Sputnik, Eisenhower told a television audience that MIT had been summoned to the rescue again. This time it was contributing its President James B. Killian, to give science "an impressive new voice in the inner circles of government." He would be an American President's first personal science adviser; he would help on all matters concerning national security. For support he was given the President's Science Advisory Committee. It had been moribund through the years when military science, with its Edward Teller, Ramo-Wooldridge, and others, was the favored wizard.

Thus another branch of the elite—the "civilians" now—had been summoned to power. And it began putting through *its* emergency programs. Funds were increased for badly needed basic research in aeronautics. With equal foresight the National Defense Education Act provided a billion dollars for more science teaching and for loans to worthy students. Here was another use for the alarums of war. That galvanizing word "defense" made possible something long overdue. It opened wider the doors of higher education, as the GI Bill had already done for actual veterans, to those whose only inferiority was financial. This was helpful. It infused the elite with vigorous barbarian blood.

In the excitement, even the National Science Foundation was at last given a concrete mission. It had been created back in 1950, after five years of congressional debate over just what work it should do. Now, after more debate, its budget was tripled and it was ordered to hurry—to equip more laboratories, produce more postgraduates, spend less time examining the merit of proposals. This crash program to create creativity was therefore a Maecenas fated to show many failings; it was not entirely NSF's fault that, as its budgets rose to a half-billion dollars, it became the softest touch in the government.

At any rate, the civilian trend was plain to see, and openly announced. Concerning Sputniks it became official policy that only the purely military projects would be run by the Pentagon. The rest of Space would be civilian territory. Here would be opportunity for such others as AEC, NSF, State Department, the quasi-governmental National Academy of Sciences; but sorely needed was an agency devoted only to meeting the space challenge, an independent agency that would work with other branches of government, with universities, with industry, yet wouldn't abdicate its R & D responsibilities as Air Force had done in the missile program.

From this concept arose mammoth NASA—the National Aeronautics and Space Administration, created by the Space Act of 1958. Six years later, its R & D expenditures—"in-house" and outside— were past an annual $5 billion, only $2 billion less than the Pentagon's research bill. But money doesn't tell the whole story. Here was a sparkling example of a democracy meeting an emergency. It also demonstrated the silliness of clichés. "Big Science" could be good or bad, depending on circumstances. Here, for such goals as reaching moon and Mars, science had to be big. The only choice could be whether it be big like a heavyweight champion or big like a stumble-bum.

Congress had been more than eager to help make NASA big. Here would be something different from the AEC, which was troublesome. Not only did it hold itself aloof; its duenna, the Joint Committee on Atomic Energy, blocked porkbarrel treatment of the atom. Where to build a nuclear plant was strictly an engineering matter: it required abundant water and abundant electric power, yet it was too "hot" to be near a population center. A former AEC commissioner chuckled when he told me about one of the hopefuls. "This congressman said he didn't care where the new plant went, as long as it went to Alabama. We put the Savannah River plant in South Carolina."

Sputniks weren't so touchy. They promised vast contracts for the aerospace and electronics people back home. Here, frankly, was the chance for a growing opportunity called Space, which could become a great new industry and mayhap take up the unemployment slack if the arms race slowed down.

Not that Congress considered only contracts and payrolls. There was genuine fright over Russia's lead. And there was something else—a challenge. Here could be a new frontier. No one tingled with more excitement over the prospects than did Lyndon B. Johnson, the Senate majority leader. His imagination leaped higher than Eisenhower's. And, unlike Eisenhower, the Texan reveled in politics. He set out to make himself chief architect of the space program.

There were other candidates and dozens of plans for overnight salvation, including the cure-all that would bypass the Pentagon's preserves but scoop most of the government's other R & D together into a new cabinet department to be presided over by a Secretary of Science and Technology. Johnson lived up to his reputation for canniness. He concentrated on setting up a potent Senate Aeronautical and Space Sciences Committee, of which he became the chairman and driving force. Though it failed to take nuclear rockets and planes away from the joint atomic energy committee, it became overseer of all else concerning Space. It fashioned NASA unto its liking. Likewise, it set up a top coordinating body, the National Aeronautics and Space Council. And when Johnson became Vice President, he moved on to head this council, whose membership also included the Secretaries of State and Defense and the heads of NASA and AEC.

Not that NASA was born full-panoplied like Minerva. It came from agglutination. The nucleus was an off-trail agency called the National Advisory Committee for Aeronautics. Since 1915, NACA had been doing basic research that kept industry and the armed forces up-to-date on the art of flying. Now, its staff of 8400 and its four laboratories, including John Stack's famed wind-tunnel one at Langley, became NASA. By the year's end, Army had formally surrendered its Jet Propulsion Laboratory in California. Meanwhile, NASA was starting its own construction program. First, in nearby Maryland, came the Goddard Space Flight Center, which was to build prototype satellites as well as be the tracking and communications center for NASA space machines, manned and unmanned. The nucleus here was a band of émigrés from Navy's Vanguard and Upper Atmosphere research staffs. NASA never got recruits more zealous than those Vanguard men, convinced that their project had been a "patsy" for blunders elsewhere. Under NASA's circular emblem—the red wishbone flaring across blue Space and the white orbit of a satellite circling moon and earth—they became a cheering section for the triumphal space bus called Delta. Its first stage was a Thor. The two upper stages were from Vanguard's unhappy rocket. Each time Delta put up another Telstar or Relay or Tiros and the like, the Vanguard men cheered. When I visited Goddard the rocket had flawlessly performed sixteen consecutive missions, and nervousness was growing. This couldn't last. Finally, on the twenty-third, Delta burned out too soon to orbit its payload, a 120-pound satellite experimenting with laser rays. But NASA, delighted with America's "most reliable space vehicle," had fourteen more on order from Douglas.

Scientists generally welcomed the NASA idea—at first. Here was civilian control. And NASA's first administrator, T. Keith Glennan, was from their world—president of Case Institute of Technology, a former AEC commissioner, and a man with a fabulous reputation as a money-raiser, which was no handicap. Columbus had needed a backer, so had the Elizabethan explorers. There was no talk, yet, of crash programs and racing Russia to the moon. NASA's goal seemed more scientific—to investigate the new ocean in all possible ways; and very laudable—for the benefit of America and all mankind.

This asked much, of course. Clearly, America was staking out its claim as a spacefaring nation. And, just as the highly regarded Atomic Energy Act had ordered civilian scientists of AEC to work closely with the Pentagon, for obvious reasons, NASA's mandate included an injunction to cooperate with the military as required, again for obvious reasons. Furthermore, the cooperation could be one-sided, as NASA learned when its flashing-light geodetic satellite was snatched away by the Department of Defense and turned into secret project ANNA, after which DOD promptly did nothing with it, "due to internal difficulties." With such cooperation, NASA was soon regarded as a weak "fourth arm" of the Pentagon. But as NASA feathered out, it became a cock quite able to resist Air Force attempts to invade outer Space, and second only to DOD in the pecking order of Washington R & D agencies.

Inevitably, however, other fowl began sounding alarms over NASA's increasing thirst for congressional appropriations and such other unseemly behavior as its raids upon government agencies as well as industry for the scientific manpower it needed. And so, as we shall see, was born a coalition of non-space scientists against an informal coalition of spacemen.

However, the first vigorous complaint seems to have come from a layman, from Eisenhower, who realized only a few weeks after the first Sputnik that satellite scientists could be as demanding as missile scientists. Biographer Hughes records this burst: "First, these science boys come to me and want 22 million dollars—and I say, 'Sure.' After a while they want 60-odd million more, and I say, 'Fine.' So they pack some trickier instruments into the thing—and want 80 million or so more. And I say, 'Okay.' But finally—when they say they need another 150 million dollars, I have to say, 'Just a minute, fellows. Where does all this *end*?' "

Washington's troubles were not only with the engineering sciences. Biology was responding to the times. From their wartime laboratories emerged physicists seeking new excitement after radar and the like. Some of them, invading life science with their theory and instruments, helped create molecular biology, which was soon in hot pursuit of the genetic code.

But most of the upsurge of interest was pragmatic. The new wartime drugs catalyzed biochemistry to seek more wonder antibiotics, more wonder vitamins and hormones, and, soon, more tranquilizers and vaccines. Here was science that dealt with cures for aches, pains, and stress, with drugs against killers. Such science, laymen could eagerly support. Congress was soon embarrassing medical research with demands for quick cancer remedies and breakthroughs for "hearts too young to die."

In a grim way, Eisenhower and other important laymen personally added to the stir. There was Majority Leader Johnson's heart attack in June 1955. Then Eisenhower's, three months later, which was more severe and certainly more dramatic; through newspapers and television a worried public identified itself with his plight and recovery. There had already been the poignant spectacle of crippled Franklin Roosevelt maneuvering his big polio-stricken body through twelve years in the White House, followed by his fatal cerebral hemorrhage. There was cancer's victory over John Foster Dulles, Eisenhower's Secretary of State. And crutches constantly reminded the public how badly Dulles's successor, Christian Herter, was afflicted with arthritis. Each of these was a dramatic challenge to research.

And it was driven by the powerful voice of the people. Experience with Social Security whetted the desire for more security: for group medical plans and government medicare and cures. Even living with dread that the Bomb might drop at any moment seemed to make no difference. On the contrary, Americans were breeding more prolifically than expected after the war. Anthropologist Margaret Mead scorned this as "a retreat into fecundity." Perhaps it was simply ecology at work. Simple creature or not, the human dutifully obeys nature's supreme demand. The race must go on. Save the mother; spare the child; smother the peril with more babies—a survival tactic that Darwin would have understood. Blindly or not, it sought what he called "success in leaving offspring."

From many directions, therefore, converged the demands upon government to help the aged, the stricken, the pregnant, the infants, the genetically misshapen, and also those who were merely the effects of a civilization gone flabby. When government reorganizers created a new cabinet-level department in 1953, the first plan was to call it simply the Department of Public Welfare. But this lacked the charm word "health," so the name became Department of Health, Education and Welfare. Eventually, with HEW's activities as the nucleus, government was supporting two-thirds of the nation's medical research.

Especially favored by Congress was HEW's major research component, the National Institutes of Health, whose nine units— National Cancer Institute, National Heart Institute, etc.,—comprise a bureau of HEW's Public Health Service. Its budgets grew in ten years from $81 million to $1 billion. The enthusiasm for NIH gave Washington something new in budget warfare. In Eisenhower years, and later as well, Congress insisted on adding another 25 per cent or so to the budget requests for NIH. Nor was NIH required to state its programs. It could hardly have done so anyway. Its troubled director, James A. Shannon, a scientist rather than trained administrator, acknowledged that he found it hard to use so much money usefully.

Consequently, NIH prospered in odd fashion. There was no doubt, of course, that its research opportunities were unlimited. Man's ignorance of his body is abysmal. Accordingly, the hope was to make NIH the world's outstanding medical research center. But it could hardly expect its own labs to do all the work, or even the major part. So it also had to be a dispenser of research grants. But to whom should they go, and for what? NIH thereupon began retaining non-government scientists as consultants to apportion the hundreds of millions it could grant their universities, medical schools, and the like. In this way NIH unloaded the bulk of its annual funds. But here came a boomerang we have seen before. The outsiders, thus financed, began luring topflight researchers from the government's own laboratories. They could offer perhaps double the money allowed under Civil Service.

Closer to the public was another side-effect. In a nation already disturbed by its shortage of capable physicians, the massive NIH spending for research was luring medical teachers and medical students away from the art of healing. Research was easy money and more glamorous.

Another result was a bouillabaisse of dedicated science mixed with mere spending. Like the National Science Foundation, the NIH became an "easy touch." Luther L. Terry, the Surgeon General, tried to pacify Representative John E. Fogarty, who complained that grantees were complaining about their being audited: "Well, there are a lot of people, researchers, who want you to have a barrel of gold coins, give them a shovel, let them dip out what they need, and not give an accounting."

At any rate, NIH could hardly provide a horror picture of research crushed by government interference. The domineering seemed to be from the opposite direction.

The 1960s

Eisenhower's administration ended in January 1961. Shortly before that he was visited by a group of senators. One of them recalls that the President, after discussing other matters, launched into a surprising and worried analysis of the increasing powers of science. Apparently it was much on his mind. Soon he was saying the same thing in his farewell speech to the nation. It startled the science establishment. He had not discussed it with his own science adviser, Kistiakowsky of Harvard, who had succeeded MIT's Killian and was an influential member of the National Academy.

Eisenhower warned against "the acquisition of unwarranted influence, whether sought or unsought, by the military-industrial complex," then he continued: ". . . Akin to and largely responsible for the sweeping changes has been the technological revolution during recent decades. Today, the military inventor, tinkering in his shop, has been overshadowed by task forces of scientists in laboratories and testing fields. In the same fashion, the free university, historically the fountainhead of free ideas and scientific discovery, has experienced a revolution in the conduct of research. . . . In holding scientific research in respect, as we should, we must also be alert to the equal and opposite danger that public policy could itself become the captive of a scientific-technological elite."

Truman had handled the postwar burden of the A-bomb and passed on the new burden of cold war. Eisenhower had handled that burden but, doing so, had allowed this new one to grow. Now, with his warning, he passed it to John F. Kennedy.

In the new climate, science saw little to fear at first. Though Kennedy was a layman, even more so in the military sector than Eisenhower, this younger President was more easily thrilled by the new, which is the product that science has to offer. Moreover, though pragmatic himself, he admired what is loosely called intellectualism and was delighted to be its patron. He quickly established rapport with spokesmen for the different branches of R & D, including "pure" science. The scholars, the sayers, became welcomed guests at White House dinners. Science felt secure; it foresaw new freedom as its budgets rose.

Meanwhile, the rearmament program was bearing fruit as far as major troublemakers were concerned. Russian scares recurred, but few could doubt now that America spoke from strength. Troubles were increasingly of another kind, the kind that bespoke affluence, like the nuisance of American farmers producing too much food. The cradle now loomed more ominous than the grave—the population was "exploding." Examining statistics a different way, doomsayers produced a horror no worse than a looming shortage of scientists.

Yet there were growing complications. The new administration spoke constantly of reaching the future via a route called "mainstream." The cliché was new, not the concept; it is a ritual of government to demand that its different bureaucracies flow with efficient togetherness. This time, however, there was special attention to Washington's science agencies. And soon enough it exposed the depth of the psychical chasm between centralized government and free science.

First, a simple example—the familiar demand for more efficiency through less duplication. The Budget Bureau counted at least eleven bureaucracies working in medical science; and so on, with thirteen, besides the Weather Bureau, in meteorology—though "everybody talks about the weather," this did seem overmuch. The clarion therefore called for coordination or consolidation of some kind.

But, what of freedom? Scientists could be very prickly, even when they were already under the same bureaucratic roof. Within HEW, for instance, NIH and the Food and Drug Administration strode alone, neither consulting the other, with the result that such dangerous drugs as anticholesterol MER/29 were released to the public. But such aloofness—specialization carried to an outlandish extreme —wasn't the main target. Nor was duplication as such. Like the usual cliché, "mainstream" was a lazy word that didn't explain itself. It could require anything from a cessation of needless competition to a surrender of integrity. At any rate, it clearly deplored vexatious nonconformity. It called for unity instead of "pluralism," one voice instead of many. Nor would science necessarily have the domineering voice. If the President approved State Department recommendation for a nuclear test ban, the AEC would then obey, though it needed tests badly.

Under some conditions such conformity might be reasonable, but it would be the reverse of scientific freedom. It would also raise internal pressures. The different agencies of science were facing vital questions of autonomy, of independence for whom. This was especially true in fields of direct public interest:

Should the Department of Interior hinder the AEC research program for nuclear power; conversely, should AEC hinder Interior's program for converting seawater into fresh water?

If the Public Health Service feared dangerous fallout, should it veto AEC's nuclear tests; should PHS, again protecting the public, interfere with the Department of Agriculture's pesticides for farmers and foresters?

And, speaking of hazards, how could AEC brook any interference with its stringent safety programs? A tragic accident in some other kind of plant would be that plus undescribable panic if a nuclear power plant blew its top.

Many such jurisdictional disputes, all different, none easy, were arising as science boomed. If the agencies couldn't or wouldn't cooperate, and had to be led to mainstream, who would do it?

Again, there was the temptation to create a new cabinet post, whose Secretary of Science would administer all of the government's civilian R & D. But during the Sputnik panic, science had instinctively shied from a polyglot polymer run by a politician. Now, with its R & D bigger, it was even more fearful of a single czar and multiple frustrations. It preferred strength in disunion.

So, for the time being anyway, Kennedy and Congress offered something milder: coordination rather than consolidation. A new White House post was created. It was called "Director, Office of Science and Technology" and went to busy Wiesner, the MIT professor of electrical engineering. He had campaigned for Kennedy and was already Special Assistant to the President for Science and Technology, namely the chief science adviser, as Killian and Kistiakowsky had been. With this automatically went other titles: chairman of the interdepartmental Federal Council for Science and Technology, chairman of the President's Science Advisory Committee. In short, here was the grand vizier of science. The responsibility was what you made it, and Wiesner had made much of it.

The new OST post did a bit more, however, than formalize what Wiesner was doing anyway. It increased his staff; it gave Congress a chance to question him (as "science adviser" he was immune). So, sometimes vague on facts, sometimes wrong, always willing, Wiesner included Congress on his tour of duty and filled pages of testimony. Within two years, his busyness roused fears that here was the future Secretary of Science. The hornets he stirred up came to roost in Congress, where one of the powerful Texans, Representative Albert Thomas, chairman of the Appropriations subcommittee that specialized in science agencies, accused Wiesner of empire-building; demanded, "How much looking into everybody's program do you do: is it invited or uninvited?"; and cut Wiesner's first $1-million budget.

Soon afterward, Wiesner resigned and returned to MIT with Kennedy's autographed photo: "To Jerry, who makes the complex simple." This was a better memento than the *New York Times* account of a tour through a rocket plant where the group halted and "President Kennedy stood by, obviously somewhat nettled, as Dr. Wiesner engaged in an argument with Dr. Wernher von Braun, director of the Marshall Space Flight Center, over the best way to reach the moon."

How much did the OST's first director accomplish? His *ad hoc* panels added to the plethora of paper that viewed with alarm. He left a challenge of unfinished coordination plans and efficiency investigations for his successor, Donald F. Hornig, chairman of Princeton's chemistry department and the first vizier *not* from Cambridge, Massachusetts. He left agitated tributaries of mainstream. And government still lacked a formula: how fast to go with this science program and how slow with that one; how to dovetail them; how to prevent one crash program from colliding with another; how, in the words of a thoughtful participant, Director Alvin M. Weinberg of AEC's Oak Ridge National Laboratory, to "nurture small-scale excellence as carefully as we lavish gifts on large-scale spectaculars"; and, in general, the question of who should control science—or interfere with it, depending on the outlook.

So, as customary, government settled for less than a grand design. The White House worked through a complex of top administrators, cabinet members, and the science advisers they were acquiring. Even the Secretary of State had one. There were also policy-makers like the influential McGeorge Bundy. In areas of national security it was this special assistant to the President, not the science adviser, who made AEC toe the line.

However, his labor was eased by AEC's Glenn T. Seaborg. This Nobelist had switched from the nuclear laboratory to administrative work and found politics to his liking. When named to the AEC in 1961 he was the first scientist to be its chairman and, because of the stature of this post, was hailed as the model for a new class of "scientist-administrators." He waded uncomplainingly into mainstream and was a peripatetic speechmaker who proselytized for it. Scientists listening to him praise research were disturbed to hear such interloper sentences as "We must conscript science and technology into government service."

Meanwhile, in Brobdingnag's biggest buyer of science—the Pentagon—Defense Secretary McNamara was demonstrating a simpler way. Unawed by the scientists and military alike, he was restoring layman control of government affairs. And judging by the outcry from experts and special interests, he was succeeding.

When I mentioned this to him he puzzled momentarily and asked to hear the question again. I repeated: "In his farewell address, Eisenhower described the growth of what he called a military-industrial complex. He gave the warning. Is it you now who are doing something about it?"

"I am avoiding the dangers he pointed to," said McNamara. How? "I make decisions in the national interest, regardless of pressures." Was it that simple? The face of the "human IBM machine" broke into a youthful smile: "I don't fear the complex, though I have been here long enough now to know that it does bring pressure on me, and criticism."

The smile was because of the understatement. The "complex" had him under almost continuous fire for the defense projects that he was killing off on grounds that they were redundant, or scientifically unsound, or had simply become unnecessary. As a result, he was accused of "trying to gut American nuclear superiority." Another charge: "He has produced no new weapon system." And the one fat new R & D project he did find necessary now had him embroiled in a congressional porkbarrel fight. In this case he had preferred the "input" from his computers and "whiz kid" advisers to that from his military chiefs; he had awarded the $6.5-billion TFX warplane contract to General Dynamics, in Fort Worth, rather than to Boeing, in Seattle. It was a debatable decision, technically. Nor was his load lightened when then Vice President Johnson soon appeared in Fort Worth to claim a Texan's credit for this Texas victory, whereupon McNamara's critics suggested that the plane be renamed the LBJ.

Actually, whatever R & D mistakes McNamara might make for other reasons—and many prayed devoutly that his self-confidence would soon destroy him—there was little chance that either partisan or porkbarrel politics would lead him seriously astray. In the Washington jungle nobody even hinted that he lacked courage or integrity. The same congressional committee that roasted his decision against a new manned bomber nevertheless toasted "the leadership which Mr. McNamara has so fully demonstrated . . . without the chaos which is the almost inevitable consequence of radical reform."

He told me that his formula was simple. It really was. As a professional policy-maker, he supplied himself with the modern advisory "input" tools of that trade. But more, he was an executive in the old-fashioned sense of the word. It was he, not the experts, consultants, and advisers, who made the decisions. And along with deciding which R & D programs to buy he reformed the purchasing procedure. Detesting the comfortable cost-plus-fixed-fee contracts, he boosted the percentage of incentive contracts, which reward efficiency —and penalize inefficiency.

So, for the time being anyway, the "complex" had met not a tamer, perhaps, but certainly a vigorous challenger. Defense was no longer a sure-thing growth industry, and defense areas like California were re-examining their future. Many companies were driven to explore the civilian market again; some were already in serious trouble. Nor was employment a certainty any more. True, the "Help Wanted" ads still shrilled for scientists and engineers; and Washington's empire-builders still cried poor, using the Russian scare for what it was worth, and extrapolating awesome brainpower shortages by 1970 or so. But reality wasn't quite like that. The emphasis now could be on quality rather than quantity. The R & D chief of a giant space company told me, "The only trouble is getting *good* scientists and engineers. We turn down nine out of ten." Du Pont's research chief looked farther: "Whatever the field, wherever the laboratory, there are more good projects to pursue than there are good people to pursue them." Apparently, then, the "scientific-technological elite" was vulnerable too.

And what was Congress doing about all this? At first, very little. It believed in Instant Science, and science was well protected by its aura of indispensability and armor of jargon. Only the joint atomic committee seemed to be doing its investigative homework. Eventually, however, excess brings reaction, whether by feedback or some other way. Here it began with sputters of resistance in the House and concerned some unheroic aspects of military science. There had already been a harbinger—the investigation by Representative Holifield's military operations subcommittee, a "watchdog" unit of the Committee on Government Operations. Consequently, it was not atomic energy but the Ramo-Wooldridge arrangement that interested Holifield in those hearings. They resulted in "shifting the fate of the nation" from a private contractor.

Another but quite different rebellion now was the one by Indiana's Representative Earl Wilson, a former high-school teacher who began digging into the electronics branch of the "complex." For his undertaking, the math and science he had learned in college were more than enough. Where McNamara trained his computers on billion-dollar "systems," Wilson went after million-dollar programs that were simpler. Where Holifield had explored subtle conflicts of interest, Wilson exposed old-fashioned extravagance, rigged contracts, and corruption. All this without a formal staff of investigators. His was truly basic information. Some was volunteered by unsuccessful bidders, some by people who found it distasteful to see science help convert Washington into an "insider's town."

However, such congressional probes were peripheral. Also, they were directed at the engineering rather than science sector of R & D. The first to examine the very structure of the new elite and its methods was in another field—medical research. This inquiry concerned the giant NIH. It produced no villains by the scruff of the neck and therefore made no major newspaper headlines. In fact, it started only as a staff study, without formal hearings and witnesses. But it made history by focusing a sharp light upon government-supported R & D and therefore the bulk of American R & D. It ushered in the period when R & D went on the defensive.

The investigating group here was the so-called "Fountain Committee," another of the seven watchdog units of the House Committee on Government Operations. This one was responsible for monitoring the efficiency and decorum of various other agencies besides NIH. In the Agriculture Department, for instance, it unearthed the activities of notorious Billie Sol Estes.

The subcommittee chairman was Representative L. H. Fountain, of Tarboro, North Carolina, a quietly competent lawyer. He had no feud with NIH. Like the average American, he hoped for good health; like many, he considered medicine a noble calling. Among his personal friends were many physicians. In fact, the man who managed his first campaign for Congress was a general practitioner— the same man who had brought him into the world. Such friendships undoubtedly have effect. Fountain wondered about the complaints that there was a growing imbalance: too few healers and too few hospitals while Congress smothered glamorous research with funds.

These doubts were not shared by an equally sincere man, Senator Lister Hill, of Alabama, likewise a lawyer and himself the son of a prominent surgeon. It was he who led the Senate in demanding ever greater research funds for NIH. His faith in laboratory results went beyond that of a laboratory man. It was unlimited. "In a relatively few short years we shall overcome the dreaded diseases that have plagued and baffled mankind through the years. . . . This breakthrough will yield the answer to heart disease, cancer, mental illness, the virus diseases, and the many other crippling degenerative ailments."

Each lawmaker proceeded according to his own lights. In 1959, Representative Fountain's chief aide, Delphis C. Goldberg, a patient investigator with a Harvard Ph.D. in political science, began the staff study of NIH. In the same year, Senator Hill got Boisfeuillet ("Bo") Jones, an adviser on government health programs, to head a special examination of NIH's performance and needs. In April 1960, the Jones committee submitted its report. It applauded NIH; it declared that research funds should be quadrupled by 1970. Whereupon Congress voted an appropriately huge budget increase for NIH.

The Fountain report was ready a year later. It did not set out to question the value of medical research as such. It did examine how the nation was spending its NIH money, four-fifths of which supported extramural research. This exposed the broad picture. It found NIH a victim of deceptive bookkeeping, sometimes outright swindling, and, most important, an all-pervasive conflict of interest. It could hardly be otherwise. The panels of consultants who dominated the grants programs were themselves grantees or representatives of grantee institutions. In addition, grants were renewed automatically upon request. And the research results had to meet few requirements, of course—that would stifle the freedom of science. In short, it was the science establishment, not the government, that was in control. Follow-up investigations, to see if the situation was improving, added to the sorry picture. This had gone past usurpation of power. Research was degrading itself to an appalling degree. NIH records show that, in four years, its number of research applications receiving a "superior" rating declined from four out of ten to fewer than one out of four. This spoke sadly for basic research that the government was supporting in the nation's colleges and universities. Two-fifths of it was with NIH grants.

What did the Fountain Committee accomplish? Little, as far as NIH itself was concerned. The agency did a little tightening; it issued a massive index to show who was getting the money. But the White House and Congress still believed in medical miracles and wrote out blank checks for them.

This, despite Vannevar Bush's warning. He tried to explain that basic research should be different from building radars and nuclear bombs: "The spectacular success of applied research during the war led to a fallacy. To solve the problem of the common cold, assemble a great institution, fill it with scientists and money, and soon we will have no more colds. It is folly to proceed thus. It will inevitably support the trivial and mediocre. The great scientific steps forward originate in the minds of gifted scientists, not in the minds of promoters."

Yet the fact that Bush spoke out shows how well the Fountain Committee succeeded as a general catalyst though it dealt specifically with life science. Self-examination now became the trend throughout R & D. Articles and letters in science journals derided government interference, or screamed at it. Other spokesmen, like Bush, dared admit weaknesses. So did Weinberg, of Oak Ridge. Concerning the panels of specialized experts who work through the President's Science Advisory Committee, he succinctly rephrased the conflict-of-interest when such outsiders decide on programs and grants: "Judge, jury, plaintiff, and defendant are usually one and the same."

In Washington the significance of the Fountain inquiry was seen immediately. Among other things it brought something new in co-ordination. Dispensing with the formality of assembling task forces to study the situation, the heads of NIH, NSF, AEC, NASA, and Office of Education began lunching together every two weeks for man-to-man solutions of the dilemma: how to satisfy both the demands from science and the challenge from Congress.

They went on the defensive none too soon. By 1963, two years after the first Fountain report, all Washington seemed to be questioning the methods of R & D. Regular committees of Congress were competing with special committees, special committees were rivaling each other, and at the White House, the OST started its own investigation. From NIH the probing was spreading into other heartlands of basic and "pure" research. The joint atomic committee sternly suggested something more practical than the $8-billion installment plan submitted by AEC's atom-smashing physicists. The National Science Foundation, infested by grantsmanship and unable to explain the fantastic mismanagement of its Mohole project to bore through the ocean floor (a skit put on by the Washington Geological Society was entitled "Mo-Ho-Ho and a Barrel of Funds") saw an abrupt halt in the steep rise of its budget curve; Congress voted $200 million less than the request. Meanwhile, NIH itself was witnessing the unbelievable, Congress was accepting its rising budgets without adding more to them.

More important than any of these developments was the insurrection against NASA the glamorous—NASA, whose tense countdowns, mighty launchings, and exciting journeys into Space were television spectaculars for the millions; NASA, whose scientists sought answers to man's age-old questions about the heavens.

Part of the growing resistance was in Congress. Some members were fretting, of course, about NASA's mounting budgets. More significant, others were losing their humility toward science and now challenging technical aspects of the big space program. Their information came from the increasing clamor within science itself. Its people were revealing what they might have kept private.

On the surface, theirs was a bitter hostility to NASA's Project Apollo—the race to beat Russia with a manned landing on the moon. But it went deeper. It was the result of science's having become big business. Though many scientists detested NASA for other reasons, the basis for the coalitions against the burgeoning space agency was competitive. Here, then, was a struggle for power. Put less kindly, here was jealousy over how to slice the federal R & D pie.

As we have seen, NASA was exploding with growth. In the Eisenhower years its budgets doubled yearly. The Kennedy administration, emphasizing the nation's prestige, went on boosting NASA budgets at the same doubling rate. The political situation made this easy. As chairman of the Senate's space committee, Lyndon Johnson had been NASA's angel in Congress. Now, as Vice President, he was chairman of the nation's space council. And he had bequeathed chairmanship of the committee to his "wheeler-dealer" friend from Oklahoma, Senator Robert Kerr, of the Kerr-McGee Oil Industries—richest member of the Senate and powerful enough to be called its uncrowned king. One of their first problems—who would head NASA in the new administration?—was solved with characteristic finesse. Scientists were pressuring President Kennedy to name somebody from their establishment to succeed Eisenhower's Dr. Glennan and join the scientist-administrators of NIH, NSF, AEC, and the like. But Johnson won the power play. The layman administrator named to head NASA was his friend James E. Webb, who had been an executive and director of Kerr-McGee.

Though this was cozy, Webb was not without other qualifications. He had the reputation of being a high-level operator who could make things work. Educated to be a lawyer, he had gone on into the aircraft industry, oil equipment, and banking. And he was no stranger to Washington politics. In the Truman administration he had been director of the Budget Bureau and then Undersecretary of State. True, he knew little science, but stocky, blue-eyed Jim Webb had not overlooked making connections in that field too. Among other things he had been titular head of Educational Services, Inc., a nonprofit ally of MIT. With over $6 million, mostly from NSF, they were pioneering new ways to teach high-school physics. Relatively speaking, this was one of NSF's better investments.

Concerning NASA, he told me, "I don't have to know science. If I did, the trouble might be that I'd try to be my own scientist." So he ran NASA with a troika: Hugh L. Dryden, his top scientist; Robert C. Seamans, Jr., his "general manager"; and himself in the center to make the decisions and the compromises. And as at the Pentagon, with its McNamara, the idea of a layman boss over science had its merits.

Both were in interesting contrast to AEC Chairman Seaborg. The difference between Webb and Seaborg was the more significant because each was the appointed spokesman for an agency set up by Congress with the express purpose of strengthening civilian control of the nation's scientific future. Seaborg, the former chemist, had a busier speechwriter than Webb, the professional politician. In his travels Seaborg sold science as the new revolution, and himself as the revolution's latest product—the science administrator. His speeches contained little about AEC's achievements and less about what support it would need in the future.

Webb, on the other hand, was a partisan who identified himself with his NASA. In selling the one he likewise sold the other. He politicked for NASA in Congress. He wooed the elite of science. For instance, he told me about his relations with the National Academy: "I work closely with its people. Unlike some, I don't consider them fogies. We get help from them." And while courting the scientists he reminded private industry that NASA was an impressive new customer. This was not a salesman's exaggeration. Industry was getting the contracts for over 90 per cent of the space agency's work. And through a liberal waiver policy, condemned regularly but unsuccessfully by such anti-monopoly senators as Estes Kefauver and Russell Long, a contractor could expect patent rights on inventions made in the course of research with the government's R & D money.

True, Webb's choice of a chief deputy for industrial relations— Walter Lingle Jr., executive vice president of Procter & Gamble —raised some eyebrows. But Lingle was equal to the situation when he addressed a meeting of space scientists: "What can a background in the soap business contribute to the space program? The best answer is that cleanliness is said to be next to Godliness; and it seemed to me that becoming associated with outer Space and its vast eternity was a good first step in trying to make this transition."

But there was one serious miscalculation for which Webb was not solely responsible. It was mainstream policy that took NASA beyond science into troublesome high-level politics. Only time can tell whether the decision to detour orderly science and race Russia to the moon was wise. And only frank memoirs by the participants can reveal the complete story of Washington's policy-making in the six weeks that culminated in President Kennedy's announcement of Project Apollo.

It was a period that gave America two more tremors. Back in 1957, Russia had launched the first Sputnik. Now, on April 12, 1961, Russia won its second undeniably major victory in Space. Its cosmonaut Yuri Gagarin, orbiting earth in a 7-ton spaceship, became the first human space traveler. The next week brought shock of another kind—the disastrous Bay of Pigs attempt to invade Cuba. The two events not only carried frightening portent; American prestige sank to a new nadir. And our first space journey, soon afterward, by NASA astronaut Alan B. Shepard, Jr., on May 5, was little solace. It showed that our Mercury program was proceeding according to orderly plan—but it was suborbital, thereby only accenting how far we were behind.

So began the Washington conferences to supply the White House with a dramatic announcement that would rebuild our self-confidence and restore our international prestige. Because of Russia's lead, we needed a goal far enough ahead. The target date became "before this decade is out"; the target, a manned lunar landing ahead of the Soviets. Thus was born crash Project Apollo—part science, part politics, part propaganda—which Vice President Johnson urged successfully upon Kennedy.

It· was a hasty decision, incorporating a staggering number of technical unknowns. But behind it, NASA could rally America's massive technological resources. For instance, there was the rocket Saturn I. This hydrogen-burner was conceived in 1959 as a super-booster to produce 1.5 million pounds of thrust, forty times the amount that launched Vanguard. By 1964 the project was competing with its $1-billion Air Force rival, Titan III, which could do the same work. And Saturn I was no longer needed anyway. For Project

Apollo, NASA was concentrating on a hotter version and also the hottest of all, Saturn V, five times stronger than Saturn I. Yet, if prestige was the goal, the first Saturn did some good. In January 1964, admiring congressmen watched it orbit 19 tons of hardware, of which 9 tons was useful payload—2 tons more than the Russians were known to be orbiting. For the time being, anyway, America claimed the world's weightlifting championship.

But an increasingly vocal coalition within science was jeering Apollo, not cheering. The experts had advised Kennedy and Webb that NASA would now need $35 billion for the decade's space activities, $20 billions of it for the race to the moon. And critics were quick to cite experience with escalating costs—the eventual bill might be much more. As always, R & D money quickly translates into manpower. Rich NASA was already a notorious raider; its program chiefs would soon dominate the nation's supply of scientists and engineers. What would happen to the nation's other R & D programs?

Adding the competition for money to the competition for people explains the power struggle that was splitting science. And from the partisan arguments it was receiving, Congress learned much. NASA had become the symbolic whipping boy for all the charges against today's science: its imperious attitude, its political involvement, its discovery of the porkbarrel, its extravagant tastes, its technical incompetence because its task forces were overpopulated with "warm bodies"; its neglect of the layman's practical needs but also, paradoxically, its neglect of basic research. And throughout ran the distasteful reminder that its scientific opinion could be bought with U.S. Treasury checks. The biophysicist investigating DNA savagely attacked NASA for spending *his* money, but the exobiologist who sought samples of life in outer Space praised NASA's name. Similarly, astronomers split, depending on whether they wanted telescopes on earth or on the moon. Participants in the fray seemed to sort out according to the weight of their vested interest, as if a mass spectrometer were at work.

Thus the war was between coalitions rather than between two sharply divided camps such as theorist versus experimenter, or scientist versus engineer, or basic research versus applied research, or, for that matter, Democrat versus Republican. The critic of

NASA's "moondoggling" might be a medical researcher guilty of healthdoggling. He might be the Mohole oceanographer wisecracking, "The ocean's bottom is at least as important to us as the moon's behind." He might even be an atom-smashing physicist—of all people!—decrying the impracticality of space trips.

Through the din it was not easy, of course, to hear the moderates who distinguished between exploring the new ocean in orderly fashion and the haste to look down on the Kremlin. Among NASA's goals, for instance, they stressed "the Big One"—is there life on Mars? Accordingly, they urged that NASA deflect some of its moon-race energy in that direction. Likewise, there were very practical dissidents like the aeronautical engineers who demanded that NASA invest more than a pittance to improve terrestrial aviation.

If the fuss accomplished nothing else it showed cracks in what had seemed to the layman a solid façade. The new elite was not yet congealed, even in its subdivisions. Though Jim Webb had courted the National Academy, and its president, Frederick Seitz, did heartily support NASA, many other members, including influential Kistia-kowsky, did not. "But," I reminded him, "NASA says that its pro-grams will result in valuable byproducts for us here on earth." He replied, "Hogwash!"

The controversy also had very tangible effects. A dedicated young electrical engineer from RCA, D. Brainerd Holmes, fresh from his triumphal construction of the BMEWS warning line, had been brought in to boss Apollo. Taking the challenge seriously, he ran the program on a "go-for-broke" basis intended to put Americans on the moon by 1967 or 1968. He was now, in mid-1963, shaken out of control by NASA's "civilians," and the target date became 1970. But this appeasement was not enough. And NASA was also on the defensive elsewhere about a series of satellite failures and other technical fumbles. Consequently, it now encountered its first skeptical Congress. Though its budget for 1964 crossed the $5-billion mark for the first time, this was $600 million less than requested. The next year's budget reached Congress with the blessing of a new President, Lyndon Johnson. Though he was NASA's godfather and despite his influence, the request was cut and the budget remained the same. As before, NASA readjusted programs. This time, for instance, a Mars probe scheduled for 1966 was quietly put off five years. Apollo was now taking three-fifths of NASA's budget, and this one agency alone was taking a third of the federal R & D budget. The moon race was still on.

Johnson made this very clear eight months later when, after six missions that failed, the seventh Ranger spacecraft sent back close-up television pictures of the moon's surface. The President took this opportunity to answer Apollo's critics. At a White House session he put Homer E. Newell, associate NASA administrator, through a unique catechism. Here are excerpts:

JOHNSON: Are you satisfied?
NEWELL: I am. In fact, I am delighted.
JOHNSON: Elated?
NEWELL: Elated. . . .
JOHNSON: Is it desirable to get there [the moon] as soon as you can?
NEWELL: In my opinion, yes.
JOHNSON: As quickly as possible?
NEWELL: As quickly as possible, yes, Mr. President.
JOHNSON: What do you lose by backing down?
NEWELL: You lose leadership.
JOHNSON: Leadership in what?
NEWELL: Leadership in world science and technology, in achievement and accomplishment.
JOHNSON: Leadership in the world?
NEWELL: Leadership in the world. . . .
JOHNSON: Do you have any comments?
NEWELL: I agree completely.
JOHNSON: Why? I want to develop that a little bit. What are some of the byproducts of your effort to this date? List three or four. I assume you made unbelievable progress in weather forecasts, haven't you . . . ?

The nation now had another layman President, this time the bounciest, hardest-driving one it could remember, and no more abashed by science than by anything else. Definitely, a doer was now in the White House, and his ideas were quaint about the "creativity" cherished by science. He immediately drew jeers with his command call "on the nation's top scholars, thinkers, writers, teachers, and specialists in all fields to generate fresh, new, and imaginative ideas." But the motives of men and the methods of politics he did understand. Mars might be too visionary; how to solve growing problems of automation and genetics might be too complex; a moon race or hospital-building program he could comprehend easily and direct with combative zest. How would science fare under this bustling President? We will meet him again. It is sufficient here to point out three indicators:

1. With or without Johnson, with or without new tremors and crash programs, the budgets submitted by science would now be examined more closely. Partly because policy-making laymen were now less awed by science. Partly because, after twenty-five years of exploding science, an automatic control was operating. The change began with the budgets for fiscal 1964, with the querulous reception that Congress gave such glamor agencies as NIH, NASA, NSF, AEC. The next year's federal investment in R & D showed the impact of the change. The figure was a record high—but $2 billion less than extrapolators had predicted. The 1966 budget followed the same new pattern. Indispensable science would go on growing. But for the time being, anyway, the era of R & D Unlimited had ended, except for an agency like NSF, whose programs for the elite could sound like programs for education.

2. More than any president since Franklin Roosevelt, Johnson knew how to wield power. Better than any, he could deal with the checks-and-balances system. The Senate was his alma mater. In the House, fortune favored him with a new chairman of the powerful Appropriations Committee—his friend George Mahon, another Texan. And wherever else they might differ, Johnson and Congress would not be far apart in their preference for people of feelable, seeable R & D rather than partisans of the more remote kind. The administration would want crops rather than seed knowledge.

3. Johnson was lucky as well as eager, and nowhere more than in the stage that R & D had set for him. It provided him a nation armed with mighty nuclear power and no longer humiliated in Space. And much more. Quietly, the "peaceful atom" had become adult. Chairman Seaborg of the AEC had not mentioned this in his speeches. Johnson seized upon it to announce the breakthrough of cheap, abundant electric power from the atom. To this he added that nuclear power would provide cheap desalted water from the oceans. This layman President seemed to poke everywhere in Washington's R & D cupboards for goodies. He speedily announced the A-11 supersonic

plane; an airborne jeep; missiles that would intercept enemy satellites. Facing the November 1964 election, he snapped out directives that would give him more material for 1965, "The Year of Science": from the Department of Commerce, by October 15, R & D plans for high-speed rail service linking Boston, New York, and Washington; from NASA, by September 1, a reassessment of the space program; from AEC "no later than September 11, an aggressive and imaginative program to advance progress in large-scale desalting of seawater."

Many scientists shuddered at this pace but joined the majority in more mistrust of the other candidate, Barry Goldwater. The nucleation point for "Scientists and Engineers for Johnson" was Donald M. MacArthur, an executive scientist of an aerospace firm, and married to a niece of Mrs. Johnson. He was quickly joined by luminaries of the establishment: Kistiakowsky and Wiesner; Harold Brown, director of the Pentagon's R & D; Donald Hornig, the President's chief science advisor; Detlev Bronk, head of Rockefeller Institute and former president of the National Academy of Sciences. A half-million-dollar campaign fund was quickly raised; the drive became a crusade. "By the time we were through," exulted David L. Garth, the professional campaign director, "any guy in Pittsburgh in a T-shirt with a can of beer in his hand knew that the smartest people in this country considered Goldwater unfit."

Johnson was grateful. But he was also grateful to many other groups in the nation. His State of the Union message had surprisingly few words for the people of R & D, and even the sentence he gave to basic research carried its reminder of the practical: "To develop knowledge which will enrich our lives and ensure our progress, I will recommend programs to encourage basic science, particularly in the universities—and to bring closer the day when the oceans will supply our growing need for fresh water."

This, and the compromise budget that followed, provided a program for agencies building the future from breakthrough ideas of the past. It could hardly be otherwise. Neither the science establishment nor government could program for creativity, the solitary idea—subtle yet simple—that rewards the searcher and may come in the night.

III: *Today's Laboratories*

> "I started doing a bit of cooking on my own.
> Unorthodox cooking, illicit cooking. A bit
> of real science, in fact."
> —Aldous Huxley, *Brave New World*

If prosperity is a sufficient indicator, the potential of American science is tremendous. For comparison we remember the era of the magnificent Medicis. Possessed of an aberrant passion that led them to assassinate each other, they were also passionate patrons of learning and made Florence the Athens of the Renaissance. Far more opulent, however, is the patronage that our science receives from government and industry, universities and private foundations. And though this support may vary, both in kind and in growth curve, it promises an outpour of knowledge that could gratify the boldest dreamer, if there were not the questions about who is to control science and how it is to nourish creativity in its work force.

Let us now get tangible bearings on this prosperity. Where do we find the bustling research laboratories, observatories, test stations? Putting it another way, where would we find the scientists, engineers, and technicians of this new knowledge industry called R & D? And what are some of its interactions with the rest of the community?

A detailed answer would require a bulky Baedeker. And it could not stop with the nation's borders. It would include researchers manning outposts in the remote arctic and antarctic. It would include those in the now booming science of oceanography who go down to the sea in such vessels as *Atlantis II* and *Te Vega*. It would not overlook the far-wandering archeologists, who try to reconstruct man's past, and who thereby escape blame for tampering with his future. Not that they are always above suspicion. On a homebound

85

ship a researcher told me of his trouble in the Near East. His native diggers went on strike. Why? Their answer: "We understand well. You do the work out here because our wages are less."

Limiting our survey to the homeland, we find a host of laboratories varied enough in appearance to satisfy lovers of the antique or of the trenchantly modern: from sedate ivy-clad Agriculture Experiment Stations still surviving at land-grant colleges, to the white-collar factories betokening a space age, nuclear age, biologicals age, or whatever we wish to call it. If nothing else, R & D has primed the construction industry and given an appropriately busy new look to the labs.

Once upon a time not long ago, the researchers were pretty much limited to university facilities. It was on the seventh floor of Columbia's Pupin Hall that physicists first investigated the potential of nuclear power for war and peace. The possibilities were proven when the first controlled chain reaction went successfully "critical" in a reactor hidden under the west stands of the University of Chicago's Stagg Field stadium.

Once upon a time, too, researchers sought aid from private benefactors. Consider Clarence Cook Little, the properly bred Bostonian who was a great-great-grandson of Paul Revere and equally restless. But his interest in genealogy focused elsewhere. As a Harvard sophomore enamored of biology, he began the brother-sister matings of laboratory mice that developed into precious instruments—all members of a strain designed to look and act alike. Later, he was the dynamic biologist whose crusades for such things as birth control got him into hopeless controversy when he was president of the University of Michigan. So, in 1929, he packed up his mice colony and moved to Bar Harbor, Maine, where such patrons as the Rockefellers, Potter Palmers, and Pulitzers had their palatial summer homes. There, he founded his freelance laboratory with the aid of wealthy Detroiters who wanted to fight disease. His sponsors included Mrs. Roscoe B. Jackson, widow of the Hudson Motor Company president, and her first cousin, Mrs. Edsel Ford, whose husband was to die later from cancer. Jackson Memorial Laboratory became world-famous for its work in genetics, and unique too. A third of its income is from selling surplus mice, which have been inbred for hundreds of generations, to other researchers. And untrammeled, imaginative research is the tradition at Jackson. Why is mankind pugnacious? Is this an instinct? For a clue, the lab went to animals. I remember my astonishment when a rabbit lunged toward me, clawing at its cage bars like a wildcat. The chewed fingers and torn lab coats of attendants showed that he was not being selective. Researcher Paul Sawin called him "a little runt with a big heredity chip on his shoulder." The animal belonged to puzzling "Race 10," which began twenty years earlier from crossbreeding a dwarf Polish rabbit and a Flemish Giant. Each was meek as a Milquetoast. But each evidently possessed submerged possibilities as a fighter, and the gene combination gave an odd anomaly to the researchers working on the principle that conditioning is sufficient to make and break habits. At any rate, such research was done at three gigantic remodeled barns on a farm donated by a J. P. Morgan partner when he abandoned his hobby of breeding prize bulls and stallions.

Many other present-day laboratories proudly trace their ancestry back to such hand-me-down origins. But these have become almost invisible in the proliferation of what are unquestionably practical buildings, though dissenting scientists call them sexy: glisteny expanses of extravert windows; air-conditioned for the well-being of computers as well as humans; alluring colors where they dare. They are most striking when they shriek dissonance, when their rectilinearity crowds up next to pseudo-Gothic or pseudo-Romanesque or pseudo-Mission architecture on genuine university campuses. They are definitely a break with tradition. Yet many of the new structures have antecedents too, of a sort. To house a spanking new Institute of Microbiology for Selman Waksman, its discoverer of streptomycin, Rutgers bought a bankrupt golf course. Not far away, nearer Princeton, RCA bought a New Jersey tomato farm for its Astro-Electronics Laboratory. This led to the problem of what address to give it. It was at Locust Corners, an impossible name and not seminal enough to suggest anything better. Nor could the address be Millstone, the name of a nearby creek. What with the sharp rivalry between RCA's communications satellite called Relay and Bell Telephone Laboratories' Telstar, RCA's public-relations people couldn't risk having the foe dub the new lab a millstone around RCA's neck. Princeton was near enough to provide the best kind of answer. That name was rich with the prestige that makes it easier to hire good scientists and engineers. Princeton meant the Ivy League university; it also meant its neighbor, the renowned Institute for Advanced Study. The lab's address became "Box 800, Princeton."

The same back-to-the-land movement spans the nation. In Canoga Park, which is in San Fernando Valley, which is in Los Angeles County, most of which, Los Angeles-fashion, is now in Los Angeles, the ranches and orange groves have given way to a community of R & D centers opening the way into outer Space. Farther north, in the San Francisco region—outside Los Angeles—on pasturelands owned by wealthy Stanford University, cattle browsing around the drooping live oaks were watching earth-movers dig and pack a two-mile tunnel for an atom-smasher. Back east, near Boston, Mitre Corporation had settled its electronics facilities on a pig farm, and NASA's great Goddard center was housed on a chicken farm in the Maryland hills. And so on—like other industries the knowledge industry seeks new elbow room. No longer is a new laboratory crowded into a shed, or a factory corner, or an antique campus building. Space, on earth, is needed for the Space-simulation chambers that shake and tumble and freeze and roast the satellites inside them, for the high-energy accelerators called atom-smashers, for the swarms of workrooms that biology requires. Along with test tube and slide rule, the bulldozer has become a symbol of today's science. It cuts down the hills and fills the bayous for the labs. It can repair mistakes too. When the biggest radio telescope at Green Bank couldn't tilt back far enough to scan the sky properly, a dozer snappily dug out a trough so that it could.

The foregoing examples show that today's science is no longer geographically parochial. It settles where it must. When we symbolize Chicago by meatpacking and Iowa by corn, these are stereotypes. They ignore the social and economic changes in a highly mobile nation of 200 million people. The same danger of oversimplification awaits the mapper of American science.

To be sure, much of the major R & D has been drawn into five major clusters, three on the upper East Coast, two on the lower West Coast. The East and West, already rich in R & D, are becoming even richer. But this does not necessarily mean that the poor areas become poorer. They, too, are finding opportunities, and not always receiving only the leftovers. So, before visiting the major centers, let us glance at two samples of what else a condensed Baedeker should include about the outpour of science and technology.

Certainly it should mention the Space Crescent, a complex of NASA facilities for the moon-landing program. Originally there were the launching pads of Cape Canaveral, which rocketry's R & D people of the West Coast airily dubbed Disneyland East. Then the situation changed. Cape Canaveral became Cape Kennedy, but more important, NASA had gone off trail for massive new support of its Project Apollo. It extended the lunar boom from Florida, along the Gulf of Mexico to the Michoud plant outside New Orleans for building and assembling rocket stages; to a $500-million site in nearby Mississippi (near the town of Picayune) for hauling them by swamp canals and testing them; and on to Texas with a project costing perhaps $200 million—the Manned Spacecraft Center near Houston. Besides designing and testing the spaceships, this is the new command post for the missions from Cape Kennedy; its electronic brains will control flights of Apollo.

California had wanted this center. Texas won, and Houston began booming with something newer than petrochemicals. Already the nation's sixth largest city, it now called itself Space Center USA, and Lloyd's of London guessed it might become the world's largest city by the year 2000. Why did Houston win? The logistics of easy sea transportation was on its side. So were its loyal and powerful Texans in Washington, porkbarrel or not. So was the feeling that California was perhaps overfat with R & D. So, too, was eagerness. Wealthy Rice University, for instance, donated 1000 acres for the NASA center. As a result, both Rice and the University of Houston quickly profited from the arrival of their opulent neighbor. They began tailoring courses for flocks of students from NASA. They began providing consultants to NASA. The chain reaction continued. To be near the big government customer, R & D companies began sending in their sales engineers and planning branch plants. In sum, though Texas was still no California (and occupied thirty-seventh place in the amount of state money spent on higher education) the South had new proof that the East-West grip on R & D was not a hammerlock.

The second area that should be noted is the Midwest, traditionally rebellious against domination by the eastern seaboard and unhappy to think it is now oppressed by the western one as well. For example, one of its claims, by the angry men of MURA, led President Johnson to complain, "I have devoted more personal time to this than to any nondefense question during the budget process." This concerned the $170-million atom-smasher that MURA—a consortium of fifteen Midwestern universities—had been promised for Madison, Wisconsin, and was not being given.

Mixed with this area's understandable jealousy of East and West is a self-consciousness grown from regret over lost opportunities. It has called itself a vacuum, even a "science desert," between the two coasts. This is backed by evidence that too many of the scientists and engineers it educates move on to an atmosphere more conducive to R & D. It is understandable, for instance, why Detroit's automobile industry hasn't attracted them. Here is no trail-blazer in technology. It favors sales engineers. Its new cars change their colors and curves annually; nothing really creative changes the ancient gas engine. Even the addition of something so simple as safety belts for the seats, and afterburners to stop air pollution from the engines, had to await research elsewhere and came only after government pressure.

Nevertheless, if the Midwest is a science desert, it has a wide variety of oases. If Iowa is symbolized by corn (and also has the nation's lowest illiteracy rate), it also symbolizes diversified research. For the home gardener, State College of Iowa developed the outstanding sweetcorn called Iochief. For the very distant traveler, Iowa State University proudly presents James A. Van Allen, the physics professor who discovered the radiation belts around earth that now carry his name.

Similarly, if Chicago is symbolized by meatpacking, it also has the University of Chicago, which operates the AEC's nearby Argonne National Laboratory, a $300-million employer of 2500 scientists and engineers. One of the lab "instruments" is its busy $70-million synchrotron. And Argonne's influence reaches far—out to Idaho, where it tests nuclear-power reactors of the future.

The influence of Battelle Memorial Institute, a pride of Ohio's diversified R & D, reaches even farther, from Columbus to the Far West. Already doing $30 million worth of business a year, roughly half of it for government, half for industry, Battelle won the contract to operate another of ubiquitous AEC's research centers, the $85-

million Hanford Laboratories at Richland, Washington. This is the famed "Plutonium City" and laboratory that grew out of the war's A-bomb program. Battelle's influence reaches farther still—to its two foreign branches, a lab in Frankfurt and another in Geneva. Founded by the heir to a steel fortune, it started in metallurgy, now works in the physical sciences, the life sciences, even the social sciences. In sum, it is the world's largest private research organization of the not-for-profit type. And because it is tax-exempt it is no joy to the for-profit ones, who argue: "It's in business like the rest of us—why not tax it?"

In general, then, hardly any geographical area in the nation has been untouched by the boom, and the "underprivileged" have their politicians who continually remind Washington's policy-makers that porkbarrel is an inalienable right. Nevertheless, there has come an inevitable clustering. Knowledge factories go where research-minded industry is, just as the production factories are attracted to favorable labor supply and transport facilities. And always a powerful magnet for R & D is the opportunity to join a community of scholars. The newcomer laboratories hire campus graduates, send them back for higher degrees, compete for professors who will serve as consultants, and are often directly affiliated with the university. In this elite industry the umbilical cord is not easily broken. Its people are most content when they can continue the filial relationship, with alma mater or any other campus that is socially and intellectually stimulating; and where, if it be true that "scientists are idols-oriented," they can join disciples of the Nobelists and other maestros. Few labs are so self-sufficient, like General Electric's pride, that they can attract talent to a Schenectady. The usual pattern would call for this lab to be adjacent, say, to Cornell University. But even at GE, automobiles being what they are, it is no hardship to hop over to nearby Rensselaer Poly or back to MIT.

It is the truly isolated who have trouble. Consider the National Science Foundation's laboratory for radio astronomy: the observatory operated by Associated Universities, Inc., a consortium of nine northeastern institutions. Its object was laudable enough—"pure" astronomy rather than intelligence work for the Defense Department or space chores for NASA. The choice of a site seemed sagacious. Radio astronomers "see" with a special antenna that captures very weak radiation signals from the planets and enables the mapping of new stars in deep Space. Consequently, they detest the interference of radio transmission and other electromagnetic "noise" from earthly neighbors. To escape such static, the observatory was erected near the hamlet of Green Bank, in a natural bowl deep in the Alleghenies of West Virginia. The surrounding mountains would block off most of the interference.

But this was one of NSF's less fortunate ventures. The time came when Congress overlooked the worthwhile at Green Bank; for instance, the 300-foot supertelescope fathered by the observatory's own J. W. Findlay, from plan to completion. Minus its auxiliary electronics, this "big dish" had cost under a million dollars. Instead, Congress wanted to know how much research per dollar the staff and group of telescopes at Green Bank were producing to justify a $5-million budget for the coming year. At one of the nation's rival observatories an astronomer grimaced. "Yes, blood is pouring out of poor Green Bank's ears. But it was bad planning. The people on the committee had an obsession about electromagnetic interference; it's something we'll have to live with. Anyway, they got fine junkets out of it. They toured from Vermont to Florida, and westward. Finally, they said Green Bank was it."

As it happened, even the climate was miscalculated. When I visited Green Bank, its massive 140-foot telescope had been dismantled and the components were strewn about. The instrument was being rebuilt by Stone & Webster, a new contractor, and workers were preparing to hoist a new 400-ton piece of steel structure into place. Steel incorrect for Green Bank's harsh winter temperatures had been used. It had embrittled, then fractured, much as some Liberty ships cracked during the war.

Parenthetically, concerning government's role in science, there is some sort of moral in all this. The NSF's troubles at Green Bank demonstrated the need for stronger government supervision over programs it pays for. If government does take charge, however, it should do so with knowledgeable men and listen to them. This was neatly demonstrated coincidentally with NSF's troubles, and only fifty miles from Green Bank. At Sugar Grove was truly a fiasco. It involved a supposedly secret piece of hardware that Navy policy-makers wanted mainly for intelligence work—the world's largest steerable radio telescope. Various scientists had warned against plans for the oversize 600-foot dish, and engineers then spent futile years trying to design and build it. The consensus is that it would have been militarily useless even if finished on time. Meanwhile, its estimated cost had grown from $20 million to at least $200 million, perhaps $300 million. One of incoming Secretary McNamara's first "meat-ax" decisions at the Pentagon was to chop off the project. By this time the astronomical venture had cost around $95 million.

Returning to Green Bank, climate and radio interference are only part of the story. At least as serious is the isolation, which today's researchers abhor. The nearest railroad station is sixty miles away. By plane, the flight from Washington is easy enough, but followed by over two hours of mountain driving distinguished by a memorable series of hairpin turns. Another astronomer described the unhappiness. "It's such a damned lonely spot that astronomers don't want to go there, certainly not to live. When they do, they find no intellectual stimulus for themselves, and insufficient schooling for their children. The place is barren—nobody cares to landscape it. They wander thirty miles away to find a home they can rent. Few dare build their own—it could be sold only to another astronomer, whose wife might have different tastes."

Ironically, Green Bank's people found there is indeed no place to hide. They had to agitate for a "radio quiet" zone to keep radio transmitters far enough away. The ignition system in all observatory automobiles had to be doctored to suppress its radiation. Such remedies helped, but outsiders remained a problem. I found a checkpoint where "foreign" cars must stop until given permission to proceed. Suppressors were being urged for neighboring farm tractors. A campaign was under way to move Route 28 so that its traffic would be on the other side of protective hills and its tourists less likely to stray into Green Bank. And always dread that the FCC would allow the ultra-high-frequency transmitters of television to crowd into wavelengths that radio astronomers desperately claim for their "radio window" into Space.

Green Bank illustrates various problems of R & D. But its very isolation shows that it isn't a major center for the new elite and the influence they wield. What, then, of the important areas?

The fact that they receive by far the biggest portion of federal

R & D support has caused much viewing with alarm. The Census Bureau found half of the nation's scientists and engineers working in six states. Other surveys have shown two-fifths of military R & D, the biggest single item, going to California. Such imbalance is not as overwhelming as it seems because the clustering here of leading aerospace companies can account for much of it. And as prime contractors, they then distribute some of the subcontracts elsewhere. But the situation is nonetheless lopsided and breeds fear of both geographical and industrial monopoly. Furthermore, it is not limited to defense R & D. Utah complained that from NASA's billions it was receiving 20 cents per capita while Texas was getting $25 and California led with $143. Here again the spread of subcontracts doesn't change the picture much. California received $30 per capita; Indiana received $1.

A similar concentration of power-through-wealth harasses the calm of the academic world, where giant "hardware" contracts go to the big universities, and so do the big research grants. For instance, 17 per cent of annual NIH grant money was traced to five research-oriented institutions that received over $3 million apiece, and 17 per cent went to 659 in the below-$250,000 class. The five also furnished over twice as many advisers on who should get the money.

The defense is that the biggest are also the best qualified. "When government comes to us," a leading university's provost told me, "it wants quality research. It isn't spending money *on* science, but *for* it. We aren't naïve. The government isn't thinking about education."

Adding it all together—industrial R & D, university R & D, the government's "in-house" R & D—one result is such statistics as federal support averaging $4000 per Wyoming scientist but $189,000 per Californian. More significant is the reason—the clustering into five major areas.

After visiting them, one has seen the spectrum of science at work —from theorist, experimenter, and tester to policy-maker and pay-master; from traditional university and industrial laboratory to "research park" and "think tank." One has also seen how like attracts like: to the Greater Boston area; to the New York-New Jersey area; to the Washington, D. C., area; to California's two coastal regions, around Los Angeles and around San Francisco. Designating these is only a convenience, of course, New Jersey could as well go with

Pennsylvania and Delaware. And the trend toward Clustermegapolis is already such that everything between Boston and Washington might be called one seaboard immensity of science and engineering.

Area 1, Boston

Start down the East Coast and the first powerful magnet for R & D is Boston—the city itself plus such environs as Cambridge and the area served by circumferential Route 128. This is the Electronics Highway toward which everybody in the applied-science world, and not only its electronics division, seems to have been attracted, even if only to erect a branch plant. A major reason is to nestle close to the talent and facilities of Massachusetts Institute of Technology. Greater Boston has much else; for instance, its major medical research centers. And its intellectual Cambridge has Harvard departments strong in psychology, in astronomy, in physics. Furthermore, as mileage goes these days, Boston's claim to being a supplier of scientific knowledge can easily extend inland to such examples as Worcester's noted Foundation for Experimental Biology, and down the coast to include Woods Hole Oceanographic Institution, the largest private employer on Cape Cod. But the area's science is unquestionably dominated by MIT, the Vulcan whose avowed purpose is investigating the theoretical and converting it into the practical.

Once it was merely "Boston Tech," the plebeian neighbor of cultured Harvard. And today Harvard's student body is twice as large. MIT has barely 7000 students, divided almost equally between undergraduate and graduate. Both the University of Michigan and Michigan State University have a student total four times larger; New York University counts six times as many; others are still larger. But the bigness of MIT is measured by its influence. Its skilled hand is found everywhere—in its laboratories on the crowded home campus; in the labs that grew too large for MIT's comfort and were urged forth to stand on their own; in the think tanks and national laboratories it manages in association with other universities; in the productivity of its alumni, a long list of whom have founded their own R & D plants, the nearest being right next door along "Research Row." Other alumni: Alfred P. Sloan, Jr., and Gerard Swope, who became president of General Motors and General Electric, respectively. From MIT's staff, too, have come wielders of influence: organizers of R & D companies, and a multitude of consultants to industry and government. Vannevar Bush headed wartime science for President Roosevelt; Killian and Wiesner were chief science advisers, respectively, to Presidents Eisenhower and Kennedy.

Hence, publicists for MIT need not speak loudly. They are content to call it an uncommon university. And it demonstrates that bigness of itself need not necessarily ruin quality, any more so than smallness—of which Oregon's Reed College is an outstanding example. For one thing, despite MIT's emphasis on postgraduate work, and its embarrassing amount of contract work for the government, it has struggled manfully to become and remain a true university. Its interests have spread past science alone. It does what it can to confront undergraduates with capable teachers who will take time from sponsored research. An R & D vice president in industry remembered back to the 1930s: "For physics in my sophomore year I had William Shockley, who went on to co-invent the transistor; and I'll never forget what inspiring Norbert Wiener did to math in my junior year."

The most immediate worry, of course, is this one about how to handle government R & D without disrupting the normal education process. Another problem is strictly local, peculiar to MIT—and neighboring Harvard. This is a cloud that isn't black, but neither does it vanish entirely. It is the feeling of efficiency folk that the two institutions should join. Why step on each other's toes? Why not become a great University of Cambridge?

A previous merger went some distance before it was balked by a legal tangle. Students from one institution took credit courses at the other (Bush received his engineering doctorate from both in 1916); today, some professors still teach at both places. And pro-merger logic is even stronger than fifty years ago. Geographically, these two campuses across the Charles River from Boston now almost touch anyway. Intellectually, the tastes of both have grown more alike—more humanities at MIT, more science at Harvard. Financially, the same paymaster at Washington underwrites heavy R & D at both. It is not surprising, then, that both already manage a $12-million electron accelerator jointly for the AEC, just as both operate a Joint Center for Urban Studies.

Meanwhile, MIT tends its various own gardens. The Great Dome rises above the Great Court where the rhododendrons bloom. Across Massachusetts Avenue, what seems another, lower dome turns out to be a nuclear reactor for research, but what seems a tiny red brick blockhouse surrounded by a moat becomes the turret-like chapel designed by Eero Saarinen. Architecturally, it matches nothing else. It need not. Inside is escape, and asceticism, but also two rich offerings. The bare bricks encircle a pulpit of sheer white marble and the golden metal curtain behind it. In front, starkness again, the few arced rows of prim straight-back chairs. A chamber for meditation, or for counsel from the wise.

But what of MIT as a center of scientific excellence? My most interesting talks were with two men in fields seemingly far apart but actually linked closely. Both men had pioneered the way to automation. Yet both, significantly, scorned exuberant predictions that machine brain will obsolete human brain.

One was Norbert Wiener, the father of cybernetics, which underlies the techniques of automatic control. We will meet him in another chapter. The other was Charles S. Draper, America's much-honored "Mr. Gyro," the professor heading both MIT's Department of Aeronautics and Astronautics and its affiliated Instrumentation Laboratory, notable for the inertial-guidance systems it has developed for the government. It was Draper's shipboard gunsight that ended the threat from Japan's kamikaze airmen in the last war. After that, he moved logically to jam-proof automatic guidance for bombers, then missiles. Such control enabled accurate launching of Polaris missiles from a submerged submarine; it has been redesigned to navigate Apollo's spacemen to the moon and back.

Like MIT, its "Doc" Draper, ex-boxer, ex-pilot, is uncommon. I found him overweight for boxing but still fast on his feet. While walking down the hall, while at lunch, he continually popped into telephone booths to keep in touch with developments. Originally, he wandered onto the campus simply as a sightseer, a young Missourian with a B.A. in psychology. He stayed to study some more and became a legend—the student who took more credit courses than anyone else in MIT history. This was hunger for knowledge; it took him into various fields. Finally, urged to make up his mind, he settled for a doctorate in physics.

Another characteristic of his mind is that he speaks it with Midwestern earthiness, and tartness lies behind the dimpled smile. Some samples at lunch:

Speaking as chairman of the National Inventors Council—"The old-fashioned inventor, that fellow in the attic, will either be dead soon, or cease to be a little fellow." As the engineering professor who tried a few years in private industry—"Sure, I could go back and pick up loads more money than I get now. Why stay at MIT? Because industry is dead from its neck up, controlled by the bookkeepers. Quick money is their only plan for the future." Concerning systems engineering—"It's all the rage now, and it's malarky. Breadth of interest isn't allowed. The electrical engineer, for example, stays just an electrical engineer."

At his Instrumentation Laboratory, too, he used simple English. The inertial method is more calculated than the verbal blueprint he supplied at first while pointing at the internal organs of a basketball-size sphere, his latest guidance system: "As you can see, just three accelerometers, three gyros, and a plumb bob."

Nowhere was the Draper attitude reflected better than in these buildings that were doing $37-million worth of government work a year, more than MIT's entire nongovernmental income. They would be a shocking sight on chic Route 128. But Draper, the quondam habitual student, wanted the lab where he could continue communion with scholars. So, when it couldn't qualify to go on campus, he infiltrated it into adjacent warrens: a vacant garage, a warehouse that had stored wool, an old shoe-polish factory.

Keeping it off campus illustrates MIT's precautions against allowing abnormally large government projects, especially those that carry secrecy labels, to kill with kindness. It does allow less embarrassing contracts and grants, and the total for these corresponds to MIT's stature, but they are construed somehow as being part of conventional departmental research. Figures show the over-all awkwardness. In 1963, MIT jubilantly announced that alumni and friends had pledged $98 million to its Second Century Fund. The same year, it received a total of $12 million more than that from Washington. This, while spurning another $100 million worth of federal research.

How to retain MIT's focus on education—how to exercise self-discipline when challenging defense contracts are offered, how to say a tactful no, how to suggest some other way? One way, if the government is desperate, is to say yes but disentangle MIT by organizing an affiliate and bundling it off campus. The outstanding example is Lincoln Laboratory, set up twelve miles away during the Korean War. Its emergency assignment: to translate MIT concepts of new radars and computers into protection for North America against surprise Soviet air attack. Here were born SAGE and the succeeding computerized defense systems against bombers, then missiles. Lincoln Lab is now working with still farther advanced electronics, still makes no pretense of using its $55-million budgets for educational purposes. It has no student body; most of its technical staff are not even part of MIT's faculty.

Even this arm's-length operation became embarrassing. When the lab had figured out SAGE, MIT was asked by the Air Force to expand the operation, to carry on with the systems engineering all the way to overseeing installation of the actual defense system.

Here was a challenge for the MIT vice president in charge of such troubles: loyal alumnus James McCormack, a retired Pentagon major general whose specialty is administration. "In the short term, yes, you do your duty," he later explained to a congressional committee. "In the long term, government and university would be well advised to look for other solutions."

He already had experience setting up "nonprofit" corporations, and this was the tack he now took: "The request seemed painfully far from MIT's basic academic mission so again we begged to be excused, but offered to divide out that part of the Lincoln Laboratory staff, about a third then, which was most closely involved in this function, and to sponsor the formation of a new corporation to run it."

Thus was born strangely named Mitre Corporation, which set up shop a few miles away with five hundred employes donated by Lincoln Lab's Division 6, and has gone on expanding. I asked its president, C. W. Halligan, if choosing the name "Mitre" was an acronymic way to claim blood ties with MIT. He grinned. "The work was classified. We wanted a meaningless name for the company but couldn't find one. One day, a few of our people were sitting around and, being originally from MIT, looked in the dictionary for words beginning with *mit.* They saw 'mitre.' Among its meanings was 'shield,' which seemed apt for a company doing defense work."

Functionally, the nonprofit companies set up specifically for cold-war duty are two kinds. One is the think tank. Working with charts, computers, and the like, its research groups produce reports and recommendations—the paper called "software." California's Rand Corporation, deeply involved with cost analysis and with statisticians who can calculate Overkill down to the last gasp, was the first of this type. It started as a service for worried strategists: "When the Air Force general was pacing up and down the room, there was a Rand fellow lying on the couch listening to him." Set up in 1948 by Douglas Aircraft and the Ford Foundation, Rand has worked for a management fee—6 per cent of costs—and its net worth has risen to several million dollars. Such companies, dealing with the economics, sociology, psychology, politics, and Realpolitik of war, are mainly sayers.

The other nonprofit type, though not mute, is more of a doer. It gets down to the necessary hardware. The first one, also dating back to 1948, taught General McCormack how to organize such a company. He was then the Pentagon's spokesman in the AEC, and the company was Sandia Corporation, a subsidiary of Western Electric Company, set up to do the actual engineering of nuclear weapons. This freed AEC's Los Alamos Laboratory researchers for the basic physics behind bomb-making.

Sandia helps explain Mitre, another doer. It carries on where Lincoln Laboratory's research on computerized defense leaves off. Though it doesn't actually manufacture the equipment, it is the government's technical adviser that directs those who do. Its lab people prepare feasibility studies, design the system, write hardware specifications for it, and so on through overseeing tests of the manufacturer's product.

Another difference between Mitre and Lincoln is this: Lincoln seems the simpler arrangement. It works in government-owned buildings. It receives no fee as such—only a repayment of direct costs, and the indirect ones that cause continual expense-account haggling between government and universities. Mitre is conventionally "nonprofit." It works for a management fee, which started at 9 per cent to help Mitre erect its buildings, and has come down to 6 per cent in recent years.

"But," I asked Halligan, "suppose a depression hits the defense industry; suppose Mitre is no longer needed? Who owns these buildings then?"

He nodded. "People who consider working here also wonder about a nonprofit's future. Yes, we're vulnerable if genuine peace comes. But that's an if. Anyway, our charter says that the buildings would go back to the government."

Another of MIT's progeny should be mentioned here because, oddly, it happens to be a natural foe of the tax-exempt laboratories. It is Arthur D. Little, Inc. (page 37), the versatile solver of problems for industry and government alike—weather research, food technology, cryogenics, solid-state physics, charcoal filters for cigarettes. It is especially fretful over those nonprofit competitors—big Battelle, for instance—that raid into private industry.

This is explainable because unique A. D. Little is not only the nation's oldest industrial research lab but largest of the true independents. When its founder died in 1935, his will bequeathed the majority of the stock to his alma mater. MIT didn't relish the non-educational responsibility, so considered this like its other investments. The lab was told to run itself. Eventually, its seven hundred employes bought out MIT's interest for their retirement trust. Thus the lab became somewhat of a cooperative, whose members feel this way about nonprofit rivals:

"They spend easy money. They inflate our costs. They also hurt us because big industrial companies expect to get research done free by the government via the tax-exempts. But it keeps us sharp. We don't claim that we're better scientists but clients can see that we don't live the sheltered life, we can't squander their money, we have a better feel for their practical needs. It's worrisome but if it doesn't get worse, we'll get by. That's more than we can predict for the smaller independents."

Area 2, New York–New Jersey

In America's science world this is the geographic area of infinite variety. Here are Brookhaven National Laboratory and such prestige universities as Princeton and Columbia, already heavy in research programs and growing heavier. Here also, notably in New Jersey, is industrial research of practically every kind, including such leaders as chemicals, with its biological offshoot, pharmaceuticals; and electronics, with its communications offshoot, computers.

But first, what of unquiet New York City, with its feverish cosmopolitanism, its sharp contrast between outward opulence and inner man, its troubled claim to having more psychiatrists and mental-health clinics than any other city on earth? Specifically, what of Manhattan?

The strident island has its serene coves. Up in a rotunda-like room of the American Museum of Natural History, remote from the thronging halls below, was only the whine of a small power saw. The sound drew me into an adjoining lab. Here I found Brian Mason, curator of geology and mineralogy—an ex-New Zealander, one of our many "brain drain" acquisitions from abroad. He was cutting a small piece of meteorite into slices. These are then delicately ground down to transparencies. Mason showed me the result under a polarizing microscope. It resembled a resplendent design in stained glass, indicating the mother meteorite to be an aggregate of pellets called chondrules.

Why the interest in them? Because, chemically, they contain some significant carbon compounds—organic matter. Consequently, these samples feed a hot controversy: Do such meteorites prove the existence of simple life forms out in Space? If they do, might life on this planet have originated from such visitants? Aside from that, the early history of our solar system—the past five billion years or so—is written in the chemistry and physics of meteorites. Mason's problem is obtaining suitable fragments, like the precious 100-gram piece he had from the Orgueil meteorite, which fell in France a century ago. Meanwhile, to provide researchers with samples, he dips into the collection he stores in pillboxes and goes on hoping that "a nice one will fall right here in Central Park."

Across town, beyond the park, is tranquillity of the medical-research kind sponsored by private foundations: famed Rockefeller Institute, proud of its Nobelists; and Sloan-Kettering Institute, part of a cancer-fighting center that is the world's largest. Because each institute now fosters a community of graduate students, each is a sumptuous quasi-university. Certainly Rockefeller Institute can boast a tree-lined campus—and lives with fear of what a new subway tunnel would do to its quiet, and to its nervous laboratory instruments.

These two, in turn, betoken Manhattan's distinctive influence on research. Here is where most of the big private foundations have their headquarters. Notable, for instance, are those grown from the wealth that came to men who served motorists: from General Motors, its Alfred P. Sloan Foundation as well as Sloan-Kettering (Charles F. Kettering headed General Motors' R & D); from Ford, the $2.5-billion Ford Foundation; from Standard Oil, the Rockefeller Foundation and Rockefeller Institute—plus many subsidiaries and such crossovers as Rockefeller Foundation's exchanging 89,000 shares of its Jersey Standard stock for 122,000 shares of Ford Foundation's Ford Motor stock, and Laurance S. Rockefeller becoming chairman of Sloan-Kettering's board. There are also many links with Washington. For example, Dean Rusk, the Rockefeller Foundation's president, became Secretary of State, and Detlev Bronk, while president of the National Academy, became also president of Rockefeller Institute.

Even when truly independent, the foundations present problems because of their power and nontaxable income; because a foundation's financial life presents more snares and nets for an investigator than does a for-profit company owned by stockholders; because the government is even uncertain about how many foundations there are. One result: an NSF report on foundations in 1964 had guesses no fresher than for the year 1960.

It is no secret that many foundations are shams set up for tax sanctuaries, for "self-dealing" business masquerades and the like; consequently, others suffer through guilt by association. As a whole, persistent Congressman Wright Patman and others charge them with adding to the taxpayer's burden (in 10 years, 534 of them had $7 billion of untaxable income); and wielding dangerous financial power with their portfolios of securities (by 1963, a low estimate for the assets of 15,000 foundations was $14.5 billion).

The biggest worry of the foundations resembles that of their offspring, the nonprofit corporations: namely, the accusation that they enable their founders and directorates to live in pompous circumstances "out of the public trough." They fight it with a counter-argument equally appealing to parsimonious congressmen—if foundations were driven out of the philanthropy field, government would have to assume the burden. Their other claim, that they provide "seed money" vitally needed for research, has become weaker through the years. Too many scientists of the Martin Arrowsmith type say foundations are flabby and uninformed; that they gamble not on ideas but on big-name scientists or projects with publicity value. Moreover, the government's annual expenditure of multibillions on R & D now makes help from the foundations relatively trivial. Of the perhaps $650 million that the foundations give out in grants annually, the physical and life sciences receive about $80 million.

Meanwhile, the government's competitive R & D has had an odd effect. The foundations have trouble finding enough worthy recipients for the money they do care to spare for science. They can hardly compete with a giant like NASA or a giantling like the National Science Foundation. The usurpation by NSF has its irony, for here is a federal agency created in the image of a private philanthropy, with all the faults of grantsmanship. Of course, a private foundation with its own laboratories, like Rockefeller Institute or Carnegie Institution, is not seriously affected. And Sloan-Kettering even less so. Its cancer program is so big that it is itself a solicitor of grants—from NIH, from other private foundations; it even takes donations from such odd bedfellows as the American Cancer Society and Reynolds Tobacco Company. But the foundation depending on intramural research belongs to a small minority. The rest suffer from a condition that a foundation director defined as "competitive philanthropy." "We're in competition," he told me glumly, "both with government and with each other."

Obviously, he didn't consider competition healthy. Nor is it—for the languid. For others, it can be. A case in point is the $10-million Research Corporation, one of the smaller large foundations. It was created in 1912 by F. G. Cottrell, a young chemist-teacher-inventor. He endowed it with his patents to the Cottrell precipitation process, which reduces air pollution by electrostatically eliminating the "smoke nuisance."

The major part of Research Corporation's income is unique. It handles patent rights for about 150 universities and others who dislike bothering with the expenses, bookkeeping, and possible lawsuits.

Among the hundreds in its portfolio, for instance, are patents for the maser and for cortisone. With its other hand, Research Corporation passes out research aid of about the same amount, around $1.3 million a year. This helped Robert Goddard with his rocketry, Ernest Lawrence with his cyclotrons; more recently, it rewarded such men as Rudolf Mossbauer, Melvin Calvin, James Watson, and Charles Townes before they became Nobelists.

President J. W. Hinkley stresses another oddity about his authentically creative foundation. In 1945 it saw the beginning of a trend—lavish aid to schools for graduate researchers, little or nothing for the smaller colleges that turn young people into those graduates. He minces no words: "The liberal-arts colleges are the backbone of our system. It would be disastrous to permit them to be degraded in the sciences or, on the other hand, forced into the mold of the university system. Our dominant theme is strengthening the sciences, primarily at liberal-arts colleges."

Young professors benefit. An example is the physicist at an unglamorous smaller school. He wanted to do a neutrino study down a mile-deep mine shaft. But his proposal for an AEC grant was rejected; he was told to try again after he had actual data. He got it with a Research Corporation grant.

"Yes, competition has hit us hard," said the foundation's vice president, S. B. Yates. He chuckled. "You might say we've been driven to do low-pressure soliciting—both for patent clients and for grantees. But it has been a healthy challenge. It doesn't let us forget reality: the unconventional researcher may have exactly the idea that science needs."

Meanwhile, the new conditions have forced some of the more corpulent foundations to begin exploring edges of the real world: For instance, from the $250 million that it passes out yearly, the Ford Foundation set up a useful $8-million program to help those engineering students who promise to make a career of teaching engineering students. It also touched on the integration problem by setting up scholarships for elite Negro students, the counterpart of "blue chip" Negro athletes for whom campuses compete eagerly. The Rockefeller Foundation has dug a bit deeper—into why those schools that do want to integrate can find so few "qualified" Negro students of other kinds and why such R & D employers as NASA are embarrassed because they can find so few "qualified" Negro engineers. The result: a pilot remedial program, at Dartmouth and elsewhere, designed to turn the socially and academically underprivileged, now delicately called the "disadvantaged," into the qualified.

No doubt, the need to do something about this problem is uncomfortably with us. One day, for example, when anti-segregation rallies and riots marked a winter of our discontents, I was at Lincoln Laboratory, the electronics center operated by MIT near Boston, therefore in the North. A Negro walked by and I realized that he was the first I had noticed in several weeks. I asked about him. "Oh yes," my guide said. "We have another, upstairs." This at a lab employing 600 professionals plus 1200 others, and a $55-million budget, met entirely with government contracts. Why so few Negroes? The answer was "We hire anybody who can meet the requirements." Fair enough but—why has education failed to qualify Negroes to meet the requirements? The question goes farther. It happens that the Negro's color serves somewhat like a radioactive isotope—as a handy "tracer." Others cannot be noticed so easily. What about the white-skinned youngsters who also lack opportunity to meet requirements? If we decline to believe that it is nature who sets up intellectual castes, then the answer lies in one's social-economic status. Those who have, also have the chance to learn. The American Council on Education reports one winner of the National Merit Scholarship per twelve thousand fathers who are professional workers, and contrasts this with one scholarship per three million manual laborers.

At least, the Rockefeller Foundation's new program recognizes the challenge. This is part of its new look. When founded in 1902, it believed "disease is the supreme ill," and for proof it contributed martyrs to the fight against tropical fevers. In 1928 its interest expanded to other sciences; for instance, it helped finance what was then the world's costliest research tool, the $6-million 200-inch telescope being built at Mount Palomar. Today, bothered by competition and exploring new paths for philanthropy, it has discovered "an increasing association between nutrition and health"; has embraced the ecological approach to human problems; has ventured into such areas of "pressing need" as birth control, conquest of hunger, and *equal* educational opportunity.

But what of industrial R & D? The best over-all view comes after crossing the Hudson. The catalyst here was Tom Edison. His biggest invention was not the incandescent lamp or phonograph but the concept of professional invention—at Menlo Park, in 1878, when he hired a crew and began creating on an assembly-line basis. His progeny are many. In New York, for example, he led to the formation of General Electric. And he dreamed up—literally, one sleepless night—the Naval Research Laboratory, which he then disowned angrily when Navy built it along the Potomac rather than at Sandy Hook.

In his New Jersey, R & D has today spread far past the Edison effect, into such fields as biochemicals and petrochemicals; and into electricity far beyond Edison's imagination.

Here, for instance, are centered the technical brains of RCA, the world's largest electronics company. It is distinctive also in that its policy-makers are not electronic computers, though RCA uses them, and also builds them. Nor are its top men human computers brought in by the twentieth century's management revolution. Rather, they are truly executives—almost old-fashioned—possessing technical as well as business acumen: David Sarnoff, chairman of the board, the onetime telegraph messenger who grew up with radio and radar engineering, wisely gambled on color television and was rewarded when laggard rivals had to come to RCA for their picture tubes; and Elmer Bergstrom, research vice president elevated to the presidency in 1961, the electrical engineer who directed development of RCA's color TV, radar systems, satellites, and the rest of its ultra-modern products.

This is industry's version of competitive R & D, and more familiar than that of the foundations. For New Jersey's electronics has much more than RCA's research centers. Among others, it has the rival Bell Telephone Laboratories at Murray Hill. This is the R & D arm of a service complex far bigger than RCA—the $30-billion Bell System, built from the most valuable single patent ever granted, and often chided for monopolistic practices. In any event, it is self-contained. Its management company is the familiar American Telephone & Telegraph Company. The equipment that AT&T needs is manufactured by its associated subsidiary, Western Electric Company.

And the researchers who convert theory into design for this communication equipment are at Bell Labs: star of New Jersey's research theater, and the world's leader as well. It employs 14,500 scientists, engineers, and supporting staff. Its research vice president, William O. Baker, red hair, pixy face, and with a mind far sharper than his soothing voice indicates, has one of the most enviable R & D jobs in industry.

Bell's self-sufficiency works nicely. Available for its experimental Telstar, as an example, were such "in-house" contributions as maser amplifiers, solar cells, and, of course, transistors, for which three Bell physicists won the Nobel Prize. Furthermore, the lab can count on support from parent AT&T, whose contracts with such giant government agencies as Air Force and NASA read like pacts between potentates of equal power. And with good reason. Its $5-billion budgets are a match for NASA's; in its Telstar deal with NASA it could point out that it spent its own money creating the communications satellite and was willing to pay for NASA's launching rocket too. In return it was getting valuable experience, patent rights, and the like. Its independence also netted publicity that chagrined RCA, who orbited the rival satellite called Relay. An RCA executive mourned: "Our show had only three publicity men because NASA worried about the reaction if Relay failed. So NASA, who paid to build Relay, was calling the tune. But the Bell people could make a spectacular out of their Telstar. And oh, how they did! They had sixty-seven PR people, from Canaveral to Maine, plus the mobile units for any newsman who cared to step in and phone long-distance."

Like MIT, Bell Labs is uncommon. And its $350-million budgets represent four times the amount spent on science by all the foundations. But lordly Bell is no spendthrift. I found it finally getting around to air-conditioning one of the main buildings, which dated back to 1939. The company station wagon that took me to isolated Murray Hill was a rattler whose heater didn't work. At lunch, Baker grimaced when an assistant shimmed up a table leg with match folders while apologizing, "Something wrong with the floor—all the tables are now wobbly."

But elsewhere Bell makes sure that its image shines resplendently: "We can't afford to have a man putter, building his own equipment.

If he needs a $20,000 magnet, we buy him one." A visiting metal-lurgist had come here to talk to the laser experts. Afterward, we compared notes. He was ecstatic. "They wouldn't have to pay me. I'd pay to work in such a lab."

The image is reflected in Bell's productivity: in its microwave networks, dial phones, and automated switchboards, and also in its basic research that led to transistors, solar cells, and lasers, to metal "whiskers," superconductivity, and information theory.

Bell does not skimp on lab equipment. It does nourish creativity: "Teamwork is a kind of dirty word around here." It proudly counts the research papers that it adds to the communal literature, much as a university does. But it requires discipline too. Recruits fresh from the campus go through an indoctrination that tries to explain this is no place for idle curiosity. However visionary, research here must envision the practical somewhere along the line.

In 1932, Bell's Karl Jansky was investigating radio static that plagued the company's transatlantic circuits. He found that not all of the interference had an earthly source. Some was "cosmic," apparently from the Milky Way. But Bell didn't share his enthusiasm for exploring this new mystery. "Your Jansky was the father of radio astronomy," I reminded Baker, "but England, and our amateur astronomer, Grote Reber, had to carry it further. Why did Bell drop Jansky's discovery?" "We didn't drop it," he parried, "because we had never picked it up."

If such choosiness be a fault, it is also found along the university circuit, where a research project often smacks too much of the ivory tower—or the converse. After thirty years, for instance, Yale finally expelled its Center of Alcohol Studies. This lab was started in the Prohibition era by dedicated researchers who felt that alcohol-ism sorely needed the scientific approach, rather than merely preach-ments and emotionalism.

However, what Yale disdained, New Jersey's Rutgers University welcomed, and it supplied a new home for the *émigrés*. For this, it had to scrounge for funds. But as a state institution rather than grandee among universities, it learned long ago that money doesn't come as easily as science may like. True, it did have one stroke of luck. In fifteen years, the antibiotics discovered by its Selman Waksman brought $12 million in patent royalties. Hence Rutgers' continuing fascination with biochemicals, the effects of pesticides, and other such medical research.

Not that this alma mater on the Raritan disdains the unpragmatical. No important university can afford to if, along with football for alumni and parking space for undergraduates, it wants to attract postgraduates and keep its faculty content. So, Rutgers now belongs to the accelerator club. Its Van de Graaff, one of the larger tandem models, can speed proton "bullets" with up to 18 million electron-volts. Though this is hardly a match for the multibillion-volt atom-smashers, it suits Rutgers. Still, the machine did cost $1.5 million and the shielded building for it cost the same. There was the usual question: how to raise the money? Rutgers scrounged. Some came from its own budget, some came from the state, some from NSF. And Bell Labs, increasingly interested in nuclear physics, chipped in with a half-million dollars. It also pays $100,000 annually, in exchange for using one-third of the machine's time.

It is understandable that nearby Princeton University, which was an important cradle of nuclear physics, aims higher than Rutgers. At its Forrestal Research Center the stream of protons is accelerated by 3 billion electron-volts, and the research machine is a $12-million synchrotron operated jointly by Princeton and University of Pennsylvania for AEC, which is technically the owner. A month after this atom-smasher began operating, construction began on auxiliary laboratories, for which AEC supplied another $8 million. Also, Princeton is the research contractor paid around $8 million yearly to explore possibilities of the fusion kind of nuclear power. Its group of AEC-financed machines is led by the Model-C Stellerator, whose equipment required $35 million.

In such ways, Princeton indulges in massive experiments. Beyond its campus, on what was nearby farmland, is a center much more tranquil and often believed erroneously to be part of the university because the two are unquestionably symbiotic. It is the Institute for Advanced Study, a retreat for scholars, financed by philanthropy, with a housing development for its own people, and, in Director Robert Oppenheimer's words, "very highbrow." This quasi-university has somewhat over a hundred "students" of postdoctoral rank who are called "temporary members." The two dozen professors, who are "permanent members," do not teach. The relation was explained this way by Freeman J. Dyson, professor of mathematical physics and another of our valuable acquisitions from England: "To begin with, I help select qualified scholars. After that, I serve as a sounding board. By talking to me an hour or so when he wishes, the scholar may clarify something in his own mind. You see, communication is a serious problem. For example, mathematical physics is full of subgroups. Each goes off into its corner. They cannot understand each other."

Here, then, is definitely no hardware. It is a center for thinker-sayers, not experimental doers. Specifically, some are historians who specialize, perhaps in Greek archeology. Most, however, practice either pure mathematics or theoretical physics. Once, in 1947, the institute did venture deeper into the real world. That was when mathematician von Neumann pioneered here with computer theory and, on the side, built up a group of theoretical meteorologists. But, just as Bell Labs couldn't accept Jansky's "impractical" radio astronomy and Yale, on the other hand, expelled its "practical" researchers on alcoholism, so did the institute's "pure" scholars grow uneasy over this foreign intrusion. Meteorology, however theoretical, smacked too much of "engineering." The resulting unpleasantness led to an exodus of the outlanders. Some fled northeast to MIT.

Flight was easier than remaining to quarrel over definitions of materialism. In nothing, for instance, are Princeton's university and institute more symbiotic than in the extent of their responsibility for the nuclear age—both its good and its terror. Here came Denmark's Niels Bohr, immediately after reaching the United States in 1939, to discuss abstractions with the institute's most illustrious member, Albert Einstein. And he brought a pregnant tip for his former student, J. A. Wheeler, and other scientists at the university: namely, Germany had just split the uranium atom. The result, in physicist Leo Szilard's words, was that Princeton became a "stirred-up ant heap."

Thereafter, this university town provided much genealogy of the A-bomb and then the H-bomb. Here, as residents, have been such leading physicists and mathematicians as theorist Einstein, of course, but also Oppenheimer, Wheeler, Henry D. Smyth, and the noted ex-Hungarians von Neumann and Eugene Wigner. Here, too, came such associates as Enrico Fermi, Bohr, and Szilard. And it remains rich in nuclear talent.

Princeton is therefore a sharp reminder for laymen who feel inadequate to judge serious matters of science, specifically the nuclear kind. Its experts have trouble too. The city is midway between New York and Philadelphia. If nuclear war comes, Princeton would be part of both targets—grim proof that the human race might not be obliterated but, likely enough, the cities, and with them the centers of science, would perish. Yet, in 1963, the university was just beginning to examine "the defense concept of the walled town." It wondered if its buildings could provide enough fallout-shelter space for its own population of six thousand plus perhaps double that from off campus.

This was thirteen years after the start of the USA–USSR race for hydrogen weapons. Why such delay in nuclear Princeton? For the same reasons that braked shelter programs elsewhere: distaste for "back to the caves"; uncertainty over how helpful the shelters would be and a feeling that they might only be cruel deceptions; suspicions that a national expenditure of $5 billion for fallout shelters, or up to $200 billion for blast-proof ones, would be just another Washington plan to spur the economy; a blend of insouciance and fatalism. Thus, Princeton had guesses, not answers. One of its leading nuclear men said, no, he had not built a family shelter. Why not? He shrugged. "Oh, our children have grown up. There are just me and my wife now. Maybe our basement will help."

However, physics also deals with atoms for peace. Far out on Long Island, beyond the R & D centers of such aerospace companies as Republic Aviation and Grumman Aircraft, is what was once Camp Yaphank, immortalized in song by a World War I sergeant named Irving Berlin. It served again in the next war. Some army buildings remain but with them now are noted atom-smashers and also nuclear reactors, one of them on Rutherford Hill. Some streets retain Army-given names but others are named for major northeastern universities: MIT, Harvard, Yale, Columbia, Princeton, Cornell, Rochester, Johns Hopkins, Pennsylvania.

This is Brookhaven National Laboratory, where you see no military uniforms and where, on departure, you are checked not for military secrets but for how much radiation you absorbed. The $200-million research center is doubly a captive lab. It belongs to an absentee owner, the Atomic Energy Commission, which also meets the $50-million budgets. And the nine universities are absentee managers. They operate Brookhaven through their nonprofit cooperative called Associated Universities, Inc., whose other big government job is operating the Green Bank observatory for NSF. Green Bank, though smaller, is likewise a "national laboratory."

We have seen many versions of government-paid R & D, and the differences among them can be subtle. Hence it helps to make a sharp distinction between national laboratory and "government laboratory." The latter is exemplified by Naval Research Laboratory, actually run by the government and with government workers. A national lab is run at government expense by outsiders who might otherwise not be able or care to invest in expensive extracurricular facilities. But it is unlike MIT's Lincoln Laboratory, which, though government-owned, is virtually a private preserve and is strongly program-oriented. Brookhaven typifies a banding together by universities to serve a wider, "purer" scientific community, even though it is not truly national, certainly not enough to placate Midwesterners. One other contrast: it resembles only superficially its European ancestors. Pasteur Institute, for instance, was set up by France as a satrapy for an idolized individual. And because of the breadth of Brookhaven's interests—physics, biology, chemistry, and basic research that reaches to such materialism as the irradiation that "cold pasteurizes" foods—it is a better example than Green Bank. Also, it has fewer management embarrassments, thanks to scrutiny by the AEC, which, in turn, is watched by its congressional overseer, the joint atomic committee. National labs, then, are held with government reins, tight or not. And their research programs, like those of government's other nonprofit captives, must depend upon government policy. The direction of mainstream is changeable.

Moreover, Brookhaven and Green Bank face a similar problem. Neither can attract the elite by offering an MIT or Princeton next door; nor can either promise community living. If Green Bank is in remote mountains, Brookhaven is on a 3500-acre dreary flatland of scrub pines, oaks, and sand. But it offers relief. From Army it inherited a fine gymnasium and outdoor swimming pool. Its three thousand workers, including the eight hundred staff and visiting scientists, can find suitable homes in towns within twenty-five miles. They, their payroll of over $20 million, and their community spirit if they care to participate, are very welcome now that the natives seem convinced that Brookhaven builds no bombs. And Manhattan's intellectual resorts are only 75 miles away.

Such is Brookhaven, a testimonial for realistic planning. It was deemed unwise that one university dominate this co-op laboratory. So, as a researcher said wryly, "They chose a site equally inconvenient for all nine."

Area 3, Nation's Capital

It has long been argued that the man—the leader—makes his times. And, vice versa, that the times make the man. Equally interesting, and fruitless, could be another debate. In an era of growing federal responsibilities and power, is it the policy-making of Washington, or what the rest of the nation needs, that fashions the other?

This is certain. Whether Washington leads or follows, it has had to keep in step. A symbol of government, it is also a symbol of change. It is now both the nation's scientific and governmental capital, and the line between the two is as nebulous as the physical boundaries of this federal city surrounded by its ring of satellite towns and science centers. The administrative buildings of the AEC at Germantown, Maryland, the administrative buildings and the government's own research labs in the NIH hills at Bethesda: these and others help explain the increasing blur in any distinction between massive science and massive government.

They also help explain eye-opening statistics. For instance, the Census Bureau says that this metropolitan area—the District of Columbia plus neighboring sections of Maryland and Virginia—is not only the fastest-growing of the nation's large population centers but has the highest proportion of families headed by college graduates. And Navy has now rechristened the Potomac. In advertisements for researchers it invites them to inspect what it can offer at its eight different kinds of labs along "Research River."

There are also the other signs of change. Suburbs bloom with new government buildings, and the focal city has likewise been in a turmoil of construction, reminiscent of what it underwent in the world wars. As late as 1963, I found parts of great NASA still scattered around town in rookeries called "A" building, "T" building, and the like. At one, the expert on rocket fuels was unworried about the thrust needed to send a rocket thirty stories tall into outer Space. Glancing around the small office, of which he claimed one corner, he said, "It's living space on earth that NASA needs."

Technology erected new buildings to solve this problem. And while doing so, it created other problems. Unable to compete with airports, once-booming Union Station was now becoming a useless mausoleum, a Romanesque one. With the last streetcar tracks torn up, the city was left to crawl with taxis—only New York City, with 10 times the population, had more of them: 12,000 as compared with 9,000. A government chemist died, not from a lab explosion, but from adding to his Civil Service pay. A robber shot him while he was moonlighting as a weekend cabdriver.

And what is this science that permeates today's Washington? It is most easily understood by noting that it fills two roles. One is that of the administrator-paymaster who directs and supports three-fourths of the nation's R & D, whose contracts and grants heavily finance work done by the universities and by industry of both kinds, profit and nonprofit.

The other role is that of the Washington who is an actual employer, who reserves roughly one-fifth of its federal science budget for government installations staffed by government workers. The percentage of this intramural activity has dropped, but the total is hardly negligible. It costs upward of $3 billion yearly. And it throws its own distinctive light upon our science in transition. Though much of this research is overlooked by glamour writers, much also is directly concerned with the needs of the average man—stronger metals, better weather forecasts, harmless highways, safer foods, and so on.

In government's first role, its controlling hand operates in many ways. One, as we have seen, is to nourish nonprofit companies that are quasi-official. Of these, none is more definitely a servant of government than IDA. It is the Institute of Defense Analyses, set up in the nation's capital for intimate relations with the Pentagon. As a think tank it is unique in that it contains a deep inner tank called Jason. To build it, IDA enticed two dozen promising new-generation physicists from universities, exposed them to guidance from four elder statesmen of military science—Edward Teller, Eugene Wigner, John Wheeler, Hans Bethe—and turned them loose on weaponry problems, the detection of Russian nuclear tests, and the like. IDA has no laboratories as such. Its product is "software." It was organized in 1956 to serve as expert adviser to the Secretary of Defense and his Joint Chiefs of Staff. The individual and often warring services, Army, Navy, and Air Force, have their own loyal braintrusts. The Defense Secretary has IDA. Here is another of MIT's offspring. Again, MIT feared straying too far from academic activities but was willing to sponsor the formation of such a nonprofit. Ten other universities joined, and Ford Foundation gave a financial boost. IDA does $10 million worth of government business a year and charges a 5-per-cent management fee: "It pays for things we can't charge on the contracts—coffee, furniture, bowling-team trophies, trustees' meetings, and the like." Its problems are typical of today's science. A former IDA president warned against "impending mediocrity in twenty-five years." A more recent president resigned because he feared IDA was losing its objectivity and academic freedom.

The capital's older forms of quasi-agencies seem to live more happily. An example is the National Academy, a private organization but not strictly private. It was chartered by Congress, is required to serve as adviser to the government, and receives about 70 per cent of its income from government contracts and grants. Washington also has the unmatched mecca for tourists, founded in 1846 with a half-million dollars bequeathed by the English scientist son of a duke. His objective: "The increase and diffusion of knowledge among men." The result: Smithsonian Institution. To the story of our changing science it contributes an architectural example.

The nation's capital happens to be more than the seat of federal government. It is also history revealed in symbols. One is seen most easily from that long tourist lounge called the Mall, which runs from the United States Capitol to the Washington Monument and on to the Lincoln Memorial. All three bespeak the strength and ideals of the Republic. Another symbol contrasts science of the past and present. It is the group of buildings that border the Mall for a few blocks. These are the home of Smithsonian, a ward whose official guardian and heaviest subsidizer is the federal government.

Most people, of course, look upon it only as a museum. Others know that it has laboratories and working scientists; that its first director was Joseph Henry, a pioneer in electromagnetism, and later directors included Samuel P. Langley, who pioneered in modern astronomy and aviation, and Charles G. Abbot, the "sun scientist"; that, since its birth, over 2000 expeditions have crisscrossed the planet to build up its collections of specimens and masses of scientific data; and that at Harvard you find one of its many outposts, the Astrophysical Laboratory, whose mission is to keep nonmilitary vigil on all artificial satellites orbiting the earth.

To the usual tourist, however, Smithsonian is Uncle Sam's official attic, jam-packed with everything from the gowns of Colonial dames to trophies from outer space. And the chronicler of science finds history in the buildings themselves. One side of the Mall speaks of the America that was. Here is the Arts and Industries Building—an ancient museum of red brick, with curious adornments and whimsical towers that take it into exciting fairyland. It had been Smithsonian's main attic. It is now a museum piece itself, overpowered by Smithsonian's new version across the Mall. When opened to the public in 1964, this Museum of History and Technology bespoke the cool affluence that has come to science. It is a $36-million monolithic mausoleum of marble.

And what of the other Washington, the government facilities run by the government's own people? We meet some elsewhere in these pages. Here, let us visit three others.

The National Bureau of Standards is a nonglamorous agency that depends upon its own devices. Its relation with outsiders is that of a reference laboratory upon whose pioneering methods and precise data the nation's other laboratories rely in war and peace. The 1500 professionals here and at the major branch laboratory, in Boulder, Colorado, typify the government scientist who is no prima donna, is rarely elected to the National Academy, and does science more "pure" than that of most universities today.

Only once since it was founded in 1901 has NBS been tormented by publicity. That was in the 1950s, when it uncompromisingly stood by its tests showing no merit in AD-X2. The manufacturer had claimed this mysterious additive would extend the life of ordinary storage batteries. Compared with the stature of other NBS projects, its series of tests this time would seem trivial. But the argument went into litigation and, more important, the manufacturer applied political pressure. The case went to Congress. The Secretary of Commerce demanded that NBS Director Allen Astin resign. MIT and the National Academy entered the fray and merely added to the confusion. But to the rank and file of scientists, the attack upon the scientific integrity of NBS was like rocks hurled by hoodlums through the windows of a respectable family. They rallied behind Astin and behind four hundred of his scientists who were ready to resign if he did. NBS was allowed to go back to its work in peace.

Eventually, however, the times became insistent. NBS needed big equipment: a nuclear reactor, an electron accelerator, a dead-weight machine that would measure missile and rocket forces of up to a million pounds. So it emptied its buildings and joined the trek to open country in nearby Maryland. In the District of Columbia it left other government agencies to vie for possession of its old-fashioned but nonetheless envied home out on Connecticut Avenue. Here, on a campus as large as many a city park, scientists can work where exotic shrubs bloom and the mockingbird trills.

The effects of NBS science on the average person are unusually indirect. In this it differs from its sister in the Department of Commerce—the Bureau of Public Roads. Here, researchers work for the greater contentment and safety of on-the-go America. Yet they, too, do not gather headlines. Partly because the bridge or highway that stands up is not newsworthy, unlike the one that collapses. Partly because these men are few in number and their "slowest wind tunnel" in the world cannot match the excitement of the big-throated fast ones.

In their tunnel the BPR physicists test small models of bridges and anything else that might cause havoc—for example, they learned how to design the heavy instructional signs that arch over freeways, so that swaying will not cause metal fatigue and then a crash upon motorists. Bigger projects are handled elsewhere. The biggest in recent years, of course, were concerned with the $41-billion program to build 41,000 miles of Interstate and Defense Highways by the early 1970s.

And aside from that? Television control for traffic emergencies was pioneered at Detroit, and other control methods are being designed. "In Washington, for example," said O. K. Norman, head of research, "we drive no slower across town than we did in 1930, but neither have we gained. Our traffic-control methods have been obsolete for years. And we're putting psychologists on the staff because engineering concentrated on the car but overlooked the driver." Meanwhile, his people go on poring over analyses of how to handle the driver problem another way—the various schemes built around cars programed to travel highways that control them electronically.

Finally, let us look at the dowager in the government's science establishment and see how it has been faring in this new generation. Its story best parallels that of America itself. To visit a NASA space center or AEC nuclear center is part adventure; to visit a soils laboratory or genetics station of the United States Department of Agriculture is part pilgrimage. Here is a reminder of the America that was, with its yeoman farmer whom Thomas Jefferson regarded as salt of the earth, backbone of a virile democracy.

Nostalgia is for fiction, of course. Not all yeomen were as vigorous as pictured, nor was the milkmaid always rosy-cheeked. More important, the yeoman vanished a long time ago. Or rather, he evolved into the twentieth-century farmer who plowed and milked by machine, whose home had electricity and modern plumbing. The concept of the farm family as a sturdy self-sufficient unit was still familiar. But revolution was now sweeping the land—the tillable land. And a once sizable farm is today the "small farm" absorbed into a mechanized factory farm; the lad who picked off the beetles he called "potato bugs" has been demobilized by the machine that blows tons of parathion spray—and kills its human operator who cannot understand safety warnings. Elsewhere, the independent farmer has joined the job force and abandoned his acres to nature's unrelenting pressure; the result is brushy wilderness, ideal browse for wild deer—and in some geographical areas they are now far more abundant than in days of Hiawatha. Or else, this farmer succumbs to other pressures: his land becomes industrial sites and suburbs and vacation retreats. For whether America is as "cool," as urbane as it likes to think, it is increasingly urban, suburban, exurban.

One result is a United States Department of Agriculture troubled by uncertainty over which directions to take. Until the world wars,

USDA was the government's leader in science activities, certainly so for the ordinary American dependent on food, fiber, fresh water, and freshened air. And in the mid-1960s, Secretary Orville Freeman could still reassure the Weed Society of America: "There are more Ph.D.s per square foot in the Department of Agriculture than in any other federal agency." The focal point remains its research center at nearby Beltsville, Maryland; elsewhere, it counts 55 locations working with animals, 135 with crops, and so on. And the controversial curse called crop surpluses, one result of a job well done, has produced treasonable sentiments. These labs still have researchers who consider it virtuous, and scientific virtuosity, to convert aridity into fertility, to harvest two blades of grass where only one blade grew before. In defense of such treason, they assert that if abundance is a burden, then it is one that many nations would jubilantly accept.

Nor has purely scientific controversy disappeared—the healthy kind between peers, and delightful when they write letters to the editor concerning each other. Thus, the attack by researchers of the Army's Natick Laboratories upon researchers of Beltsville's Entomology Division, who had reported isolating and identifying the sex attractant of the female American cockroach. "This claim," said Army, "can be supported neither by [their] evidence nor by our own knowledge of the behavior of the substance. . . . The proposed compound could not in fact be the attractant. . . . The effort to identify natural insect attractants and use them for the control of various pests is highly commendable. Great caution must be exercised, however, to avoid premature claims of success." To this reprimand, Beltsville retorted: "Our tests with more than 100 organic compounds show that a number will elicit wing-raising in these insects. Our bioassay procedure therefore requires, as a positive response, no less than a complete behavioral cycle in the male—namely, intense excitement, wing-raising, *and* attempts to copulate. Of the many compounds tested, only our natural attractant evokes the complete response."

This might be an example of "damned if you do." However, it has been USDA's fate in recent years to hear new voices damning it if it doesn't—if it doesn't spend research time on ways to sterilize insects or trap them with sex-attractants or afflict them with mass-produced viruses, rather than go on trying to poison them. Big as it is, USDA has been a twig bobbing on waves of public uproar against pesticides, aimed at crop-destroyers and disease-carriers, but also finding their way into humans, as well as other innocents. Some of the furor, but by no means all, has come from runaway emotionalism. Likewise, the USDA does merit censure for insufficient vigilance, but much blame for the poisoning belongs elsewhere, and not only on the chemicals industry. Not quite Jefferson's upright yeoman is the factory-farmer who impassively drenches crops with toxic chemicals and pumps antibiotics into the milk supply of his cows to cure mastitis, itself an udder infection resulting from mass-production carelessness.

At any rate, USDA's bureaucracy has squirmed under adverse publicity—for poison on the Thanksgiving cranberries, for poultry meat oversexed with synthetic hormones, for milk carrying pesticides and penicillin, and more. These were blameworthy, but the excitement didn't stop here. The USDA had to defend pure eggs and pure milk too. Medical statistics offered them as villains during the anti-cholesterol terror. And to that statistical nonsense, the popularizers of "Science says . . ." soon added an idea for which there was yet no laboratory proof: the same foods were guilty somehow of producing the blood malignancy called leukemia. In short, if those traditional mainstays, milk and eggs, caused both heart disease and cancer, what foods then could USDA's nutrition experts recommend?

Even success had its irony. USDA was in disgrace for not breaking through faster with the biological controls it had shown possible when it found a way to control the highly destructive screwworm fly, a killer of livestock. The method here is to sterilize young flies with gamma rays from radioactive cobalt, then release them to mate eventually with wild flies. If there are any offspring they are cripples that die soon. The highly infested island of Curaçao was chosen for the first test, in 1954. It eradicated the pest (Curaçao was still free ten years later). In 1958 the war moved to Florida. Here, 50 million irradiated flies were released per week. By 1960, the fly had vanished—an $8-million campaign was saving the cattle industry $20 million yearly. Two years later came Rachel Carson's rousing book *Silent Spring*.

Since then, bedeviled and bewildered by the anti-pesticide crusade, USDA has had to move at a brisk pace. This has been good for its soul. Discouraged from showing farmers how to produce more, becoming the big farmer's crop-supporter, marketing specialist, and tax adviser, it had allowed its science to become stodgy.

It is now back deeply in research, but in keeping with the times. For one thing, as in other fields of science, here is a return to basics. In 1962, USDA's Agricultural Research Service released eighty-three new varieties of crops. But all stemmed from the discoveries made sixty years earlier that led to disease-resistance and hybrid vigor. Now, there are such new directions as nuclear irradiation, to produce valuable mutations.

There is also the growing health awareness. For instance, Beltsville has been testing a method to sterilize even the diabolically stubborn housefly. But not all concerns new methods of insect control. To protect the future of its tobacco-growers, USDA is trying to identify the harmful components of cigarette smoke so that they can then be changed chemically, mayhap, to something safer.

Meanwhile, surpluses take research into industrial chemistry. For a nation that now prefers the lean, USDA has been working on ways to use animal fats in a novel way. The goal is detergents more palatable to destructive bacteria than the petroleum-based ones which, unhappily, have gone on unaltered—busily frothing all the way from Mrs. Smith's sewage to Mrs. Brown's fresh-water faucet. Likewise, to use surplus materials, cereal starches are being turned into rigid foams of the kind that could be used for insulation and other construction materials.

Nor has the era of the great plant explorers vanished entirely. Even exotic ornamentals are not overlooked. Two USDA horticulturists have brought back hundreds of varieties from Nepal, in the high Himalayas. A magnolia grows there at the same latitude as Florida but is unusually hardy because of the 9000-foot altitude. This version of R & D, too, will be useful. Time was when a USDA yearbook was the scientific retort to bucolic advice in the farmer's almanac. In 1937, for instance, it was a 1500-page volume whose information and readability made it one of the best books available on plant genetics. Its title was simply *Yearbook of Agriculture*.

By 1963, however, USDA had recognized new realities—the farms becoming summer homes; the orchards becoming housing developments; the gentleman farmers otherwise known as "tax-loss" farmers; the countrymen of another kind. But USDA also recognized another reality. Not yet banished, like Jefferson's yeomen, were all of the modern but small-scale farmers. They, too, wanted to live on the land. They valued their privacy and what was left of their independence. They were proud of their 4-H children. They deserted television for the annual county fair. USDA wrapped the new situation into its new yearbook. It was titled *A Place to Live*.

Area 4, San Francisco

California is unique both by its own acclaim and by various generally accepted claims. As a result, it attracts many kinds of people, including those of R & D. It offers them the spectrum from basic research through engineering to testing the final product. When such isn't enough to lure scientists and engineers from elsewhere, the tempter can sing of its climate. Or it can boast of prestige universities—University of California (UC), Stanford, University of Southern California (USC), and influential California Institute of Technology (Caltech). To support that name-dropping it claims almost half of the Nobel laureates in American science. Stanford, for instance, had five researching there recently, and far-flung UC claimed a dozen, of whom nine were at its campus in Berkeley.

All this helps growth of the Golden State's knowledge industry. To the gold found by its prospectors was added gold from its oil, its fruit and vegetables, its banking, its shipping industry. Today, California's harvest of golden R & D surpasses that of any other state. It comes mainly from two geographical areas, each with its own specialties.

Concentrated at the mushrooming Los Angeles region is the nation's biggest aerospace industry—companies that design and build commercial aircraft but also bombers, missiles, rockets, spaceships. Such others as Martin-Marietta, centered at Baltimore, and Boeing, at Seattle, merely prevent southern California from winning all the prime contracts. This brawny industry, along with university research and the like, definitely qualifies Los Angeles as one of California's two major R & D areas.

The other is Los Angeles' rival farther north. Here, too, is much else—electronics and biology at Stanford, for example—but the dominant specialty is nuclear physics. This science, in all its ramifications, also typifies the rest of the region around San Francisco.

Perhaps the difference between the two areas has to do with what the San Francisco Bay area considers its superior culture. Or, closer to visible cause and effect, with the fact that one of America's great experimentalists, Ernest Orlando Lawrence, invented and developed his cyclotron at Berkeley. That was in the early 1930s, and he is now legendary, not forgotten. His monument is Lawrence Radiation Laboratory, which UC, the state university, operates for the AEC. "Rad Lab's" main product has been new nuclear weapons. But the border is hazy between atoms for war and atoms for peace. Even before the war, Ernest's brother, John Lawrence, was using cyclotron-made radioisotopes for his medical research and the treatment of disease. Thereby he built a pillar for modern medical physics. More recently, Rad Lab has worked on the AEC's Project Plowshare: the nuclear method for mining, for blasting out harbors, and the like. Also, of course, the lab spearheads AEC's dogged attempt to control the nuclear reaction of the hydrogen bomb in some way that will produce nuclear electricity—the so-called "fusion" method. Among other places doing fusion research is Los Alamos Scientific Laboratory, in New Mexico; operating Los Alamos is another of UC's contract jobs for AEC.

Meanwhile, there is the other road to nuclear power, obtained by splitting uranium rather than fusing hydrogen. This offspring of the cyclotron era has arrived—so definitely that the experts rely on its safeguards sufficiently to go on designing ever bigger nuclear reactors. But the methods used commercially so far cannot yet be called conventional. Consequently, California also spearheads industrial R & D that seeks the more efficient reactors that AEC wants for the future: General Electric continues with experimental ones near San Francisco, at Vallecitos and San Jose, just as General Dynamics and North American Aviation do in southern California.

This happens to be industrial R & D. It is university research, however, that better symbolizes the San Francisco Bay area. So let us cross from hilly San Francisco to hilly Berkeley and UC's mother campus. At first, the view from here is that of a mammoth university —and proof that bigness need not necessarily be bad? For California is a dynamic state and its state university has not been overlooked by the taxpayers. California's Master Plan offers tuition-free higher education to all who can benefit. The plan operates on three levels. The best high-school graduates qualify for the university. Others can go to the seventeen state colleges; these, in turn, are backstopped by a network of six dozen two-year junior colleges. At all levels, the state thinks ahead to the twenty-first century. Even before that, by 1990, UC's nine campuses are expected to reach capacity—each a full-fledged modern university with a student body limited to 27,500. Already, Berkeley and the Los Angeles branch, UCLA, have approximated their limit. In sum, UC has been called Multiversity and Ideopolis; also the University of the Future.

But the bigness lacks something. UC has no comparable Master Plan to give the conventional student—the one who doesn't plan to be a scientist—sufficient literacy in science. Research is the darling. Research is the invading cowbird, a parasite in the ecological scheme of things, whose young crowd the other fledglings out of the nest. Directly, because of the laboratories and equipment it needs. Indirectly, by depriving the undergraduates of sufficient capable instructors (shortly after I wrote this, student protest movements at Berkeley, Brooklyn College, and Yale were associated by the *New York Times* with "opposition to academic policies that reward research while ignoring the quality of classroom teaching").

True, Berkeley has its new in-the-round lecture hall for undergraduates who take physical sciences. They face one-third of a rotatable stage. For the next class, and then the next, the stage will bring into view a new instructor and his demonstration equipment. This and the closed-circuit TV may or may not be equivalent to "Give me a log hut, with only a simple bench. Mark Hopkins on one end and I on the other," but the argument is needless. Whatever the state may wish, its university has become conventional in the modern manner. Its heart belongs to research; its claim is not the caliber of its undergraduate instruction but of its record number of Nobelists, of having the largest membership in the National Academy and the largest number of faculty members who have won Guggenheim Fellowships. In the prestige race this is necessary, but it doesn't teach young America. UC's new branch near San Diego was built around a graduate science school and the world-famous Scripps Institution of Oceanography. Here is a young university that opened with graduate programs and without freshmen—undergraduates would have to fit into the rest somehow.

And back at Berkeley, even those who pursue higher degrees, even the professional students who go on indefinitely with their post-doctoral grants, must compete in the nest with an even bigger cow-bird. As we shall see later, some have their chance to participate in fascinating research. But UC, like MIT back East, does big contract jobs for Washington—and worries less about its educational virginity. On such contracts, the graduate students, if allowed at all, can be only supernumeraries.

This throws another light upon big UC. Its budgets seem to be past a half-billion dollars, which could buy a lot of education beyond high school. But it does more federally supported R & D than any other university. Well over half of its budget is Washington money, and the bulk of this portion, about $250 million, comes for operating two $200-million properties owned by AEC: the one at Los Alamos, and Lawrence Radiation Laboratory. Both have only the flimsiest connection with education. They make sense only when we remember how much big science is indebted to big government—and, in turn, how much big government depends on big science. Just what is this "Rad Lab"?

It is two. The older part is in Berkeley, above UC's home campus. Here, Lawrence's cyclotron fathered a family of atom-smashing machines, and a teamwork version of graduate research is still found. The newer half was set up in 1952, when we were in the race to beat Russia to the H-bomb, much as MIT was called on to spin off Lincoln Lab for computer-radar defense against attack. Its job was to step quickly past the academic and into the practical—to help Los Alamos with secret work on nuclear weapons. So the lab in Berkeley underwent fission. Ernest Lawrence and Edward Teller moved a small group of its young scientists forty miles away to Livermore, away from student researchers and into the gray buildings of a naval air station surrounded by vineyards of white grapes. These became what Rad Lab later called its "Young Turks" of Livermore, bouncy with Lawrence boldness, confident that the impossible takes only a little more time.

They succeeded. So did the Russians. Lincoln Lab stayed in weaponry. So did Livermore, but there was a difference. Lincoln was supported by the Department of Defense, whereas AEC was Rad Lab's paymaster. And AEC has peaceful as well as warlike missions. This explains why Livermore branched into fusion power and Plowshare. Its half of Rad Lab has outgrown the Berkeley half— five thousand workers compared with three thousand; and a budget four times as large.

The times change, however. Research was fun at Livermore. Now it's big business, and red tape is no longer something to scoff at. Or else, as in the test-ban controversy, Livermore is caught in the cross-fire of what is correct to say and what is politically correct. In a generation or less, men can change considerably, too. Not all, of course. I found Livermore's director, John S. Foster, still the infec-tious Young Turk (an American raised in Canada). And Nicholas Christofilos (another American, who had been raised in Greece) was, as we shall see, again startling the nuclear-physics world—this time with Astron, the most complicated of fusion machines. But in general the old fires had cooled. Ernest Lawrence died in 1958, and, in the power struggle to succeed him, Edwin McMillan emerged as Rad Lab's new director. Thanks to the cyclotron, he had helped find elements heavier than uranium; now, at fifty-six, he was an ad-ministrator trying to solve other kinds of problems. More signifi-cant, perhaps, was the busy traffic to Washington. Glenn Seaborg, codiscoverer of plutonium in the older days, had become a cautious politician, like McMillan, but had gone farther—to associate director of Rad Lab, to chancellor of the Berkeley university, and on to Washington as chairman of the same AEC that supports Rad Lab. Also in mainstream, but operating as the Pentagon's director of R & D, was Harold Brown, Foster's predecessor at Livermore. And the first of Livermore's directors, Herbert York, had likewise pre-ceded Brown in this Pentagon post but then changed caps again, returning to UC. Not to Rad Lab, however, but as chancellor of the new branch university at San Diego. He remained here but became also a member of President Johnson's Science Advisory Committee. At the Pentagon, Brown chuckled when I mentioned that many university men were voicing fears of government control: "It's the reverse. In only twenty years, the universities seem to have taken over the government."

After this shifting of chairs it is restful to move thirty miles down the peninsula from San Francisco to Stanford University. Its people peregrinate less than those at Berkeley; the flow of top scientists is more often *to* Stanford. Its campus, despite the usual expansion pressures, remains one of the most beautiful in the nation, thanks to strict planning and the comfortable fact that it received nine thousand acres of elbow room from its founder, Leland Stanford, the railroad tycoon. Long before the modern flight from cities, this private university was "the Farm." And despite its participation in big science it tries to remember its undergraduates. Luminaries like Nobelist Robert Hofstadter and Arthur Schawlow, codiscoverer of the laser, have mixed their research with teaching the most elementary physics. Nor does Stanford starve the humanities. I found it buoyant with plans for its first Summer Festival of the Arts. Frost Memorial Amphitheater was being converted to an open-air reproduction of an Elizabethan theater; the festival would mark the four-hundredth anniversary of Shakespeare's birth.

Stanford's role in R & D is energetic too. Considering its size— one-third of Berkeley's student population—Stanford outranks Berkeley in percentage of Nobelists. Moreover, it is very much the MIT of the West—a somewhat larger student population, second only to MIT in the number of advanced engineering degrees granted to full-time students per year, and likewise a magnet for imaginative industrial companies that flock here to be near university talent. Then there is its own research, both "pure" and sponsored. For instance, its Center for Radar Astronomy spreads equipment through two thousand of the handy acres. And, three miles from the mellow mission-style buildings of the campus, I found AEC fulfilling an $114-million authorization from Congress to construct America's costliest scientific instrument, for which the annual operating budget is estimated at $20 million a year.

This is a mighty atom-smasher, the world's largest electron accelerator. And as its operator-to-be, even secluded Stanford was already having problems with environment. One was scientific. It concerned the nearby San Andreas fault—uncertain bedrock that has shifted in the past, notoriously so during San Francisco's earthquake in 1906. What might a new quake do to this accelerator, especially because its highly precise beam must travel underground? Several defenses have therefore been built into the system.

The other problem: even a nine-thousand-acre property has neighbors. And they have had to be placated. These residents are reasonably well-informed; theirs isn't blind terror. They understand fairly well that this isn't a nuclear reactor in any sense, for either research or power production. It is an atom-smasher. Stanford's physicists will study neutrinos as well as neutrons, positrons as well as electrons. Their business will be not to split the nuclei of atoms but to knock basic particles out of them, to explain the particles, create new ones, decide and measure what forces hold them together, and so forth. In other words, there might be an industrial-type accident (for instance, the hydrogen blast that blew up a bubble chamber serving the Harvard–MIT accelerator in Cambridge); but this, like earthquake damage to Stanford's "linac," could be scientific calamity, not a public catastrophe. Stanford's neighbors were troubled by something else. To see how even "pure" research can be massive enough to bother the layman, let us glance at how this high-energy accelerator works.

The physicist will start with an injection gun that shoots bursts of electrons into a tube. The idea is somewhat that of a TV picture tube, but here the tube is a 1-inch passageway down the center of a 4-inch copper pipe almost 2 miles long. This pipe, the heart of the accelerator, builds up the striking power of the pulsating beam of electrons. As they move along they are electrically prodded 240 times, each time with a pulse of up to 24,000 kilowatts. But soon the power input can add little to their speed because they are moving almost as fast as light, which Einstein postulated to be the limit. Now, the additional energy primarily increases their mass. By the time the beam reaches the "switchyard" at the exit end, where it is deflected to strike atoms in different target areas, its relativistic electrons are 40,000 times heavier than they were at "rest."

All told, Stanford's newest linac will need an increased power supply of around 200,000 kilowatts—and more later when the machine's maximum energy is doubled, from 20 billion electron-volts to 40 billion. How to deliver the required current is what became a free-for-all involving the AEC, Pacific Gas & Electric Company, Stanford, and Stanford's neighbors. Groups such as the Save Our Skyline Committee feared the atom-smasher less than what the looming transmission towers would do to their admittedly soothing landscape. The university expressed sympathy but pointed out that it "could not justify devoting its own funds to a national facility of this kind," that it was only the operator, that the owner of SLAC (Stanford Linear Accelerator Center) was the federal government. So the AEC offered various compromises, such as its paying something extra for lower, less objectionable power poles, but balked at spending perhaps an eventual $4 million extra to run the high-line underground. Finally, the courts and Congress had to deal with the controversy between AEC and wealthy, rustic Woodside.

Elsewhere, the university's ecological life has run with more smoothness. For much of the practical research desired by both government and industry, it set up Stanford Research Institute a few miles away, at Menlo Park, and maintains an appropriately distant relationship with this offspring. At home it is the landlord of a development where its people may lease land and build attractive homes in pastoral surroundings.

Then there is its other original thought. It was the first university to set up a so-called "research park." This was the brainchild of its provost, Frederick E. Terman, son of Lewis Terman, who originated "Stanford-Binet," the standard IQ test. Interestingly, the son has a noted record for spotting talent in students whose "C" grades might indicate otherwise. He is also proof that some university scientists can become outstanding administrators.

In the 1930s he was head of Stanford's electrical engineering department and author of the technical bible *Radio Engineer's Handbook*. When war came he was summoned East to head the counter-radar laboratory at Harvard. When he returned to Stanford, as dean of engineering, he knew what he wanted to do. He could see the coming boom in science; it would be drafted to provide new seed knowledge. "Industries that want to grow," he argued, "will realize that for creative work they should be near a center of brains. A university with a good graduate program will be more important to them than the old requisites—proximity to raw materials, transportation, factory labor, or even markets."

Thus was born Stanford's Industrial Park. Under provisions of the Stanford will, the university was forbidden to sell any of its land. But this did not preclude leasing. If the result is an academic super-market, as some have called it, the fault isn't noticeable. The seven-hundred-acre park is strictly zoned; buildings must meet esthetic standards that prevent the factory appearance; only R & D and light manufacturing, such as publishing, is allowed. By 1964 over forty companies had taken long-term leases and built. Such contagions can spread. To this Palo Alto–Stanford area other R & D firms have come in by the scores and given an electronics appearance reminiscent of the Route 128 area near MIT. At last count, two hundred electronics firms were within a fifty-mile radius of Stanford.

In the park itself, some are new companies, some are branch labs of national corporations. Appropriately, the first lessee was Varian Associates. In 1937, the late Russell H. Varian was earning his master's degree at Stanford, where, twenty-five years earlier, Lee De Forest had experimented with the amplification and oscillation characteristics of his audion tube. Varian had the idea for something different, a power tube that might help defeat Hitler, for whom he had a bitter hatred. Stanford physicist William W. Hansen helped him with it. Varian and his brother, Sigurd, also received some laboratory space and $100 worth of materials. One result was the klystron tube, which did war duty in microwave radar. Another was Stanford's participation in patent royalties, of which $1 million helped build the Russell H. Varian Laboratory of Physics. A third was Hansen's use of klystrons when, immediately after the war, he pioneered with the first linear accelerators.

Area 5, Los Angeles

In 1810, New York overtook Pennsylvania as the state with the largest population; in 1964, the United States Census Bureau acknowledged victory in the West—California was now ahead of New York. For this triumph, southern California's seductively easy living —its climate, patios, swimming pools, freeways—can claim the major credit.

Here, the biggest concentration of scientists and engineers is in the area centered at Los Angeles, the city that swallowed most of its county. During recent years, for instance, 90 per cent of Greater Los Angeles' growth has been in San Fernando Valley, whose cattle ranches and orange groves are therefore vanishing. But beyond the valley are the Santa Susana Mountains. Their tilted landscape is familiar to anybody who has seen cowboys run on the movie screen or re-run on the TV screen. This is the outdoors of big canyons and big boulders, of cactus and mesquite and rattlesnakes. To this, the movies added the horse operas with their six-shooting bad men and good guys.

Today's technological people call these mountains "Suzie," and the risks have become another kind. The hairpin turns on the road up the mountain are not serious in themselves, but one constantly brushes past the big trucks transporting liquid oxygen and hydrogen. And, at the end of the ten-mile drive to the top, one moves only when the air-conditioned guardhouse gives permission, because rocket engines are in their test stands, ready for the countdown that will start the tumult. These are captives, of course, held down for the seemingly endless static tests that are needed. When Rocketdyne came here in 1947, it thought one test stand would be sufficient. I found fifteen, and still more being erected at this outdoor laboratory of seventeen hundred acres.

Within a half-mile from Propulsion Field Laboratory's last test stand the R & D atmosphere changes abruptly but precautions remain. This is the area of Atomics International's Nuclear Field Laboratory, which must work carefully with uranium fuel and liquid sodium. One of the labs here was continuing prototype work on the kind of nuclear power plant that uses sodium instead of water to carry heat from the uranium fuel. Another was trying to adapt the same method, as part of the so-called "SNAP" program, to provide electricity for a satellite or spaceship.

The proximity of the rocketry and nuclear laboratories isn't accidental. Rocketdyne and Atomics International each has its own home base at Canoga Park, down in the valley; but these firms happen to be two of the six divisions run from headquarters of North-American Aviation, Inc. This company typifies the aircraft-missiles-spacecraft kind of R & D, heavily supported by government, that is most characteristic of the booming Los Angeles area. North American's versatility makes it outstanding among the nation's giant aerospace companies. In the mid-1960s, it was far in the lead among NASA's major R & D contractors, largely because of its big share in Project Apollo, the moon program. It had the work on all engines for the rocket expected to hurl the three-man spacecraft to the moon—the cluster of five kerosene-fueled F-1s, each giving 1.5 million pounds of thrust, that would launch the rocket; the five hydrogen-fueled J-2s that would power its second stage with a total of 1 million pounds; and the single J-2 that would propel the third stage. And North American had a $1.5-billion contract for the spaceship itself. This employer of a hundred thousand people was also in the cluster of the four leading Defense Department contractors and was seventh, just ahead of Westinghouse, on the AEC's list. Its interest in nuclear energy came by way of aviation. Shortly after World War II, it looked into the possibility of nuclear-powered aircraft for the Air Force. From that start, it branched into commercial nuclear power plants, the kind that do not fly.

Such alertness is as good a reason as any for the company's hopes to ride out readjustment problems if the defense industry runs into trouble. Another example is its new Science Center, whose job is to supply basic knowledge to North American's other laboratories. "We like it to have a university atmosphere," said B. D. Haber, the company's head of R & D. "Its people keep their own hours. They don't have to make a project pay. We look on the Science Center as our version of Bell Labs."

Even the more practical labs serving the company's five divisions in the Los Angeles area are a bit visionary. One was trying the idea of growing algae and feeding it to chickens, in the thought that poultry meat might be provided this way on the moon. Another was cooking the humidity and water of crystallization out of thousands of rock samples to see whether our explorers might focus the sun's rays to extract water out of lunar rock.

Being so space-minded, North American declines to be paralyzed by the problems of communication among its divisions and their various facilities. To move data, it soars over automobile traffic with its own microwave network. For communication in person, there are the company's own helicopters. Within twenty minutes, for instance, I was moved from company headquarters in El Segundo to Rocketdyne, in San Fernando Valley.

Another day, a few minutes brought me to the complex at Downey, in the other direction. Here, among other things, was R & D on the moon rocket's second stage, and on the spaceship. Men were at work on flyable test models of this ship, and NASA's astronaut candidates for the mission were already coming here to inspect a non-operating but otherwise real version of its command module. I found it comfortable enough—for one person; and one of the flight problems for three men, a teaser at first glance, has an easy solution. The seat for the astronaut in the center is removable. During flight, stowing it in the allotted space under the right-hand seat will allow the men to stand and move a bit. But how, when all three men are packed side by side for launching, can the one in the center later remove the seat beneath him? When "weightlessness" begins, he can—merely by floating upward and reaching down for it. However, other problems arising from conditions of abnormally high or low gravity—the best position for instruments and controls, the best way to illuminate them for a man who may be floating—aren't that simple. They require discussion and even a majority vote of the astronauts. Then there are questions that need intense research. Many concern electronics, of course. At the other extreme, some deal with something apparently so simple as paint. What kind for the interior of the crew compartment, and how to apply it? If flecks of paint peel off they will float, and that brings up the possibility of their settling upon a delicate instrument or penetrating into it.

In one version or another, then, it is the interest in aerospace that dominates R & D in the Los Angeles area. Here one finds such leading companies as Douglas, Hughes, Lockheed, Northrop, Aerojet-General, Thompson Ramo-Wooldridge, General Dynamics; such pacemakers among the "nonprofits" as Aerospace Corporation and Rand Corporation; and, of course, California Institute of Technology.

This is Pasadena's relatively small private university that is wagged by its big tail eight miles away. The tail is Jet Propulsion Laboratory, which Caltech operates for NASA, much as the state university manages the Lawrence and Los Alamos laboratories for AEC. JPL has been deeply involved in the moon program. It handles the exploratory Ranger and Surveyor programs that precede the actual lunar landing by our Apollo astronauts. JPL also is trying to explore deeper Space, notably with its Mariner and Voyager programs to reveal the nature of things on Venus and Mars.

In its conventional role as a university, Caltech gets 45 per cent of its $21-million budget from the conventional array of federal R & D contracts and grants. But in addition, there is the budget of over $200 million yearly as manager of JPL, which has a work force of four thousand and where Caltech's faculty and students are treated like other outsiders. For operating this plant, Caltech receives a management fee of about $1 million yearly and an "overhead allowance" that doubles this income. Combining the campus and JPL budgets, Caltech depends on the government for around 95 per cent of its operating funds.

Neither such imbalance nor JPL's apartheid from student education has worried Caltech's president, Lee DuBridge. The outlook of this former physicist goes back to the war, when he headed the government's radar lab at MIT. That led him to advocate the idea of government facilities under private management, with the civilian researchers exempt from Civil Service regulations. "Let's face the fact," he warned. "A civilian scientist, as a scientist, just doesn't care to take his orders from a colonel."

However, I found that his former self-assurance had turned to defensiveness. Congress was blaming mismanagement for the failures of a series of space explorations emanating from JPL and was demanding that Caltech's three-year contracts be put on a year-to-year basis. NASA was adding that, though it is a civilian agency, it couldn't get JPL to listen to orders. DuBridge mentioned another worrisome portent: a House committee had just cut the National Science Foundation's budget proposal. "It's an extremely confusing picture," he said wearily.

Something else worried him. Like leading scientists whom I met during the same period, he was disturbed to a surprising degree by the report, "Science, Scientists and Politics," just issued at Santa Barbara by the Center for the Study of Democratic Institutions, an offshoot of the Fund for the Republic. For example, this taunt contributed by the center's president, the noted educator Robert M. Hutchins: "A scientist has a limited education. He labors on the topic of his dissertation, wins the Nobel Prize by the time he is thirty-five, and suddenly has nothing to do. He has no alternative but to spend the rest of his life making a nuisance of himself."

The principal target of the report was military science, but DuBridge and others apparently interpreted it as an outbreak of jealousy from the other of the "Two Cultures." And he sent Congress his applause for the idea when various groups, including the American Council of Learned Societies, recommended that the government's financial support of science, via the NSF, be matched by support of the other culture, via a "National Humanities Foundation."

The climate was different at the campus of University of Southern California. Like Caltech, USC is neither state-owned nor denominational; established in 1880 through the efforts of a Protestant, a Catholic, and a Jew, it is the oldest and largest private university in the West. And like any important university, whatever the type, USC is in the race for federal support of its science. But unlike many, whether through design or circumstance and probably a combination of both, it still concentrates on the business of education. Even its undergraduates remain important. It was building interdisciplinary labs for them and supplying efficient equipment, though not all of the type suitable for a graduate researcher. "It's results that count," said Arvan Fouharty, at the biosciences lab. "After all, these undergraduates are paying $2 an hour for their education. A $3,600 spectrometer is certainly adequate. A new weighing balance does in thirty seconds what the old kind did in fifteen minutes, and only costs twice as much."

Similar alertness to competition from the booming state university extends to graduate programs, certainly to work supervised by Alfred Ingersoll, dean of engineering, a man who almost runs while he walks and talks. In his new Hall of Engineering, a gift from the Olin Foundation, he disdained the elevators as he showed me his sparkling new equipment, such as the $85,000 electronic probe analyzer. With equal energy he was trying to convince private industry that it should contribute to USC rather than merely warn against taking government money.

What Ingersoll did at USC was profit from a ripe situation. He realized that California employs 15 per cent of the nation's engineers, and half of these are within commuting distance of USC. Furthermore, he was aware that many engineers want to earn a higher degree while remaining with their employer. Accordingly, he arranged part-time schedules for them and could now claim a total of fifteen hundred graduate students, the largest number at any university in the nation.

This consciousness of the community's practical needs was echoed at USC's Medical School. One of its labs had the usual collection of small animals that indicated cancer research was under way. But not only on cancer, and not only this lab. It was one of four, in different sections of the Los Angeles area, at which USC was working with the United States Public Health Service to learn the various effects of smog. For example, half of the laboratory rats breathed raw air; the other half breathed air as purified as technically possible. A specific objective was to learn the "threshold" effects, the cumulative harm done even when air isn't polluted enough to give outwardly noticeable trouble.

Such research was badly needed, of course. Despite what else it offers, California has smog and Los Angeles has unhappily been the nation's smog capital. There are many varieties of smog. Los Angeles produces the classic photochemical type, explained by three conditions: abundant sunlight; a group of noxious chemicals formed by action of the solar radiation upon fumes, especially those from the exhaust pipes of heavy automobile traffic; frequent "inversions," when warm air higher up is an abnormal blanket that prevents polluted air nearer the ground from rising.

For this, the city had a warning system ranging from the first alarm, when the telltale ozone content of the air indicates damage to growing plants, through the brownish-haze stage, to the final alert, at which the population would begin fleeing. Meanwhile, California was hoping for relief. It couldn't banish the sunlight or the inversions. But in its desperation it did legislate requirements that automobiles in the future be equipped with afterburners and other antipollution devices.

To one group of people, however, the elimination of smog would bring a mixed blessing. These are the astronomers at Mount Wilson. The observatory here, like the newer one at Mount Palomar, is operated jointly by Caltech and the Carnegie Institution of Washington. Palomar, snug atop its block of granite 15 miles long and 5 miles wide, has had few environmental problems. It is 130 miles from Pasadena and far from any other interference. Wilson, however, is only 30 miles from Pasadena. And unlike radio astronomers, such as those at Green Bank, who receive radiation from Space in the form of radio waves, Wilson's people work with conventional wavelengths in the optical part of the spectrum—their famed 100-inch telescope is the "seeing" type.

When this observatory was erected in 1904, the location was superb. Ira S. Bowen, director of both viewing centers, told me: "Wilson's sky was three to five times clearer than at Palomar." But at that time, cities were not strongly illuminated and Los Angeles had only a hundred thousand people anyway. Since then has come the boom and the cursed city lights that interfere with the astronomers' celestial photography and spectrography. This is why they have been grateful when they could look out at end of day and see smog rolling in below. For a precious few hours it might conquer the lights.

IV: *The New Elite*

"I agree that there is a natural aristocracy among
men. The grounds of this are virtue and talents."
—Thomas Jefferson

At the universities a few science professors still wear goatees, and
some of their research students have grown beards. These are outside
the norm. Wherever people "do" science—industry, government,
campus—they challenge the usual stereotypes. The American scientist
or engineer looks like any other prospering member of society. If he
needs a haircut that is because he needs one, not because he is another Einstein. If a scarecrow, it is because his metabolism works
that way, not because he is the starving inventor, now as rare as the
whooping crane. His home is mortgaged, or unmortgaged, depending
on his need, his taste, his wife.

Such superficialities aside, what is this member of the new elite
like? If power is his objective, how much does he wield, and in what
way? If money, how much does he earn as salary and how much may
his specialized knowledge provide in some other way? What is this
about an establishment, and a "same old gang" at the top? What of
those in the middle? Farther down, what about the budding scientists
who are energetic or idealistic, or both; those who are content to do
a job; and those who are simply warm bodies living on perennial
grants, the "grantsmanship bums" who swell the size of research
teams and task forces?

From a seaside laboratory, a researcher's wife writes: "August is
best. Come see scientists in colorful native summer plumage, torn
clothes, no shoes." A lab administrator is equally wry: "It's research from 9 to 5, a $500 exemption for each in the family, plus
$300 for the poodle." And about task force research, even unworldly

Einstein had wondered: "Can you imagine an organization of scientists making the discoveries of Charles Darwin?"

We have already seen that when our science falters—in courage, in creativity—this is because it has grown corpulent, with the various ills that implies. The condition can pass when and if it learns to adjust healthily to its new environment; to adjust its troubled relations with government, campus, industry, and, in general, with society. Meanwhile, what do we find?

First, let us brush away three representative myths:

. . . Despite the prejudice commonly held and frequently preached by those intellectuals who happen to be illiterate in science, the man with the slide rule or test tube is not necessarily a Philistine. When he is, the reason may well be that he has become overspecialized. When he considers Shakespeare only as an assembly of chromosomes, he is a cultural goon but no more so than the Henry James cultist blind to all else—or the taxidriver who knows only baseball's batting averages. In television, on the *College Bowl* quiz program, the questions ranged through history, art, science, music, literature; and the student team from Drexel Institute of Technology triumphed week after week in competition with teams from better-known and less technical campuses. This was not accidental. It was a tribute to Drexel's way of instructing the young.

. . . Despite the scientist's association in the public mind with such modern villains as pesticides and nuclear weapons, he is no less but also no more antisocial or unmoral than any other individual. True, he is able to concoct more wholesale harm. But war can be defense as well as offense. Furthermore, not all R & D people work in military science and, among those who do, the people out in the laboratories and drafting rooms are no more bloodthirsty than the file clerks and truckdrivers paid from the same weaponry contracts. Whether or not the science folk go to church as faithfully as others, they certainly match others in support of the United Nations and test bans, of CORE and CARE. In the Schenectady area they went farther, organizing their stay-at-home version of the Peace Corps. This VITA (Volunteers for International Technical Assistance) started with Robert Walker, a General Electric physicist, and has spread across the country to include over a thousand scientists and engineers. As unpaid consultants, they dodge such questions as the one from

Africa on how to turn the wastes from lead mines into bullets. Instead, they advise on how to purify water or build a solar cooker.

. . . Despite what scientists like to believe, though with increasing doubts, theirs is no longer the creative field it was. It has been diluted by mass-produced mediocrity; by the swarming of all sorts of people, not always the suitable ones, into our mushrooming science. In this, America is not alone. A study in England's foremost science journal, *Nature*, asserts that the most creative among high-school students shun science and turn to the arts instead. Be that as it may, today's science cannot even claim exceptional intelligence. It is generally conceded that, more than ever before, the Ph.D. diploma has become mainly an identity card betokening a member of the establishment. All this is another indication that the elite is self-perpetuating. Figures from the United States Census Bureau confirm the obvious: that sons of the college-bred have by far the best chance of going to college.

To be sure, science still has its inspired people, and not only among students with stars in their eyes. How to explain the others? Many still want to teach the young. At Columbia, Menelaos D. Hassialis was chairman of the Henry Krumb School of Mines; I found him also leading an undergraduate class of would-be engineers through thermodynamics. The class ended at 1 p.m. This winner of the Great Teachers Award then took me to his office, where he lunched on hard-boiled eggs and a cup of tea while he explained why he had not moved into government science or a vice-presidential post in industry. In sum it was simple: "I don't feel stifled here." At another university, a professor showed me his pregnant, smallish research project on the carrier molecules called chelates. There was no major excitement in this field. He knew what he was missing: "While I've been teaching here, former classmates have been scooping me on research. Yet I don't think I'm wasting my life." Here was a brisk young man, far yet from Sir William Osler's condition when he confessed to "a deep autumnal yearning not unnatural in a man whose best years have been passed with undergraduate students, and who has had temporarily to content himself with the dry husks of graduate teaching."

The dedicated are not limited, of course, to those who find fulfillment in teaching. There are dedicated researchers like Harmon

Plumb, of the National Bureau of Standards, who showed me charts proving the superiority of his ultrasonic thermometer over gas thermometers, then added casually, "It cost me seven years of my life." And high up in the hierarchy a Nobelist, remembering his younger days, was explaining to a congressional committee the thrust of curiosity that drives the genuine researcher: "Do you really think that any outside group, congressional committee or otherwise, could have told a rather unknown scientist by the name of Harold C. Urey that it was important to work on the discovery of heavy hydrogen? I think not."

There are many such examples of the profile that science prefers. But it has been badly blurred by the louder examples showing science in trouble. Personal observation finds them easily. They also abound in flagellant reports by self-studying scientific groups, in critical testimony at congressional hearings, in the complaining letters about the state of their art that the people of today's R & D write the editors of their professional journals.

Besides printing such letters, *Science* magazine is occasionally a crusading reporter. For instance, it described the true career of William Fox although, under today's conditions, the story might seem to belong to science fiction. This New York City policeman patrolled a night beat so that he could use his days for studying chemistry. After earning his Ph.D. at Columbia he went right on with the physics of fluids—now doing basic research in the basement of his home. Definitely outside the establishment, he had to buy his own equipment. When he applied for government aid, he was lucky to receive even an answer from the Medicis of Washington, such as: "The statutory authority permits the making of grants only to educational institutions and certain other nonprofit organizations."

Inside the establishment it is otherwise, and sometimes equally grotesque. A medical researcher told me that he was no longer pleased with the private foundations. He had gotten $150,000 from one of them for a three-year, part-time project, "and the only special equipment I needed was a microscope that cost $2000." But later he had been quizzed about his new typewriter—was it really necessary? So, he said, he was now switching over to a fat five-year grant from NIH. I happened to have dinner the same day with another scientist who was doing well with the interdisciplinary approach. He explained that he was supported by the AEC, NIH, and NSF, and went on to tick off how busy he was. With one grant he was doing some research; with a "piece" of the second, he was starting a magazine; with a "piece" of the third, he was flying cross-country to attend a friend's wedding.

But the foregoing examples, of good and bad, give an incomplete picture. To simplify a complex situation, let us look at some components of this massive new knowledge industry; at its illustrious and its rank and file, its influentials and its leaders.

The Laureates

Not outward appearance or even financial income best distinguishes one scientist or engineer from another. It is prestige. In *Now It Can Be Told*, Lieutenant General Leslie R. Groves, who headed the A-bomb project, wrote of his touchy relations with the scientists he needed for it: ". . . I felt that my position would be stronger if they thought of me from the first as a general instead of as a promoted colonel. My later experiences convinced me that this was a wise move; strangely enough, it often seemed to me that the prerogatives of rank were more important in the academic world than they are among soldiers."

Of course, scientists shun actual uniforms for themselves. But in their mind's eye they are very conscious of their epaulets and service stripes. And they judge their associates likewise (physicist Leo Szilard: "I was not quarreling with third-rate scientists: I was quarreling with first-rate scientists").

Prestige dominates, for itself, or as the provider of power or money if one of these is the end goal. In this, science is like show business or any other where the notices count. Among other things, they differentiate the various castes. In industrial and governmental science there is the pecking order from raw recruit at the bottom to R & D chief at the top. Universities and the like also have their castes. Below are the graduate students learning research. Toward the top are the full professors and department heads. At the pinnacle are men of renown.

If rank varies, so does the way of winning it. Many, the drudges and others too, measure their progress in papers: "Publish or perish."

Those who are good joiners and verbalize easily move faster by serving eagerly on *ad hoc* panels and permanent committees. Others, through foresight or luck, choose a field where stirring scientific events will occur. And if talented enough, persevering enough, or lucky enough, they may win international renown by becoming Nobel laureates.

Many can be nominated for this distinction; few can be chosen. But there are a multitude of other honors available, and many rank high. Some are an accolade, like the National Medal of Science, or the Presidential Medal of Freedom, though the latter is not restricted to scientists—it also goes to a John L. Lewis and Walt Disney. On the other hand, there are the very restricted ones, for one field of science only, like the American Chemical Society's Priestley Medal.

Also, of course, is the honor accompanied by a check, such as the Lasker Foundation's $10,000 award to medical researchers. Likewise, the $25,000 Vetlesen award, somewhat of a consolation prize because it is for earth scientists—geologists, for example—whose achievement is not in one of the five specified Nobel categories (physics, chemistry, medicine and physiology, literature, and promotion of international peace).

Then, in terms of prestige and money combined, come the three major awards. Financially, the biggest is the gold medal plus $75,000 given by the Ford Motor Company Fund for outstanding contributions to the peaceful uses of atomic energy. The first winner of this Atoms for Peace award, in 1957, was physicist Niels Bohr, already a Nobelist (also the only commoner received into the Order of the Elephant, his native Denmark's highest order of chivalry).

Likewise in atomics, but not restricted to peaceful usefulness, is the Fermi Award. Its origin was permission given the AEC by the Atomic Energy Act to recognize an "especially meritorious contribution." The commission thereupon awarded $25,000 to Enrico Fermi for history's first controlled nuclear chain reaction, which led to the A-bomb. After that, it became the annual "Fermi Award," the honor accompanied by a tax-free $50,000. After that, also, it became controversial. The AEC left the choosing of winners to its General Advisory Committee, composed of nine scientists. Of the first seven chosen, all but two were GAC members at one time or other, and this led to the complaints that members of "the same old gang" of bomb-makers were taking turns as Fermi winners. At any rate, when Princeton's physicist Eugene Wigner shared the Nobel Prize in 1963, he became the first to have won all three top awards—Atoms for Peace, Fermi, and Nobel. And AEC had meanwhile started giving Ernest O. Lawrence Memorial Awards of $5000 to console those outstanding nuclear researchers who were under forty-five years of age.

Unquestionably it is the Nobel Prize, with its gold medal plus a sum now risen past $50,000, that carries the most prestige: partly because the judges are instructed to reward the deserving, regardless of nationality; partly because they announce winners in several fields rather than just one; partly because these prizes have been publicized the longest. Named for Alfred Nobel, Sweden's inventor of dynamite, and endowed with $9 million from his fortune, they have been given since 1901.

Meanwhile, Stockholm's annual affair has grown into a gala week. The winner still presents his Nobel lecture, still drops by at the Nobel Foundation to pick up his prize money. The rest is ceremony and glitter. From *Medical World News:* "The Nobelists joined 800 guests in drinking red wine with smoked salmon, sipping champagne with roast duck . . . then the King watched with obvious enjoyment as the crowd of elegantly gowned ladies, African diplomats in native dress, evening-coated professors, and white-capped students vigorously twisted and twirled until the small hours of the morning. . . . The weary prizewinners returned to their suites to fortify themselves for another day."

Nor does it end in Sweden. When I visited microbiologist Selman Waksman to talk about antibiotics, the short, blocky man detoured a few minutes to discuss the extracurricular activities his award had brought.

In the adventurous but grubby past now were the days when his assistant at Rutgers was a deaf-and-dumb dishwasher and his lab was a cubbyhole, from which he ran out to a chicken yard at the rear of the building for another spadeful of soil teeming with microbes. In 1943, after twenty-eight years of search, he set off a chain reaction of antibiotic events by discovering the "wonder drug" streptomycin—killer of tuberculosis. He collected so handsomely from his share of patent royalties that the Nobel Prize money eight years later meant much less than the prestige and associated by-products. Now a professor emeritus, he merrily proceeded to describe the life of a Nobelist:

"The honor does have its advantages. For example, a wealthy man has set up an organization called Friends of Nobel Prizewinners. In several places throughout the world he has châteaus and the like where he will lodge you and your wife. And pays the airplane transportation too. He will also pay at some hotels but only after the first $10, which is a kind of deductible—after that, it's free."

It was Waksman who coined the word antibiotic. "I have now invented three new ones to describe the ailments of a Nobelist," he said, "Lecturitis, Awarditis, Banquetitis." As a celebrity, he continued, he had agreed to be at seven ceremonies during the coming month. Others he had turned down because he still needed time for some research and also because, at seventy-two, he had to conserve his strength. In the month, for example, he would help dedicate a science building in Minnesota; he would be at a White House dinner honoring all living Nobelists of the Western Hemisphere; he would attend a dinner in New York, where Henry Luce was fêting celebrities who had been pictured on the cover of *Time*. "Of course, I might have refused Mr. Luce." He twinkled. "But how could I? I would meet so many more interesting people than at a White House command performance."

Such is the increasing respect for scientists. And within their own society, the prestige value of a Nobel Prize has increased proportionately as the value of its $50,000 has decreased—not through inflation so much as because other money is now easier to come by in the form of research grants. Certainly the Nobel check has lost the value it had for financially troubled Marie Curie, whose work with radioactivity made her a laureate in physics in 1903 and, eight years later, the laureate in chemistry. Compare her with Caltech's chemist Linus Pauling, the experimenter who produced a remarkably workable theory of the electron bonding that holds atoms together. This led to the chemistry prize in 1954, and he became history's only other two-time winner when he received the Nobel Peace Prize for 1962, this time as a pacifist enemy of nuclear war and testing. The point is that in his role as chemist his research grants from The National Foundation and its March of Dimes totaled over a half-million dollars, a sum that dwarfed the Nobel prize money he received for personal use, research or not. The same vigorous foundation has helped support the research of other Nobelists-in-the-making.

Such aid devalues the monetary importance of the Nobel Prize even when the money all goes to one scientist rather than, as frequently happens, to two or three sharers in the same field. But none of this is serious. The prize money has been mainly a reward for a *fait accompli*, rather than a grant to help the researcher. "What are you going to use the prize money for?" a newspaperman asked. The answer: "I used the money already ten years ago." Government aid, of course, now provides much of the seed money. For example, NIH "career awards" have supplied up to $25,000 a year for the duration of the researcher's career. This is equivalent to a full Nobel award every two years, and has brought the suggestion that Washington give a lump sum of perhaps $700,000 to a gifted, proven researcher to finance the rest of his career. The sum is large only at first glance, certainly when compared to the million and more that a big-team man receives per year. Some of the money would pay for necessary assistance; most of it would "buy the rest of the scientist's working lifetime, then give it back to him."

None of this, however, diminishes the prestige of a Nobel Prize. On the contrary, it is augmented. The number of scientists grows; the number of Nobel Prizes per year remains the same. Nor has the prestige been dimmed any other way. True, the candidates are nominated and judged by humans; the choice isn't always easy and is sometimes questionable. Einstein received his prize for a lesser part of his work. The Canadian Charles H. Best was bypassed as co-discoverer of insulin. Some others have had to wait years longer than need be before their work was rewarded. Nevertheless, nothing else in science provides so much unquestioned prestige. And, though winners in literature sometimes reject their Nobel Prizes, scientists do not.

The Rank and File

The United States can now claim that between forty and fifty living American scientists, native-born and *émigrés*, hold the Nobel

Prize. But this is the tiniest of minorities. What is the total population within the boundaries of our massive science and technology?

Here, where science hasn't done research upon itself very well, we find many guesses, some counting of heads, and tabulations that come out differently, depending upon which heads are counted and how they are classified. Chemists seem to outnumber physicists 4 to 1, but many work as physicists. There is also the blurred distinction today between those chemists and biologists who are doing medical research. Even the ratio of engineers to scientists is uncertain. It may be calculated at 5 to 1 but is usually considered between 2 and 3 to 1. For totals, one official set of figures, the nation's 1960 decennial Census, counted 1,022,692 "engineers, technical" and "natural scientists" (which doesn't include social scientists; neither does it count such obvious outsiders as locomotive engineers or people in the "science of boxing"). The Bureau of Labor Statistics, by including some statisticians as mathematicians and some physicians and dentists as medical researchers, counted 1,157,300, which is not far from the Census figure. But the National Science Foundation climbed to 1.4 million by including not only psychologists and anthropologists but sociologists, economists, and the like, plus high-school teachers of science and mathematics.

Whichever figure one prefers, how much of a portent is it in terms of the pressures that science can exert? Since 1900, the nation's total labor force has increased 2½ times, but the number of scientists and engineers has grown more than 25 times—10 times faster. This helps explain how the power of this professional class has risen. More important, it poses the question of how much more influential will science become? Here we must go into extrapolation, a useful method found all through science, but tricky when overdone. For instance, only exuberant extrapolation, or including all technicians and others who are normally outside the pale, could explain the estimate by Paul M. Gross, a recent president of the American Association for the Advancement of Science, that the nation had 2.7 million "scientists" in 1963. Even by using the NSF's optimistic figure for 1960, this would have been a doubling in only three years.

The only practical answer is to choose what seems most appropriate from these and other varying estimates. For instance, the genuine scientist or engineer does not always work in what is literally "research and development," but the government's manpower estimates usually slur over any difference. Likewise, following the trend that includes the 100,000 social scientists, we can balance those who aren't really scientists with those physicians and technicians who may really be doing scientific work. In sum, for the year 1965 this gives a workable estimate of 1.5 million active scientists and engineers, including those who teach at the college level. The figure corresponds to an estimate reached by Congressman Carl Elliott's Select Committee on Government Research.

It is tempting, of course, to include more of the technicians because they do what the scientist or engineer is being paid too much to do, does not wish or is unable to do. In this sense they correspond to the noncoms whose usefulness rivals that of many junior commissioned officers. But whether they have had on-the-job training or have been graduated from a technical institute or junior college, they do not have proper credentials. They lack the required minimum of a four-year college degree in their specialty (which brings up a slippery distinction between a trade school and four-year colleges that cater to the "practical"). Can the situation change? Already engineers are recognized as an important caste by both the NSF and the National Academy, and a citizens' group went so far during the 1964 Presidential election as to also include physicians under its banner: "New York Scientists, Engineers and Physicians for Johnson-Humphrey." Already also, the technicians are occasionally included in tabulations to show how powerful science has become. They do indeed swell the figure, and here the manpower shortage has been genuine. The 1960 Census, for example, showed that the number of technicians in electronics had risen 679 per cent in only ten years. There are now over a million technicians in various fields, and the need for more of them continues. But the barrier also remains. Unless and until the elite needs him to increase its political power, the technician, no matter how skilled in R & D, is by definition barred from membership.

This still leaves a potent professional group of 1.5 million. How much more powerful, numerically, will it become? Using its figures for 1960, the NSF foresaw 2.5 million by 1970. But aside from including social scientists and high-school teachers, this figure was influenced by the idea of the exponential increase: charts showing that the number had been doubling almost every ten years. A projected growth curve, however, is not a fact. There are too many variables in this profession that is so much a ward of the federal government, therefore dependent on the amount of cold war and the mood of Congress.

It even depends to some extent on immigration. The rise of dictatorship sent notables like Einstein to our shores. Likewise came such valuable Hungarians as Wigner, von Neumann, Teller, Theodore von Karman; another two thousand scientists and engineers arrived after the Hungarian revolution was crushed in 1956.

And the motive has not continued to be only flight from persecution. All told, for one reason or another, America acquired 43,523 such immigrants between 1949 and 1961 alone. The rich do get richer in the sense of attracting the scientifically talented. They come from underdeveloped nations, and from highly developed ones too. Many of Britain's scientists and engineers pack up and depart to double and triple their wages, receive easier research grants, work with America's resplendent laboratory apparatus. The UN has found Britain losing 12 per cent of its output of Ph.D.s annually, more than half going to the United States. In percentage, Canada loses twice as many across the border. And not all are brand-new scientists. Many are men of repute. An English newspaper headlined "Another One Down the Brain Drain" when John Pople, a division chief at England's National Physical Laboratory, moved to Carnegie Institute of Technology. And brilliant physiologist Ian Bush brought his entire nine-man research team to Worcester Foundation for Experimental Biology.

For many reasons, then, the voice of common sense has come through the outcry about America's manpower shortage of scientists and engineers. This was another of the terrors created by Russia's first Sputniks and our "missile lag." One reaction was to worry about America's women, who, because of their own disinclinations as well as prejudice against them, were providing only ¼ of 1 per cent of the nation's engineering talent—contrasted with 35 per cent in the Iron Curtain countries. A more significant reaction was the shower of programs calling for mass production of Ph.D.s.

A few years of realities placed the shortage in a different light. They showed that massive R & D programs were massively wasting manpower; that in the quest for youth, recruiters were bypassing experienced engineers in favor of graduates fresh from the campus; that there would be more science graduates and better ones if teaching were better; that a shortage of mathematicians, say, might coincide with a surplus of chemists; that the real need throughout was for quality rather than quantity; that supply-and-demand was still very much at work and will continue fluctuating. By the mid-1960s, though empire-builders like the National Science Foundation still urged mass production, business analysts were worrying: "The demand for scientists and engineers shows no signs of picking up," and ads were promising "How to Get a Better Job in Today's Market."

Even surveys that still foresee shortages now stress quality and explain how to get it: through teachers who know enough science themselves and know how to teach, of whom there are too few in grade and high schools; and through college teachers who know sufficient science and don't disdain classwork. A Presidential panel headed by MIT's Killian bluntly insists that scientists who accept faculty posts should also "assume an obligation to teach that is as clear and compelling as their commitment to research." Otherwise, the pedagogy is forced upon junior researchers. From one of them, still a subsidized student after receiving the Ph.D.: "The post-doc is not eager to take over the menial teaching chores of members on the staff so that they can have more time in the lab." And James M. Finn, professor of education at USC, offers this dig at them: "It's not that I am prejudiced against graduate students, you understand, but would you want one of them to teach your daughter?"

But the prospects for improving education happen to be another variable. So, disregarding quality, counting the incompetents as well as the competents, the nation can expect to employ about 2 million of the science people by 1970; and this without counting "the women and little children," as Rabelais stipulated in his Gargantuan tabulations. But it is not improper, as spokesmen for science have been doing, to remember not only that there are women in science but that scientists do have families, and to increase their voting potential accordingly.

In any case, here is an elite that is very sizable and growing fast. It is already six times bigger than the medical or legal profession, neither of which has as much latent power to begin with. Whether or not all these professionals of science will ever vote alike, which even members of labor unions do not, is less important than the pervasive other influences they wield. As modern wizards, their inventive people revolutionize industry and daily change our physical way of life. As modern viziers, their political people daily ponder new situations for government and influence its decisions.

All this despite the fact that science has not yet shown any real unity of purpose, or even of organization. Most of the political pressure it can exert on the rest of society is still potential. It is the kind that a civilian population dislikes seeing in the hands of a military class; the difference here is that it is the scientists who are being distrusted. Even during the proselytizing opportunities of the Great Depression, the disciples of Technocracy won few converts to the idea that governmental control should be placed in the hands of scientists and engineers.

The Emoluments

Billions are spent upon booming science. Some of its people are rewarded bountifully for their work—in dollars, prestige, power, or all three. But like any other industry, it does not pay everybody handsomely. This is certainly true of its salaries (including the educational area, NSF reports the median in 1964 was an annual $11,000). Thus many in the rank and file, and in higher echelons too, stay in the profession for other reasons. To some, the work is inspiring; to others, it is a status symbol; others value job security.

Take physics, for example, because of its importance. One would expect its salaries to be munificent, the more so because it is not an overcrowded field; to help with its work, it must call upon many chemists and engineers. The situation is further revealed by the fact that in an average year only 300 Americans become fully qualified physics teachers (another indication of why our science education is so faulty). The situation is also blurred: by the fact that the American Institute of Physics says it could find only 21,000 physicists in 1964, but the Bureau of Labor Statistics stated the figure had already reached 30,000 in 1960. Anyway, one would expect the institute to know what its people are earning. It says that the physicist with a bachelor's degree and 20 years' experience is paid about $7000 as a teacher. If this person has a master's degree and works as a researcher rather than teacher, the figure is $13,000. Again with 20 years' experience, if he is a Ph.D. and heads a laboratory or is elsewhere in management, he gets about $18,000—no more than the average for physicians, whom the pecking order definitely excludes from science; their hobby may be birdwatching or stargazing but they remain ineligible unless they do actual "research" in ornithology or astronomy.

Although technicians are noncoms rather than officers, a wage comparison is helpful. Like the X-ray technician at a hospital, the technicians of R & D are considered skilled but noncreative. Their role varies. Some are akin to corporals or sergeants. They not only help the veteran colonel but may have to teach laboratory technique to a shavetail lieutenant. Thus a technician earning $5000 or $6000 guides the new scientist whose bachelor's degree brings $7000 or whose Ph.D. brings $9000 or $10,000; or he may serve a perpetual drone content with a master's degree and $6000 grant after seven years of so-called "research." Other technicians may be draftsmen working with engineers. In newer fields they tell computers what to do and they monitor what automation does. Then there are the highly experienced, highly dedicated ones who serve as crew chiefs. But even so, the technician who knows every tantrum of his multi-million-dollar atom-smasher may be earning only $8000.

At the other end of the scale, far above the noncoms and also the lieutenants, the wages of science are comparatively so low as to be really startling. Industry, of course, pays its leaders with salaries and stock options that keep R & D vice presidents content. The private foundations and nonprofit corporations also pay competitive wages. And the $18,000 full professor at a university, unlike the supergrade Civil Service scientist who may get comparable pay but is forbidden conflicts of interest, can easily double his salary with extracurriculars. But at the very top are the government administrators sorely needed to get best results from the billions poured into industrial and university research. Washington has had to beg and lure them with fascinating projects, or appeal to their patriotism, or point to the intangibles—power, connection, prestige—that a year or two in important government service can provide.

Otherwise, for instance, it would have been senseless for a D. Brainerd Holmes to leave RCA, where he had supervised construction of the $1-billion BMEWS missile-warning system and was headed for a vice presidency, to take command of gigantic Project Apollo for a NASA salary of $20,000. The Los Angeles water and power department had thirty-five executives receiving more than that. So were the executive janitors, called "custodians," of New York City's schools. Or consider Joseph Charyk, Undersecretary of the Air Force and its top scientist, who was another $20,000 man before he stepped over to $80,000 as president of the newly created United States Communications Satellite Corporation. In the same period, seventy salaries at the nonprofit Rand Corporation, which worked for Charyk, were between $20,000 and $50,000. And Defense Secretary McNamara, who had left the presidency of Ford Motor Company to take responsibility for the nation's biggest R & D programs, was himself receiving only $25,000. When Congress revised federal wage scales soon afterward, the salaries of top-rated Civil Service scientists were benefited by as much as 22.5 per cent, but this still could not be the sole reason why they remained with government, or why non-Civil Service appointees like McNamara, raised to $32,500, and AEC Chairman Seaborg, raised to $30,000, stayed on. As far back as 1962, Seaborg, newly arrived from the Berkeley campus, had explained to congressmen that traditionally low-paid professors could now earn between $25,000 and $30,000 yearly, counting the extra compensation for work during the summer months. And this did not include the other extras.

These campus people, especially the full professors and department heads, are the most interesting element in the entire picture. The money they can earn if they wish is only part of it. They have acquired influence as well as affluence. In the establishment they are the colonels whose influence pervades all R & D, off and on campus. Their specialized knowledge is one major advantage. Another is their freedom, because most of them now belong to research rather than teaching. This means freedom from rigid schedules not only in the summer months but through the academic year as well.

It is now conventional to allow the professor one day of the week for his private affairs. Of his remaining time, 15 per cent typically is spent with the paperwork of administering research grants, another

15 per cent for supervising the graduate students whose work builds his prestige. It has been said that "he doesn't research, he doesn't teach, he just sits and deals and reads Machiavelli." This is an exaggeration. He finds time to do extra campus work for extra pay and can be a prolific writer of books, with the aid of his own grants and his government-subsidized students. Most important, he has time to be entirely extracurricular. Today's university, says Director Shannon of NIH, "is felt to be the scientist's boarding-house rather than his intellectual castle."

For one thing, industry ardently woos him as a consultant, the bargain being money for brains. His fees run anywhere from $50 a day plus expenses, to $200 or $300, with $125 considered a standard. Or the specialist may take a retainer of anywhere from $2000 to $12,000 a year. The magazine *Science* quotes a valued physical scientist: "For the past five years, I've averaged $50,000 a year in consulting fees. I spend a total of one month a year consulting."

Government is the other big customer for their extracurricular services, and here influence is often more important than fees. The professor can serve not only as a conventional consultant but belong to groups serving as overseers and policy advisers. Despite Washington's mainstream efforts, or because of them, the number of these is soaring. The AEC alone has twenty, including its General Advisory Committee, whose $100 per day is insignificant compared with what it offers in prestige and influence over the nation's nuclear future.

In such panels, boards, and advisory committees, the experts from universities are associated with experts from industry, who likewise appreciate the value of influence. Membership frequently includes the names of such R & D chiefs as Guy Suits of GE, William Baker of Bell Labs, E. R. Piore of IBM. Baker's name, for instance, is found among the lists of those serving the President, the NSF, Air Force, and Navy. These, of course, are not the only places of rendezvous for members of the establishment. Industrial scientists belong to the official visiting committees that come to the campuses, and often are guest lecturers. University men send their graduates to the industry men, or come personally as consultants. Both groups furnish directors and trustees for corporations, profit and nonprofit; both furnish officers for the many science and engineering societies.

In their Washington activities, however, there is a subtle difference.

Though industry's representatives can claim to be as trustworthy in Washington as politicians are, they must be discreet lest the public associate them with loathsome "lobbying" of some kind. The university men are less hesitant. The rocketry professor can be openly for space programs, in committee and in public. Likewise, the biologist or nuclear physicist in another committee can openly espouse his own favorite. And such is the usual respect for the "free university" and the scientific method of its researchers that the faculty expert arouses suspicion only when he is grossly careless with facts or is a palpable fool.

All this brings a revision of the image showing the dreamy professor moving in an academic world where intellectualism, liberalism, and freedom were equated. Today, if money is his object he can certainly find it. He starts with his university salary. When his research team is lucky enough to invent something he collects from 12 to 15 per cent of the royalties paid by industry, his university taking the rest. He is a busy author, or editor of material supplied by underlings. He is a consultant to both government and industry, and may also benefit indirectly through his influence, such as being on a government panel that awards research grants in his field.

How valuable his mental service can be when it is so diluted is one question. And physically too, how can he do so much, along with joining all the conferences, colloquiums, seminars, and symposiums where his prestige and influence require him to be? The campus becomes his mailing address. And his refuge as well. He need not work under the government's relatively low salary scale and be troubled by its injunctions against conflict of interest. Nor need he formally join private industry, which would also restrict his activities and whose demands for the practical would lower his prestige. His income-tax situation is also less troublesome now. Though he has not asked for a mental-depletion allowance, as athletes have done for depletion of their physical strength, a recent ruling allows him to deduct what were formerly considered personal expenses that enhanced his prestige. The bills for extracurricular trips, secretarial work, and the like are now adjudged necessary for his "fulfilling the duties expected of him as professor."

Another recent development is an offshoot of the campus expert's specialized knowledge of his field. He need not work only for consultant fees. He can become a businessman outright. One way, of course, is to develop his research results into a new product, then set up his own company to manufacture it. Another is simply to become a director or trustee of an established company. Wall Street has many mutual investment funds eager for these experts on which is truly a "growth stock" and which is not. Then there are the non-profit corporations. There are also the manufacturing firms hungry for knowledge of what competitors are planning and for educated guesses on what new products should be tried. Stanford, for instance, counted eight faculty members in its electrical-engineering department who were board members of various companies.

Meanwhile, there is the new trail blazed by Quadri-Sciences, Inc. (the name refers to the earth, oceanographic, atmospheric, and space sciences). The half-dozen scientists who founded this prospering company—including three Nobelists—demonstrate how financially alert the scholar of yesteryear has become. They reject the idea of fees in exchange for letting their brains be picked. Instead, they work out a deal with a relatively small company that shows promise of being able to handle advanced R & D. For their expert help they require a piece of the company, receiving some of its stock in exchange for some Quadri-Sciences stock. Here, certainly, is "pure" science being applied by men seeking the practical. Here, too, is evidence of how easily campus men move about these days. The company is based in Washington, D. C. Among its founders, Harold Urey, the chemistry Nobelist, is from University of California; space scientist James Van Allen is from Iowa State University; Polykarp Kusch, a physics Nobelist, is from Columbia.

All six are prominent in the establishment. And all, obviously, are ambitious. For instance, Josiah Lederberg, who won the Nobel Prize for his work in bacterial genetics, has a satrapy at Stanford, where he heads the genetics department and the Lieutenant Joseph P. Kennedy Jr. Laboratories for Molecular Medicine. Here he receives massive research grants from both NIH and NASA. The medical research deals with what he calls euphenics, the hope to alter human beings by changing their molecules of heredity—the nucleic acids of their cells. The NASA work is in exobiology and primarily concerned with finding extraterrestrial forms of life, especially bacterial forms on Mars. Meanwhile, Lederberg has become scientific adviser to a privately owned laboratory built nearby in Stanford's Industrial Park. This is the Syntex Institute for Molecular Biology. Its stated purpose is to work on nucleic acids "for a better understanding and control of the physical and mental welfare of humanity." The laboratory is one of the far-flung properties of Syntex Corporation, a pharmaceuticals company based in Panama. It spread into Mexico before reaching the United States. Its products were based originally on mysterious jungle plants, but since then Syntex has risen as a manufacturer of synthetics. Its "breakthroughs" with new steroid hormones, including skin medicines, sex drugs, and oral contraceptives have already made its stock one of the most spectacular gyrators on the stock market.

The Administrators

Prestige and wages are part of the picture. More important is the matter of power. Where are the bosses and influencers of our science? Outwardly, of course, most scientists and engineers work for government, or university, or industry, or a varying mixture of all three. But how are these people mustered for the politics of peace as well as emergencies of war? Who are their accredited spokesmen? Where actually are the corridors of power that England's C. P. Snow considered fictionally? These people have no mass labor union. They are in professional societies which, like droplets of mercury, seek to amalgamate. When and if they do, will the result be a more impersonal, much larger, much stronger version of the American Medical Association? Or might the nation's condition—an economic depression perhaps—bring back the agitation, this time with effective power behind it, for a controlling technocracy?

Obviously, such questions quickly enter the arena of politics, and the administrators in Washington wish somebody had the answers.

I remember an example of this concern very well because of a fast taxi ride to the Pentagon one day. The hurry resulted from almost conflicting appointments that had been made for me. They called for my talking with NASA Administrator Webb in early afternoon and with another layman, late-working Defense Secretary McNamara, after that. With a little bit of luck, this could be done leisurely enough. But record-breaking heat hit Washington; taxicabs seemed to have vanished; and worse, Webb seemed unable to break off. Happily, the world was not in uproar that day. I was late reaching McNamara's office, was late leaving it, and General Maxwell Taylor, chairman of his Joint Chiefs of Staff, was therefore late ushering in a dignitary from Germany.

The trouble with Webb was that after we finished discussing NASA, his drawl, hoarse and insistent, kept me anchored there on the lounge in his bureaucrat-moderne office. It was unexpected quid pro quo: he had given me his time; he now wanted mine. As a habitual politician, he was vigilant and had easily detected in science an impressive but still imponderable new force. He threw probing questions. What did I think about this science journal, that university, this professional society or band of societies, that advisory group? How were they rated, which was influential? And on into the big question—how much power does science want, and is it capable of handling? Webb's interest was understandable. This hard worker from Tally Ho, North Carolina, had become head of America's most adventurous, expensive scientific project. Now, though he had himself begun counseling some restraints over the moon race, the antispace scientists continued centering their fire on him for "moon-mad" spending of *their* money. He felt hurt personally, and congressional response to the pressures hurt NASA's budget. But on this day it was the political potential in science that most aroused this veteran of Washington's ever vigilant industry—politics. "Why," he demanded, "should science want to be united and have its own strong leaders? If it insists on having a stronger voice in government, what right does it have? For instance, this desire for more influence in the State Department. There's nothing to stop them—they could have had it years ago if they had been interested enough to ask for it."

This aroused memories. It sounded like the paternalistic factory-owner of old: sincerely aggrieved when his employees, it seemed to him, went whoring after labor organizers. Regardless, Webb's responsibility for NASA's $5-billion budgets definitely enrolled him among those who boss science. Another, of course, was Defense Secretary McNamara, ruling an even vaster R & D empire. But like the usual top executive in industry, such men govern a science in which they have not had training. They need an R & D chief of some kind to be their chief expert. And he, too, is not unique. He corresponds to industry's vice president for research. A different breed of top administrator could be his own science expert when necessary. Such people do exist. The idea works occasionally in big industry; in universities too. For technocrats, this could be the man of the future. But he still hasn't proven himself in government except as head of a smaller, less troubled agency. The right man with the right genes may yet come along; but each prototype attempt to place a scientist at the top of a major science agency produced a weak testimonial. The administrative record of the National Institutes of Health and of the National Science Foundation can be graded as from poor to shocking. And though the AEC continued its respectable bookkeeping practices, it lost the vigor it had when laymen were in command.

Not that Glenn Seaborg, the former nuclear chemist, wasn't active as the AEC's new chairman. He preferred the label "administrator," but the duties he preferred were those of traveling politician. The big somber-faced man with the nuclear message from Washington tried hard to be considered just one of the fellows. His speeches let it be known that he had "helped to usher plutonium into the world," which brought him part of a Nobel Prize, and also that he had been made a Kentucky colonel; he combined the two personalities by wearing a pocket handkerchief decorated with atoms. He, or his speechwriter, spoke of his "scientific reticence," and his speeches far outnumbered those of NASA's Jim Webb. On a North Carolina campus he praised the state for awarding the first Ph.D. in nuclear engineering, and for contributing "my valued friend," the former governor, to Washington's mainstream. To the Texas Senate: "In addition, you have sent a valued member . . . Congressman Albert Thomas of Houston."

Like others, *Fortune* magazine had expected fascinating results from this politician who "can manipulate people as adroitly as laboratory apparatus." But it was not the AEC that benefited. Technically an independent agency and once proudly so, it now lacked an independent leader. Its nuclear instructions were coming from wherever mainstream happened to be at the moment. Or was Seaborg's loyalty to AEC less because his loyalty to campus was more? As his lengthy official biography cautiously expressed it, "he is currently considered by the University of California to be on leave from his post as professor of chemistry." Meanwhile, his hedging answers on scientific problems. They caused even the gentlemanly joint atomic committee to lose patience. For example, Senator Pastore: "Is it so or isn't it so? I think I am being precise with my question."

Of course, if a scientist does succeed as a top-rank government administrator, he can no longer be a true leader of fellow scientists. Along with his heavy involvement in politics, he will have definitely joined the boss class. Where, then, do we find those who can speak influentially without severing the old ties? At Washington's Cosmos Club, but where else?

The Influencers

One place to find them is in the "same old gang." But besides being impolite, especially when it happens to concern a Nobelist like Wigner of Princeton or I. I. Rabi of Columbia, or such other influentials as Jerrold Zacharias of MIT and DuBridge of Caltech, this phrase is only a makeshift. It is used by competitive younger men to describe what is really an informal club of insiders who have a bewildering number of connections with each other and the government. They are found in all major sciences.

The best example is that of big-name physicists whose reputations stem from the World War II era. At that time they worked secretly on one or the other: radar or the A-bomb. The Cold War brought them and some others together under the common roof of military science, and they have gone on from there. From this group, government moved Seaborg to AEC, and Leland Haworth took a musical-chair route from MIT, to Brookhaven, to the AEC, to succeed Alan T. Waterman as director of NSF.

"Old gang" or not, the influencers do not always see alike, whether on test-ban treaties, atom-smashers, or pesticides; and their every dictum is not obeyed. But they are pervasive because they populate Washington's advisory committees and boards so heavily. I have mentioned the AEC's twenty groups, including its General Advisory Committee of nine "civilian" scientists. An example in another field: the National Institutes of Health has about forty advisory groups, each comprising from thirteen to fifteen outsiders who judge applicants for research grants.

In this mass production of advice, one group has acquired influence faster than others, thanks to the mainstream concept. It is P-Sac, the President's Science Advisory Committee of eighteen important scientists and engineers who advise the President's chief science adviser. This topmost group is in turn advised by over three hundred consultants of various kinds whose names are not announced. If one seeks shadows, this secrecy sounds shadowy, but it is defended on grounds that it protects the experts from "pressure," public scrutiny, and so forth. Among them have been such important men from industry and the universities as William Baker of Bell Labs and Charles Townes of MIT. The latter holds an unusually high position among the influentials. Besides advising the government he is an administrator in the sense that he is MIT's provost. Financially he rates high, too, not only because of his university salary and the usual extras but because of his basic patent on the potentially rich electronic device called the maser. And his prestige is the highest possible: his work on the maser and its offspring, the laser, led to his sharing the Nobel Prize with two Soviet scientists.

A capsule biography of Townes would illustrate how active the modern scientist can become. At twenty-four, as a new Ph.D. from Caltech, he began his eight years of experience as a physicist at Bell Labs. Then, in 1949, to Columbia as a professor. The maser possibility occurred to him in 1951, when he was in Washington for a physics seminar. He turned the idea over to his research students at Columbia, and the first maser worked in 1953. When he received his patent in 1959 he was in Washington as research director of IDA, the think tank that works for the Pentagon. Then, in 1961, he moved to MIT, which was one of IDA's sponsors. When his Nobel Prize was announced in 1964, the provost was attending a California meeting in his role as adviser to NASA.

Two other influentials stand out because of similarities in their careers. Both Jerome Wiesner and George Kistiakowsky were on the committee that formulated our missiles program. Each later became not only a member of P-Sac but chief science adviser to a President, therefore automatically chairman of P-Sac. And like many other reputable advisers both have had to live with the nagging problem of guarding against conflict of interest, a problem for which government continually posts pious warnings but hasn't solved with a Sermon on the Mount's "No man can serve two masters" or with an eleventh commandment as crisp as that at AT&T: "Employees must have no relationships or engage in any activities that might impair their independence of judgment."

But AT&T's situation is relatively simple. Its employes are not likely to be wearing several hats, except in line of duty. It was simple, too, for Italy to imprison the head of its atomic energy commission for awarding contracts to favored companies in which he, his father, and others had a personal interest. Washington prefers to worry over the amorphous situation where an expert must sort out in his mind what is proper. While he was President Kennedy's chief science adviser, Wiesner himself helped prepare a report that became one more of the many, though this one tried to catch attention by wearing a pink cover. It urged the development of more "clean-cut codes of conduct."

He himself had not been in trouble but he knew the problems that could accompany the advantage of wearing several hats. In a *New Yorker* profile, he was frank about the moonlighting he did while director of MIT's Research Laboratory of Electronics: "I decided to make money. I wanted to be financially independent so that I could always express my opinion." So, before coming to the White House but while already a government adviser, he had helped set up not-for-profit Aerospace Corporation, and for-profit Hycon Electric, Inc., of which he became board chairman. Both worked on government contracts. And while a member of P-Sac though not yet its chairman, he was on the advisory board of the Television-Electronic Fund, which the *New York Times* called "one of the largest mutual stock funds with a direct interest in the direction of Government research contracts."

It was somewhat the same with Kistiakowsky, who had been Eisenhower's chief science adviser. "When I went there," he told me, "I was punctilious about divesting myself of all consultant work for industry." Soon after returning to Harvard as professor of chemistry, but still an influential P-Sac member, he went on the board of such enterprises as United Aircraft, Itek, and Dreyfus Corporation, the investment firm: "When I was leaving Washington, a whole lineup of companies swooped in to try to hire me. And after the White House salary, less than what I get here, I was glad to recoup.

Thank heaven I have life tenure here—I could return." Did his industrial and government roles conflict? "No," he explained, "my guide is intellectual honesty. For example, I refrain from ever revealing to my industrial connections any privileged information about the direction of government policies or contract policies."

The Fraternities

The laureates, the administrators, the influencers—all these are movers and shakers who operate singly or within quiet in-groups. Where allowable, or when they can spare the time, they may also be leaders of the profession. But in this they have no monopoly. The rank and file today can supply many candidates from its upper ranks. This organizational matter is important because it concerns the power latent in our booming science and engineering. It also demonstrates the changing times. While becoming a massive profession, science has been working out ways of speaking with a common voice. Some of its people have gone so far as to try labor unions. More typical are changes within their own professional societies. The amateurish coterie has been evolving or amalgamating; even the engineering societies have grown bigger and more professional. Leaders are more effective spokesmen; members are served by a secretariat. And rivalry between competing groups can be intense.

Biology, for instance, has acquired a new importance and affluence. One of its family groups is the Federation of American Societies for Experimental Biology. A news release, announcing its annual meeting in Atlantic City's Convention Hall, promised 16,000 registrants, 7500 authors of 3380 research papers, and 1500 interviews with the press. To overtake this rival, the American Institute of Biological Sciences grew from a net value of $44 to a combine of some 50 groups claiming 80,000 members and with an annual income of over $3 million, mostly in grants. Its mission: "The task of making biology important and ensuring the recognition of that importance." Then, after eight years without an audit from its major sponsor, the NSF, an alert auditor did come. Exploring one of the bookkeeping puzzles, he found AIBS liable for a third of a million dollars it had diverted to various promotional activities such as motion-picture films and entertainment. The consequences were not serious. AIBS was given three years in which to make up the shortage; the only sufferers seem to have been thirty-six employes whom the AIBS secretariat, now parsimonious, dismissed without severance pay. A year later, AIBS was unabashed again. It complained publicly that NASA was giving science only $7 million with which to seek extraterrestrial life on Mars and argued that, for a starter, the sum should be a "relatively modest" $100 million.

The older organizations vary but generally are less brash. Of these, the two biggest offer interesting comparison and contrast. One is the ACS, the American Chemical Society; the other is multidisciplinary AAAS, the American Association for the Advancement of Science. The fact that each counts about 100,000 members seems a paradox because AAAS has some three hundred affiliates, and ACS is one of them. But AAAS happens to be a dual arrangement. It is a loose federation of self-governing groups. It is also an organization of individual members. And it can honestly count as members only those individuals who actually join it. Of course, if the affiliates surrender independence, or if all their members join AAAS as individuals, and if engineers could feel more at home in AAAS, it might become a nation within the nation—an elite theoretically able to speak with one powerful voice. And such an idea does exist. The chances of its fruition depend on the people of science deciding what they want. Until then AAAS can speak only for its officers and secretariat.

Meanwhile, what of the chemist who happens to belong both to ACS and AAAS? Each organization is a giant with headquarters in Washington, but he finds that the similarity ends there. Chemistry is distinguished by two things, its practicality and versatility. It has abundant theories and theorists, but is more a doer than a sayer. And in its many ramifications—through various specialties, and from campus chemist to industrial chemist—it is our biggest, most independent science. This helps explain ACS, a professional society set up democratically and noted for its practical services; especially the opportunity to know what is happening throughout chemistry, and in the member's specialty. Its highly professional news service keeps the public informed too, but stays out of the Washington wars. For these, industrial chemistry has its own groups. Drugs, for instance, are defended by the Pharmaceutical Manufacturers Association; an attack on pesticides brings counterattack from the Manufacturing Chemists Association, though not so successfully as with its propaganda, overt and covert, on behalf of food additives.

The AAAS likewise tries to keep its members informed but, unlike ACS, pays little attention to industrial science. And, of course, it is multidisciplinary. Here, it interprets its mission so ambitiously that into membership it even welcomes laymen who want to help "advance science." Accordingly, it is heavily concerned with the socio-political and with public policy. But discussion is one thing; policy is another. The vigorous young scientist's chances of rising in the science establishment and becoming an influence in Washington are poor if he expects to do so through the AAAS. It has its tight inner government. When one of its presidents, Alan Waterman, who also happened then to be the head of NSF, described AAAS as "highly democratic," he was challenged on grounds that individual members "have no voice or vote" in the election of AAAS officers. He explained: "Any member may express at any time to its officers any ideas or criticism of the organization."

But, though accused of being run by a clique and its secretariat, AAAS is more outgoing than that. Certainly so in seeking more members and taking in such in-groups as the Society of Clinical Hypnosis and Society for Scientific Study of Religion. And certainly in staging the annual meeting and exposition that it calls "The World Series of Science." Because of the increasing clutter, several larger affiliates, like ACS and the American Physical Society, broke away to hold meetings of their own, leaving what AAAS calls "a degree of imbalance, programwise." But the conclave remains a major hotel event in whatever city it is held, and a money-maker for AAAS.

Such money is needed. The AAAS has passed $3-million budgets. Receipts come from diverse sources, including around $2000 from lapel emblems sold to members at 100 per cent profit. The bulk is from members' dues and from advertising sold by its weekly *Science*. Much of this magazine's content is for coterie readers but AAAS has also been wise enough to supply a professional staff including skilled interpreters of nontechnical R & D news. Into another account goes about $1 million in the form of grants from government and private foundations to do missionary work in science.

The ACS has a heavier workload but easier bookkeeping. To

meet its $12-million operating budgets, it draws on three major sources: dues from members; income from national meetings; and, the largest, revenue from its string of publications. Of these, *Chemical Abstracts* is an unrivaled international source of technical information; publishing it is an industry in itself. Also uniquely successful are *Chemical & Engineering News* and *Journal of the American Chemical Society*. Confidence in these magazines is such that they appeared on the "top preference" reading lists of physicists as well as chemists.

In grantsmanship, too, ACS moves with self-reliance, unlike the biologists, physicists, and others who clamor for aid. For example, I received the announcement: "This is written on behalf of the American Institute of Physics in collusion [sic] with the National Academy of Sciences." Though "collusion" here betrays something other than connivance, it does show AIP's relationship to government and quasi-government. Another announcement from AIP sharpens the point: "This will be a 'pay-as-you-go' seminar because we have not yet received support from the National Science Foundation, but we hope that attendance will be undiminished." Now NSF aid is hard to resist. It subsidizes some publications and creates others, useful or not. It finances summertime seminars and workshops in the North Woods, and wintertime ones that offer salubrity elsewhere: "The conference management will reimburse you. . . . Put out no money on your own, except for tips." However, the American Chemical Society has "colluded" with all this so rarely that one of its officials chuckled, "I'm afraid NSF is miffed because we won't help it spend money."

Such independence is not at all remarkable. The ACS can afford it, thanks partly to the magnitude of chemistry, partly also to democracy within its ranks. Engineers are allowed into AAAS but are low in its pecking order. In ACS, however, chemists and engineers are equally at home. This pays. ACS has become the world's largest organization devoted to a single science. And for support, it can draw on all segments. Thus, most of the $3 million for its new building was donated by a wide spectrum of members and various chemical companies.

This structure received Washington's "Best Headquarters Building" award because of its businesslike modernity, its aluminum louvers that move with the sun, and so forth. It also reveals the chemist's own practicality at work. Into its sub-basement, two levels of parking area, chemical engineers proudly designed a prototype shelter for protection against not only nuclear fallout but poison gas and bacteriological attack. This was educational rather than panicky. It showed what could be done at a cost of $63 per occupant. Meanwhile, the facilities stood ready to provide decontaminated air, food, and shelter for the ACS people and the first two hundred others running in from the street.

This self-reliant situation explains why, in grantsmanship, ACS is a busier giver than receiver. That is, it is its own philanthropic foundation. As usual with foundations, of course, its nest egg is conscience money of a sort. But the Petroleum Research Fund administered by ACS came from a unique source. To prevent violent bickering over patents, the major oil companies had jointly bought Universal Oil Products Company, noted for its complex of basic refinery patents. But this led to dangers of antitrust punishment. So, in 1944, the oil companies passed the hot property on to ACS as trustee, with earnings to be earmarked for basic research. The ACS in turn went through some squirming over its dependence on the patents. In 1959 it got court permission to sell all the stock and invest the proceeds in a portfolio of diversified securities. The property had meanwhile soared in value. It netted $70 million. This was how the trustee found itself with $3 million in dividends to spend annually on research in colleges and universities.

It is likely that science would be less on the defensive today if all grantees worked under ACS standards. One of them: any resulting patent must be immediately dedicated to the public, royalty-free. Another: the researcher's proposal should be venturesome, should "avoid the 'sure-fire' neat little problems which can always be solved."

The Parliament?

To conclude this hunt for power—for the leaders and spokesmen of today's science and engineering—let us return first to government because the federal science establishment pays most of the R & D bills, hence feels entitled to demand allegiance. Then we will look at the National Academy of Sciences, which is partly government, partly a prestige society, and has offered itself as an influential new force.

We have met some of government's administrators, also the influential inside-outsiders with whom they must deal. Will these "civilians" dominate government? Or will government, involved in ever bigger scientific programs, impatient with the inability of science to keep its house clean, demanding order where there is now disorder, push on for more federal control? And if so, will this be through a Department of Science and Technology, or perhaps through a truly potent science administrator at the White House? Already, science has supplied government with its new breed of authoritarians, like Wallace R. Brode. As adviser to the Secretary of State, this former president of AAAS warned scientists to support Washington policies when they go abroad under government auspices; closer home, he foresaw "pure research going out of style," citing Soviet success with integrated programs of applied science. This was before the Soviet political hierarchy deposed Premier Khrushchev for, among other reasons, failing with those programs. But it was while Russia faced its own peculiar problems. On the one hand, Soviet biology was influenced by whether Lysenkoism did or did not happen to be in favor at the Kremlin. On the other hand, leading Russian scientists were daring to scorn the kind of research that made it necessary for a highly technical paper on quantum physics to genuflect as follows: "These phenomena are a new confirmation of a well-known thesis by V. I. Lenin on the inexhaustibility of the properties of the electron and the infinity of nature."

To the usual guardian of scientific freedom in America, those words by Brode are fighting words. But there is no certainty that a destructive showdown for power is coming soon. For example, despite labors of the mainstreamers, "pluralism" does go on briskly in Washington. I was talking one day to an R & D official, important in policy maneuvers but not the top administrator in his agency. When we got on to the conflict-of-interest topic, he spelled out this practical if rather suspect bureaucratic method: "All these new rules are so much nonsense. For every new rule there will be ways to get around it. The interlocking goes on all over, including right within government. As a simple example, the man in one bureau is now forbidden to be a consultant to another government bureau. We solve that by serving on many *ad hoc* committees. The result is what we call the core group. You see, there are two things we bureaucrats can always get. One is the telephone. The other is travel orders. So, if I want something done, I get on the phone and arrange a first meeting. If one of the chaps I want present is clear across country and hasn't a travel order, his chief gives him one. Now the device is this—he doesn't come officially, only as a so-called 'observer.' At that first meeting we do little more than learn each other's language, and arrange a next meeting. At the second, we begin scouting the problem. By the time of the third meeting, we're the core group of dedicated members, each exerting his influence back in his bureau. That's how we solve the problem of one bureau not wanting, or not daring, to consort with another."

I mention this pragmatism as a reminder that in science, as elsewhere, the exercise of power need not be noisy or, worse, lead to a brawl. Brawls start when the politics of compromise fails. Already, the high councils of science and government are trying compromises in their efforts to live with a spaghetti-like intertwining of administrators, influencers, consultants, and committees beyond computer count.

The reawakening of the National Academy of Sciences is the best example. This group's potential had not been understood, which is unsurprising. The academy itself was unaware of its potential. Its secretariat recited its august history; the disrespectful opined that the main function of academy members was to write each other's obituaries. Either way, the academy remained aloof. Its policy was silence unless the government asked it to speak. It did not become boldly political until around 1962 when Congress began joining in the querulous "Whither science?" colloquies. Also, this coincided with invasion of academy interests by a host of research institutes, think tanks, and other nonprofits.

Its answer was to capitalize on its potential as science spokesman. Though in not so many words, it began offering itself as a parliament of science, an all-embracing mother, a Committee of One Thousand; anything indicating a blend of major specialties and motivations in the science world.

. . . It is quasi-official. For over a century—North Pole expeditions, the A-bomb, cancer research, Project Apollo, and so on—it has been close to the federal government, as a consultant that evaluates, recruits talent for, and sometimes has a hand in directing Washington programs. Chartered by Congress in the Civil War, it is still bound by two stipulations: to serve the government "whenever called upon"; to receive expenses but no pay as such.

. . . Its prestige is impeccable. One is elected to membership for "distinguished contributions to scientific and technological research." This may signify a notable discovery; or, more broadly, a notable career. Some lesser lights, obviously, come in on the coattails of a clique. In any case, Academicians are in the next-to-highest caste. Only Nobelists rate higher—and they are quickly admitted to the academy if not already in.

. . . Its province spans all science and technology. Originally, its membership was limited to fifty. Though university men remain in control, membership has risen past seven hundred; there is even a minority of engineers, perhaps 10 per cent—beyond this, the academy hasn't cared to go. However, to keep peace with the world represented by the increasingly powerful and ambitious Engineers Joint Council, which was increasingly irked to see scientists receive credit for what engineers do, the academy finally gave its blessing to the creation of a twin, the National Academy of Engineering, with hopes that the two will work together rather than at cross purposes. Meanwhile, its auxiliary called the National Research Council adds some three hundred scientists and engineers who can help with academy projects and also with academy politics; many of these participants represent the professional societies.

. . . It is undistracted by laboratory research. It does none. It coordinates research by others. More important, it can mobilize its people into a spearhead of *ad hoc* groups backed by an array of permanent boards, institutes, committees, subcommittees, and panels. Their work is supported by grants, mostly from the government; their chief product, varying in quality, meets government's mass requirement: more paper. The reports are prepared by those unpaid members who can spare the time, plus paid consultants chosen from a reservoir of several thousand.

. . . It is stable, not one of the nonprofit fly-by-nights. Its home in Washington was built with Carnegie gift money. Its budgets have risen to past $15 million. Though, technically, it still receives no government "compensation for services," changing times have changed the meaning of "compensation." In the form of grants and contracts, the government supplies 70 per cent of academy income. Similarly, though members prepare reports in exchange for expense accounts only, they are helped by a paid staff of seven hundred. Significant too: in 1965 the academy used new bylaws to elect its first full-time, salaried president.

Such is the *modus operandi*, evolved over many years. The academy still works on technical subjects that have more or less national importance; as we saw, it even entered the fray concerning a battery additive. The difference now is the enthusiasm with which it enters the public arena.

For this change, which began in the early 1960s, we must meet Kistiakowsky again. Eisenhower, the five-star general, has left the presidency. His chief science adviser has returned to Harvard—back to little Gibbs Hall with its quaint chemistry laboratories exuding the old-fashioned smells. Kistiakowsky's tenure is safe. But his research team needs rebuilding. And, in thirty-two years, this is the first time he has had to teach freshman chemistry. So, he does his duty—and misses excitement. This isn't astonishing. How he rose, from a seventeen-year-old Cossack tank soldier in the Russian Revolution to a Harvard full professor, is a rambling but not dull tale: "I spent most of my time running away from Bolsheviks, and changing generals." Then came the biggest war. In the Manhattan project, others prepared nuclear explosives for the A-bomb. Kistiakowsky, an expert on fast reactions, headed the Los Alamos division that worked out the way conventional explosives trigger that nuclear blast. In other words, not a theorist; rather, an active laboratory man but not in the glamour department.

And fifteen years later, when he leaves Eisenhower, the tall professor, though just past sixty and outwardly grave, is inwardly still a man of action. He returns to quiet Harvard—and cannot forget Washington. There is no need to do so. In one of his many extracurricular roles, he belongs to the National Academy; moreover, he is a restless member of its seven-man executive committee. Call him one of the "same old gang," or elder statesman, this politically minded chemist remains influential in Washington, the more so because physicist Frederick Seitz, the academy's new president, has similar hopes for the organization and the two men can support each other. Each is on its executive board. Each also serves at another focal point—they belong to P-Sac, the special advisory committee that Eisenhower passed on to Kennedy.

Here was a handy bridge between big science and big government, and Kistiakowsky began using it busily. As the chief White House adviser he had been handicapped by need for secrecy; but as an academy officer he could help "identify the major public issues and decide how the academy can best make a contribution toward wise solutions. If there is any group that can speak for science, it is the academy."

That may have been a slap at aspirations of the AAAS. It was also a challenge to the organization that Wiesner had built up at the White House for control of science. Anyway, the busiest voice in the academy became that of the newly created fourteen-man Committee on Science and Public Policy, also called COSPUP or merely "Kisty's Committee." What this committee actually produced was in no way startling. Similar information and conclusions, often provided by the same people wearing other caps, could now be found elsewhere, and free of charge, instead of paying the academy for its booklets. Better yet was getting information at first hand. But Kisty's reports were under academy auspices; and when they spoke sharply to government and science alike, science had to take note. It might scorn laymen, Congress might be ridiculed as a superstupid aggregation of laymen, but this was the voice of the National Academy.

For a starter, Kisty's panels of experts reconnoitered such familiar problems as the need for birth control, the ways in which grantsmanship evades its bargain with Congress and taxpayer, the harm that excessive research does to education, the crushing effect of big government upon useful research. To government, he stressed his committee's usefulness as an analyst of danger areas in the increasingly vast R & D programs. To science, he stressed that COSPUP provided the long-needed "chance for scientists to make themselves heard."

Meanwhile, he crossed another bridge. The academy had usually prepared government reports with the White House in mind. But Congress, too, was increasingly bewildered by sincere as well as porkbarrel battles over R & D, already taking over 15 per cent of the federal budgets. It debated ways to get expert advice, hopefully the unbiased kind that disembodied spirits might provide. The only unusual plan accepted was one allowing the academy to place an outpost in Congress. This committee, another headed by Kistiakowsky, was given a $50,000 contract to supply whatever advice a special R & D subcommittee of the House might need over a two-year trial period. Congress and the academy had never undergone such a marriage formality before.

Did all this mean the academy was "infiltrating" government? Not even the academy could tell. After all, it is a complex organization whose members have various allegiances. And Kistiakowsky? "No, I won't ever get a Nobel Prize. But I dabble, I teach, I research, I get into public affairs. All this I like." A political independent, he had switched from Eisenhower to Kennedy, he now helped write the science part of Johnson's campaign platform and became a Johnson adviser on foreign affairs as well as on P-Sac matters. But ambitious Kistiakowsky, now vice president of the academy, was growing older. Would the academy's influence inside government be continued by its newer generation? And what if this advice were brushed aside?

Very well, perhaps the academy has wandered too far. In that case, it can concentrate on its other potential role. Of course, as far as its guiding science is concerned, the academy cannot be a true parliament because the rank and file does not elect its members. Yet, until something better, it can conceivably claim some sort of leadership. It already reaches through all fields. Its influence on behalf of science is pervasive. It has been in no scandals. It has become eager to lead.

Again, decisions for the future. If science were united in this or some other way, would its power be exerted forcibly, in the fashion of a labor union or guild, demanding the freedom to do this experiment or to go on strike against that government program? Or would pressure be applied in the manner of organized physicians lobbying through their American Medical Association? Or would scientists increasingly treat their organization like an American Bar Association or other such mother club, and depend upon their individual initiative, as politician lawyers do, to gather what government powers and emoluments they can?

If the academy fails as influencer of government or leader of science, it has another opportunity, assuming its reputation is kept spotless. It might supply tribunals for science matters of serious public concern. It has already had much experience as a reviewer of scientific data and some as a referee of sorts. It could go farther. The idea here is that the Academicians need not render "decisions"; it would be enough to act as a jury of experts listening to experts. Such juries would provide concise and, above all, sufficiently unbiased judgments on the throng of subjects that start as simple differences and, if not settled authoritatively and soon, end as unbridgeable chasms. They start simply. Allowed to burgeon in today's hospitable environment, with protagonist after protagonist adding his commentator's fog of prejudice and investigator's bog of data and statistician's squirt of cuttlefish ink, they eventually reach the stage where no human, or computer either, can hope to find truth. Wretched controversies like those concerning cancer cures or the fluoridation of water, sleeker ones like the value of Moon versus Mohole, universal ones like those that concern nuclear testing or genetic manipulation of humans, and all the rest involving layman and scientist alike in a babble of propaganda, lies, half-lies, guesses, and mistakes—such could supply intellectual challenge more satisfying to Academicians than writing each other's obituaries.

II

State of the Art

V: *The Researcher's Methods*

And what of scientific method? One way to discuss it is to quote from the index of the book *Science and Common Sense*, written years ago by Harvard's James Conant: "Scientific method. *See* Alleged scientific method." To show agreement, I will save time by giving examples of science at work. They are more revealing than tributes to a vagueness that speaks too much and claims too much, from careful technique to a sure cure for all of mankind's ills.

So this chapter introduces Part II by concentrating on important examples of the concepts and tools used by science today. Besides illustrating changes in the state of the art they supply background for the biological and physical research in succeeding chapters. The first two examples, for instance, deal with basic science: how it has drawn a working picture of the atom and gone on from there to a working knowledge of electricity and magnetism. Another section concerns the elegant laboratory instruments, notably the electron microscope, born from such knowledge. The final section, with the cancer and cholesterol problems as cases in point, contrasts laboratory research with the increasingly aggressive "scientific method" built around the tool called statistics.

But first, a few words about the concept that underlies all our transactions with nature. It is the concept of energy. Here is indeed an abstraction. Neither experimenter nor theorist can offer the smallest clue concerning what energy *is*. Science can understand energy only in terms of what it can do; so defines it as the capacity to do work and busily learns new ways to manipulate that capacity.

179

A chemical explosive certainly has the capacity to do work. So does optical energy moving through the microscope that examines a speck of the chemical. The human, meanwhile, translates energy derived from food into muscular energy that manipulates the microscope. By way of the eyepiece, the optical energy then goes on through another transformation—now into electrochemical signals to the brain.

From this comes our guess about the truth. And the fact that man has learned to do so many fascinating things with energy indicates the guess is a good one: Though nature is forever exchanging this for that—why, we don't know—she does so with the only truly raw material that she owns. We call it energy. Not only is it energy that combines hydrogen and oxygen to give us water, which then becomes the waterfall, which turns the turbine, which gives us electricity. It is also energy moving from here to there (anyway, leaving here and reappearing there) that gives the radiation we call light, which unaided eyes can detect; and also the longer waves that we see indirectly when the television screen converts them into shorter waves for our eyes. The energy of sunlight builds plant life directly; indirectly, through our food, it builds our bodies, warms them, generates the electricity that works our nerves and muscles, including the once mysterious pump we call the heart. Today, and until Einstein is proven wrong, we look upon matter itself as being merely congealed energy, and upon the atom—the "building block" of matter—as itself being an assembly of electrical positiveness and negativeness. And what is life? One of the many tortured attempts at definition is "a chemical system capable of replication and controlled energy transfer."

Man surpasses all other creatures in his control of energy transfer; therein lies what science calls its creativity.

There were such experiments as Franklin's daring one with the kite and key, confirming a German theory that lightning is electricity. Later in the eighteenth century, Galvani's experiment with frog legs provided another clue by demonstrating "animal electricity." Thereafter, science proceeded onward and arrived at today's elegant electronics, which will become crude as man continues learning his capabilities. Simultaneously, he expanded the possibilities offered by energy that comes in optical form; while the artist refashions the golden browns of Rembrandt and reds of Titian, the scientist already plays, unartistically to be sure, with the purity and power of a laboratory-made laser beam that hits the moon. And always, of course, science must weigh the good and ill of what it can already do with nuclear energy, and hopes to do later.

Yet the key word remains ignorance. While man learns that energy wears an amazing number of faces, his ever-expanding frontier of knowledge does not overtake the ever-expanding frontier of ignorance in front of it. For instance, he discovers the molecule of heredity; he still hasn't reached the "secret" of life. As far as fundamentals go, he remains the optimistic greyhound who never quite catches the rabbit. Or is he simply a foolish greyhound? Those who have felt the allurement of the chase say that it is a compulsive thrust of curiosity, that it distinguishes Promethean man from primitive beast.

Picturing the Atom

The atom is the heart of the matter because it is the heart of all matter. But that presents science with something very small. The calculation that 20 million atoms are needed to cover the head of a pin shows we are dealing with a unit whose appearance challenges the imagination. This immediately brings the need to draw some sort of familiar analogy for the atom because a characteristic of the human condition is an almost childlike dependence on helpful pictures. One trouble, however, is that analogies can be taken too literally. Another: scientists keep adding to the picture. Being human, they are driven to know what the atom itself is made of and how the parts—the so-called "elementary particles"—are held together.

Any visualization of the atom, consequently, should carry the warning, "Subject to change." For here is a concept built by theoreticians, mathematicians, and experimenters whose evidence can be only indirect. To learn about inner atomic structure, for example, the high-energy physicist smashed a target he could not see with electrified bullets he could not see. When invisible particles flew out he studied them by analyzing a photograph of the vapor trail they left behind.

But this requires another analogy—the legend of the Spirit brooding over chaos. As research probed deeper with ever more powerful equipment, the comfortable two building blocks of the atom—proton and electron—increased to beyond thirty "elementary particles." And efforts to smash out of this wilderness have led to six dozen more at last count. Those that baffle even the theoreticians are formally called "strange particles" and a "strangeness" rating has been devised for them.

But all this is in the strange world of cyclotrons, synchrotrons, and other atom-smashers, which come later. Here, let us eschew dialectic surrealism and remain with the more recognizable atom, which can be mysterious enough. Assuming that the heavier atoms were built out of lightweight ones, whence came hydrogen, the lightest? Concerning this one, presumably the mother atom and therefore the first trafficker in energy, theory is discreetly noncommittal. So many other and more immediate questions confront science that only the metaphysical cosmologist wonders seriously about the first genesis. It is much less frustrating to accept the *fait accompli* of a universe that already had atoms, and try to proceed from there.

Science has indeed gone far, to the point where it dares regard the tiny atom as mostly empty space and the rest of it as particle-like blobs of energy that constitute the atom's mass. Similarly, taking courage from Einstein's $e=mc^2$ equation, we dare believe that mass converts back into free energy by attenuating somehow. This makes sense and has produced enough evidence to allow theoretical physicists to guess still further.

But it is already too far for visualization. And man does insist on helpful pictures. In science, they need not be the splendor of Shakespeare's imagery, or a Melville's "Ahab would burst from his stateroom, as though escaping from a bed that was on fire." They must be practical: "The rocket engines swivel like a juggler's palm under a broomstick." How, then, can one picture energy? Science does not try. Instead, it seeks analogies that retain the comfortable concept of a corporeal atom composed of corporeal building blocks.

Originally, to comprehend the atom, and to help others comprehend, chemists imagined the atom as a tiny solid ball: this was the smallest possible unit of hydrogen, when the material happened to be hydrogen; or of gold, when the material was gold, and so on. At the end of the nineteenth century, however, new evidence from physicists made it necessary to acknowledge that the solid atom was in reality composed of two kinds of particles: electrons—electrically negative and relatively lightweight; and protons—electrically positive and much heavier. The smallest possible unit of matter accordingly evolved into the concept of a tiny solar system. Its "sun" is the nucleus of the atom, by far the smallest part but with by far the most mass (popularly called "weight"), one reason being that it contains all of the dense protons. Each electron moves around this core in a well-defined orbit while spinning on its axis. The number of these planets exactly balances the number of protons and, despite the difference in mass, the negative charge of an electron balances the positive charge of a proton, so the complete atom is electrically neutral. In the early 1930s, the nucleus was found also to contain the particles called neutrons. As heavy as protons, they supply a considerable part of the atom's mass but, being electrically neutral themselves, they do not upset the atom's over-all balance between negative and positive charges.

Here, then, is a workable basis for today's very electrical atom. Even though troublesome questions led theory to proceed from the planetary idea and imagine the electrons arrayed around the nucleus in concentric "shells" and "subshells," the concept remains fundamentally the same. Of course, the picture can be drawn in still more complicated fashion. For instance, we will note later the attempts to envision electrons as smeared-out clouds. We will also see frustration lead to banishment of the entire model. The pictorial atom ceases to be; the analogy is replaced by an exercise in mathematics. Only its energy changes give evidence that the atom "exists." Under the circumstances this is reasonable. But it favors the atom-smashing scientist and his subnuclear particles too much. Aside from its raising new questions while answering old ones, it abandons what we call reality. Our senses insist that matter does exist. Nobelist Peter Debye admits: "Mathematical manipulation is all right, but I cannot do without a picture."

So we will stay here with a modern version of the Bohr-Rutherford atom, a version that adds some contributions of shell and quantum theory to basic usefulness of the sun-and-planets picture. Though it doesn't supply all minor answers about the earth and universe, and of course supplies no basic answers, it works well enough. Its nucleus explains isotopes and why unstable ones are radioactive. This inner part of the atom has given nuclear bombs and peaceful power plants. With it, science fulfills the alchemist's dream: breaking down atoms, building them up, transmuting one kind into another.

And the same model works very satisfactorily for the outer atom— for those surrounding electrons that spin, that can change orbits and even escape from the atom, that can soak up energy and then radiate it. Here we find electricity and electronics and optics. Here atoms remain the building blocks of substance; atom joins atom through electron bonds to form the molecules that society lives with and its chemists and biologists work with. Here modern man uses some of the sun's energy for living and for reproducing himself, some for such driving new compulsions as exploring the atom and outer space.

Such is the general picture. One way to profit from it is to convert it into something the eye can see and thereby help the brain understand. On paper, this has been going on a long time. Visualizations of the individual atom were drawn. And the chemist's formula that merely showed the number of atoms in a molecule evolved into the more useful structural formula showing how these atoms were joined. This, too, was not enough. A two-dimensional drawing became especially inadequate when science in recent years grew fascinated with macromolecules, some of which might contain hundreds of thousands of atoms. Such a molecule might be a polymer—simple molecules linked repetitively, monotonously, to form a long chain. But the chain might also have side chains. Still more complicated, a pair of chains with their side chains might intertwine and twist to give a complex network of perhaps a million atoms, requiring visualization as it really is, in three dimensions.

Only by depicting which atom joins which, their relative sizes, the distances and angles at which binding forces hold them together, could researchers fully understand for themselves and explain to outsiders how a certain plastic or detergent acts as it does, or how— at the new crossroads of chemistry, physics, and biology—the nucleic acids DNA and RNA carry the genetic blueprint from parent to child. So structural formulas on paper became the basis for physical models.

Three-dimensional models built to scale had been useful elsewhere. They made planetary versions of the atom easily understandable.

They translated experimental evidence into displays of how atoms are bonded and arranged in nature's beautifully simple crystals. Now, to show what was being deduced about macromolecules from indirect evidence supplied by the techniques of X-ray diffraction and electron microscopy, model-making became a lusty new specialty in the laboratories. The old-time craftsman who built telescopes with loving care, and the glassblower who fashioned bubbles into custom-built apparatus for the chemist and physicist, now had a rival—the technician who deftly assembles atoms in their simplest version, the solid little ball.

One of his specialties is DNA, the thin, long master molecule of heredity. It varies in actuality, but is generally pictured as an intricate yet orderly double spiral, with perhaps thousands of turns and twenty groups of atoms per turn. At one university laboratory I watched the modelmaker at work with his atom-balls of different colors representing carbon, hydrogen, oxygen, phosphorus, and nitrogen. The balls were made of foam-in-place plastic; some larger, some smaller, but all close to the size of a golfball and a hundred million times larger than the atoms they represented. He was trying different ways of attaching one ball to another; with some, he used a snap-fastener, with others, tiny magnets imbedded in the plastic. This model would cost about $1000. He was not, of course, attempting to build the entire DNA molecule. A representative section, only one complete turn of the double spiral, would suffice for this project.

Electricity at Work

Now let us return to the activity inside the atom. Among other things, the concept of its planetary electrons supplies explanations for what is commonly called electricity. This puts us back again with energy. But now the modelmaker is restricted. He cannot picture electricity, or the energy associated with it. Consequently, it is practical to look upon electricity in terms of what it does. It thereby becomes a universal working tool. Through the hidden chemical interplay of atoms, electricity operates our bodies. As electricity "in the raw," it operates our motors when it moves along conducting wire and our television sets when electrons are beamed from cathode gun to the face of the picture tube. And, of especial interest in this chapter, the working tools of modern R & D are for the most part electrical.

That is speaking broadly. Now for a sharper focus. With so much guessing about the atom it is hardly strange that electricity, as a thing, baffles us. But though it is too subtle to be described except in terms of what it does, experience and theory agree that electricity has two components, positive and negative. One unit of negative charge is defined as the amount carried by an electron. And the proton, about 1840 times heavier, carries the same amount of charge, but positive. We know that the number of each depends on the kind of atom. The lightest, hydrogen, in its common form has but one proton and one electron; much heavier uranium has ninety-two of each. And the electrons are pictured as orbiting at various distances from the protons in the nucleus. The net charge of the entire atom, then, is zero; it is electrically neutral.

However, it need not stay that way. Through an energy interchange of some kind, it may lose one or more electrons, temporarily or permanently. Now, because of its surplus of protons, the atom is positively charged. One departed electron leaves one proton too many; two departed electrons leave two unbalanced protons, and so on. Meanwhile, each freed electron is carrying its single negative charge.

It is the movement of charged particles from one place to another that gives electricity as we know it commonly—in motion. For current along the usual conductive wire, the modern concept is that the electrons move. But not without help. In the first place, a single straight wire will not do. There must be a closed circuit so that current can keep on flowing. Nor is joining the opposite two ends of the wire enough in itself. An electromotive force must be supplied. This external source of energy provides the propulsion—variously called electric pressure, difference in potential, voltage—necessary to overcome such obstacles as inertia and friction. The over-all result is a mass migration in one direction if direct current, back and forth if alternating current. Actually, it is only a token migration. The wire is so crowded with atoms that the electrons are pictured as barely able to move. Yet the telephone in New York is heard almost simultaneously in Chicago. Not the electrons themselves but the wave of their movement has raced a thousand miles in that instant.

Electricity need not move only along a conductive wire. But the fundamentals are the same whether in the lightning bolt or in electrochemistry's more placid transport of electrical charges through a battery of some sort, such as a nerve cell. Here, the picture needs more detail because in any substance—solid, liquid, or gas—atoms can be near enough to influence each other.

One result is that the electron freed by a neutral atom may join another neutral atom, giving it a negative charge too many. The convenient word "ionization" covers this give-and-take. The atom with a surplus negative charge is a negative ion; the one with a surplus positive charge is a positive ion. From here, the concept moves easily to the molecule. Under certain conditions, this combination of atoms may split in such a way that one part carries off a net surplus of electrons, leaving the other part with a deficiency. These, too, are called ions, negative and positive. They are familiar workhorses of electrolytic chemistry and explain what we know about the action of the brain and the rest of the nervous system. But ionization is universal.

It can occur violently, as in meteorology's thunderstorm: first in the raincloud's buildup of charged particles, then in the air as the discharge flashes through. Violent in their own way are the physicist's ionizing methods that strip atoms entirely free of electrons, providing the "plasma" whose bare nuclei are needed for fusion-power experiments. Also violent is ionizing radiation—whether man-made, earthmade, or cosmic—when it disrupts the balance of electrical forces in man's cells enough to mutate them or turn them into molecular debris.

Such is our skirmishing around the question of what electricity is, in order to explain what man can do with it. An increasingly important thing he can do is take advantage of the associated phenomenon called electromagnetism.

It has given science a host of practical benefits since the birth of quantum theory at the beginning of this century, but not without trouble for the theorists. The accepted explanation of electromagnetism was that its energy radiated in the form of waves—light being a familiar example. But quantum theory introduced the idea that the energy can also be considered as being in the form of pieces called quanta or photons. The result was the exercise in imagination that Sir William Bragg described in his apt apology: "We teach quantum theory on Mondays, Wednesdays and Fridays, and wave theory on Tuesdays, Thursdays and Saturdays." Today, the choice— waves or quanta—depends on which suits a situation better, a dichotomy perplexing only until one gets accustomed to it.

Further, it is easier not to worry over what magnetism truly is. As with electricity, science can only guess by what magnetism does. The best guess is that magnetism is a byproduct of electricity, because it seems to exist only as the result of the motion of electrical charges. In an iron magnet, for example, the electrons spinning like planets while whirling around the nucleus are considered the source of magnetism. At any rate, the magnetism is easily detectable. A compass needle will line up with the magnet's lines of force, just as the needle does with the magnetic poles of the earth. And with iron filings the schoolboy reveals the pattern of this magnetic field; the filings arrange themselves precisely along its lines of force.

This is not all. A magnet as such isn't needed. The compass needle will respond likewise when held over a wire carrying electricity. The needle is deflected and points across the wire, indicating the direction of the magnetic lines of force with which the current has encircled itself. The converse is also familiar. Apply a force by moving a loop of wire across the lines of force of a magnet. Now, a surge of electrons along the wire produces an electric current, and we have the principle of the ordinary electric generator—the energy of motion becomes electrical energy.

From such fundamentals, physics went on to explain and produce electromagnetic radiation. In a radio transmitter, for example, the source remains electrons in motion but now the current is alternating rather than direct. Accordingly, electrons surge back and forth between both ends of the wire. The result is comparable to that of a cork bobbing up and down in water. The electrons send out waves. Analogy ends there, however. The waves produced by electrons are an interplay of oscillating electric field and oscillating magnetic field, each generating the other as they sweep out from the transmitter. The result is regarded as a traveling disturbance of some kind through what used to be called the ether—the same kind of waves that bring us energy from the sun.

Beyond this is even deeper conjecture. Some theorists, respecting nature's apparent preference for symmetry, hope that elementary particles of magnetism will be discovered. These "magnetic monopoles" would correspond to the atom's charged particles. Others, respecting nature's apparent preference for simplicity, would rather have fewer particles than more. They hope to see proof for Einstein's unified-field theory, which seeks to treat electric, magnetic, and gravitational fields and phenomena as varying aspects of the same cosmic process.

Meanwhile, science proceeds with what it has in hand. Magnets help convert the steam from nuclear reactors into electricity. Electricity produces the magnetic pattern for the tape of tape recorders and core memories of computers. Magnets guide the charged particles in atom-smashers and electron microscopes. The interplay goes on and on, out into Space, to send back electromagnetic television pictures or other data from the moon and our sister planets.

Today's Instruments

It is obvious enough that the experimenter needs laboratory apparatus. How much, and what kind, is debatable. One scientific method is to run experiments or build things and see if they work; then go on redesigning and debugging the experiment or hardware until it does work. Another way, and cheaper, is to do more of the exploring with pencil and paper first. In broad terms, the first method has long been favored by Americans; it belongs to the same impatience that brought our mechanization and mass production. Europeans, more theoretical, less hurried, and with less experimental money, were likely to do more preliminaries on paper.

This has been changing. The advent of electronic computers, coupled with our financial ability to afford them, has resulted in our mathematicians and theorists being given more of the work. But the computer, too, illustrates our preference for hardware rather than pencil and paper. Meanwhile, Europe's researchers do not try to fight any lost cause. They badger their governments for the money that will buy expensive instruments. When dissatisfied with what they receive, as in England, they emigrate to our laboratories, where the equipment is stupendous, measured by European standards. The fact that so many of the lab tools were originally devised by Europeans simply makes the situation ironic.

Many such instruments—mass spectrometers, electron microscopes, and the like—are in the $50,000 class. The same figure happens to be an estimate for the laboratory costs required to support a professional researcher's work for one year. And if he needs a very special piece of equipment—a big atom-smasher or telescope—the cost per researcher may be a half-million dollars.

Of course, it is craftsmanlike to prefer good tools. The quality of the researcher may not always match that of his self-recording instruments, but certainly the apparatus has marvelous potential. For one thing, it works faster than the human instrument can. AEC Commissioner Gerald Tape puts it this way: "It took me about a year to do a doctoral thesis on beta ray spectra; today the same information can be obtained in approximately twenty minutes, including preparation of the radioactive source."

Today's instruments also do what the human's simple sensory equipment cannot hope to do. For example, research on viruses did not get under way seriously until after the electron microscope, a German invention, became practical in the late 1930s. In the same period, America's cyclotron physicists and chemists began creating and studying the elements heavier than nature's uranium, such as plutonium, the A-bomb material. This was work with radioactive and therefore fugitive materials, yet laboratory technique had progressed to the point where scientists could study samples sometimes weighing only a few billionths of a gram.

In this period, too, Sweden's Arne Tiselius was earning a Nobel Prize for developing his method of electrophoresis. With other innovations, like chromatography and ultracentrifugation, it sped the investigation of hormones, nucleic acids, and the like. Here were methods for quickly, surely separating the components of a baffling biological mixture from each other and from impurities—components that must be treated delicately because they behave in what Tiselius calls an "unpleasant manner." As life chemicals, they are easily damaged or destroyed. Also, Tiselius reminds us, "it seems that nature often embeds some of her most attractive research objects in a surrounding of gummy materials particularly difficult to remove."

A distinguishing characteristic of modern laboratory instruments, of course, is that they are usually electrical in one way or other. For instance, that already aging "queen of scientific instruments," the spectrograph. It not only frees chemist and biologist from much dirty cookery in the lab but can scan the stars to tell an astronomer what they are made of. Here we are back with electromagnetism: now with energy radiating directly out of an atom's electrons, as they do from the excited atoms of a red-hot stove. The method is to vaporize the material, then record the kind of light it emits when hot or absorbs when cool. The idea is that for every element or compound, the electrons will be emitting or absorbing waves of a characteristic, identifying length. In a modern laboratory, the equipment does several jobs. It vaporizes the sample. Its optical parts then spread out the resulting wavelengths in a spectrum of identifying lines, bright ones for emitted light or dark ones for absorbed light. And it provides a photographic record of these lines, showing what kinds of atoms are present and in what proportion. Moreover, lacking limitations of the human eye, and able to use specially sensitized film, it can record infrared and ultraviolet wavelengths as well as those of ordinary "white" light.

Such instruments range in elaborateness to the $120,000 setup at the National Bureau of Standards. Its work is in the extreme ultraviolet range, where oxygen would interfere, hence the need to operate it in vacuum. Down the hall, however, I found W. F. Meggers, dean of American spectroscopists, still working with his favorite desk-top instrument, still peering at spectral lines after fifty-three years of research that helped picture the modern atom and supply a succession of identifying spectral guides for scientists. Why was he doing this now that he was emeritus? "I've published 235 technical papers," said he, "and I want to finish a few more before I quit."

The semantics of science are untidy. Another analytical instrument that ranges up to $120,000, whether you call it mass spectrograph or mass spectrometer, has nothing to do with spectral lines, though the idea vaguely resembles that of a prism. It sends electrically charged particles through a magnetic field, and each kind of particle, according to its heaviness, is deflected to a different degree from the original path. The result is a fanning out that shows the relative mass of each substance present—a quick way, for instance, to sort out an element's different isotopes.

Such are ways to analyze the very small amounts of material that must be studied as science probes deeper. But, after all, "seeing is believing." What about very tiny objects no larger than a virus particle that contains only a few molecules of DNA, the molecule of heredity; or this nucleic-acid molecule itself; or even an atom? How, without bogging down in the metaphysical question of what is reality and what is perception, can we see what their structure is like so that we can understand better how they operate?

By a combination of viewing and deduction, much of this is already possible. Today's busiest way of doing it is with that triumph of the instrument-maker called the electron microscope. If the spectrograph is queen of instruments, then this microscope claims to be the young king. Furthermore, it is useful in this chapter because it gathers together several contributions of modern physics.

First, a reminder about normal vision, which starts when the eye receives waves of light reflected from an object. Like any other kind, this seeing is bound by limitations. One is that the unit of measure be no larger than the thing it measures. Somewhat as we use inches to measure a foot, and a foot to measure a 10-foot pole, when the eye sees that foot and inch it is detecting them with light waves that are shorter still. Otherwise, the waves would tend to engulf the object and continue on; the object would not reveal detail by sharply reflecting the waves back to the eye.

Next, let us abandon the idea of seeing only with the eyes in our head. This does not abandon the concept of seeing. The important thing is the ultimate optical message to the brain, which tells what an object is like. Television is a simple example. Instead of seeing the studio with the eye, we do it via such electronic intermediaries as a recording camera at one end and a cathode beam at the other. The end-product is fluorescence on the TV viewing screen. Here, after all the intermediaries, the electrical message takes the form of light, of wavelengths within the eye's range of recognition.

But, as we know, both kinds of waves—radio-TV and visible radiation—are of the same breed. They are electromagnetic waves. Whether or not theory explains them correctly, engineering manipulates such waves easily. At one end of the electromagnetic spectrum, we have the lowest frequencies and longest waves—those used by ordinary radio. At the other end are the incomparably shortwave, high-energy, deep-penetrating gamma rays resulting from nuclear events, such as in the nuclear bomb. Between both ends of the spectrum are the bands associated with shortwave radio, television, radio astronomy, microwave radar, infrared, light, ultraviolet, and X-rays.

It is the development of the electron microscope, and the training of people expert enough to handle its subtleties, that has spurred research down in the microworld where the measuring unit is not the meter, centimeter, or even the handy micron, but the angstrom. This is short indeed. Ten billion angstroms equal one meter. For comparison, radio operates up into thousands of meters. Even the microscopic micron is 10,000 angstroms. Hence the angstrom is ideal at the short end, where, for instance, the diameter of a DNA molecule may be 20 angstroms or less.

Now it is a fact of life that the human eye responds only to a narrow band whose waves are shorter than the shortest radio waves and even microwaves. Tucked between infrared and ultraviolet, these waves in the visible range are from 4000 to 7500 angstroms. They give the eye a suitable measure for a speck of dust. For anything appreciably smaller the eye needs a magnifier. But the ordinary optical microscope soon reaches its own limits. It can magnify clearly only the image of what its light is able to detect clearly. It, too, is restricted to wavelengths a few thousand angstroms long. For anything much smaller, then, we need an instrument providing suitable resolving power and, of course, magnification so the eye can then see what the instrument has seen. X-rays would do, but we lack magnifying lenses for them. Accordingly, science favors one version or another of the electron microscope.

This elaborate instrument looks like neither a television set nor an ordinary microscope but borrows from both. Here, as in the TV picture tube, we have a stream of electrons torn loose from parent atoms and behaving like an electric current, but without need for a wire to carry them. And because these are charged particles, their paths can be bent by passing them through a magnetic field. The result is a beam that can be focused. In TV, magnetic coils steer the beam this way and that in a scanning pattern. In the electron microscope the beam can likewise be manipulated magnetically as it shoots down through the instrument. In TV, the beam strikes fluorescent materials on the viewing screen. In the microscope the beam strikes a target too—the specimen being examined.

This might sound like an atom-smasher at work shattering a target with bullet-like particles. But at this point, happily, physicists use evidence for the wave-particle concept of quantum mechanics. They do a fast mental flip and consider the electrons acting not as particles but as waves. Accelerated by an applied voltage, the faster they go the shorter their wavelength becomes. So, at even a conventional 50,000 volts, we can forget they are particles and consider them as radiation whose wavelength is only .05 of an angstrom. Here is something a hundred thousand times shorter than light—certainly an easy measuring unit for virus particles and large molecules.

Consequently, after striking the object, the electrons form an image as in an ordinary microscope, but now again the focusing is magnetic. The image is then made visible to the eye, usually in two ways: directly, when the electrons light up a small fluorescent viewing screen; and by photographing the image shown on that screen. Of course, this microscopy is not for amateurs. Packed into an instrument only a few feet high are electron-emitter, power supply, magnets, built-in cameras, and so on. The work is done in vacuum, so the instrument needs airlocks through which the specimens and photographic plates must be slipped. And the techniques for preparing specimens are increasingly elaborate.

Ultra-thin slices of the specimen must be mounted on ultra-thin film and guarded against damage from the high vacuum and the electron beam itself. There must be proper contrast for photography. For instance, "shadow casting" blows metal vapor across the specimen to form a sort of snowdrift, and thereby shows three dimensions. Technicians usually do such work. Only experienced scientists try to handle the entire procedure themselves, and this is fortunate; both the instrument and experiment would otherwise be in peril.

A skilled operator also knows that size of image isn't the entire story. It is not enough for the instrument to magnify over 200,000 times, compared with the 2000 or so that the best optical microscopes can do. Incorporated in such figures is the matter of resolving power—the ability to distinguish between two separate points very close together so that one point image will not smear into another. The optical microscope theoretically can give good detail down to 2000 angstroms. But older electron microscopes handle 50 angstroms; at Caltech a technician showed me his new one that gets down to 4 angstroms; and instrument-makers hope for 2 angstroms.

What, then, can we "see"? First, of course, there are indirect methods that rival the electron microscope. An always valuable workhorse is X-ray analysis. It detects the arrangement of atoms in a crystal from the way they scatter the rays. With such evidence, the diameter of an atom has been estimated to be 1 or 2 angstroms. Newer is the spectacular field-ion microscope that uses helium ions to reveal the positions of atoms, then displays the positions as bright dots on a fluorescent screen. Meanwhile, the high-energy physicist probes deeper, into the nucleus of the atom, where elementary particles are revealed by the tracks they make. All such evidence supplies information on forces, distances, relative sizes, but it is too indirect to be called seeing atoms, and certainly not their particles.

So the electron microscope remains the most authentic aid to the human eye. Its beam has not yet seen and therefore been able to photograph an individual atom for our eyes; some day a new kind of electron lens might enable this. Meanwhile, with a resolving power reported already down to 3 angstroms, it is potent indeed because this is the size of the smallest molecules. As mentioned, the optical microscope can distinguish two points separated by 2000 angstroms, which corresponds to the span of 2000 hydrogen atoms. By contrast, 3 angstroms brings seeing down to the size of only 3 hydrogen atoms.

This figure, of course, reflects the optimism of scientists; the usual limit in the 1960s has been about twice that. Even so, the 80-angstrom thickness of a nerve membrane now looms comfortably large under electron microscopes. They also enable routine examination of the 30-angstrom parts of a virus; the virus particle shaped like a doughnut can hardly be confused with one that looks like a tadpole with a tail and six-sided head. Other research fields can benefit too. For instance, if air pollution is ever taken seriously, the optical microscope can examine bacteria and lung-damaging dust, but the electron microscope can reach smaller, to fumes and metallurgical dusts whose particles range down to the size of viruses and large molecules.

The most excitement so far, however, has been in molecular biology, where electron microscopes now routinely examine simpler forms of the difficult DNA molecule. Physicists Alvar Wilska of the University of Arizona and B. M. Siegel of Cornell are representative of apparatus men working to produce a microscope that will fulfill the biologist's and chemist's dream of directly photographing the actual structure of such a molecule. Wilska is more optimistic than most: "I see no reason why, in a few years, there could not be laboratories of people reading the genetic instructions for making humans, plants and animals, as Egyptologists read hieroglyphics."

The Statistician

Ordinarily, we could overlook mentioning mathematics because when it avoids cultistic abstractionism it is so obviously a working tool of science and engineering, of theorist and experimenter alike. What does interest us here is math in its ingratiatingly simple and mushrooming new form of statistics. This produces no Boyle's gas law, or Avogadro's Number, or Planck's constant, or the aeronautical engineer's lift-over-drag ratio. It concerns itself with "If you can't count it, it doesn't count."

Accordingly, though the average statistician cannot be held responsible for the announcement that 50 per cent of the nation's schoolchildren are below average, he cannot escape blame for leveling creativity down to an average mediocrity. Numbers prevail and a Newton disregards the accidental apple falling on his head. The statistician is a new type of worker in science. Neither sayer nor doer, he partakes of both. Inking in his bar charts, slicing his pie charts, concocting scatter-diagrams, and, of course, keeping computers busy, he is "quantifying" science from atom-smashing through geology to zoology. The result is often the square root of confusion but the fact that mass science produces massive data explains why he is kept busy.

Moreover, there are the extrapolators. In demography, for example, they do handsprings of dreadful joy when they plot a curve and contemplate man's future. Thus it is noticeable to laymen as well as biologists that people have been breeding, not like flies but perhaps like the carefree grasshopper. Consequently, the Population Reference Bureau titles one of its bulletins: *Outdoor Recreation Threatened by Excess Procreation.* And another views with more specific alarm: "In 800 years, nearly a second in the evolutionary time scale, the same rate of growth would mean standing-room-only in this country. Every citizen would have only one square foot of living space."

Fortunately, there are other extrapolators. Thus the Population Council answers with the rate of auto production: "Long before population growth will present a space problem, all the surface area of the globe will be covered with asphalt and all the asphalt will be covered with automobiles locked in a final, conclusive traffic jam."

The trouble with the first prediction of stasis is, of course, its confidence in growth curves. It can disregard the suggestion by homosexuals that theirs is "the perfect answer to population explosion," but it should not disregard the growing interest in birth-control methods, here and abroad. Nor should it overlook the Census Bureau's constant reminder that "projections are based on the assumption that there will be no disastrous war, major economic depression, epidemic, or other catastrophe." It might also remember that social attitudes change. For instance, the American woman, the *toujours gai* rebel of the 1920s, was willing to become a brood mare after the war, but has since revised downward her estimate of the "ideal family" size.

However, the prophetic statistician concerns us less than the one who performs mathemagic that seems to explain scientifically the past and present.

If the tabulation is correct, why should there be anything wrong with counting heads, counting lungs, or whatever? The trouble lies manifestly in who does what with the count: "Figures don't lie but liars figure." Assume, however, that liars are not involved, that the statistician is innocent of conscious distortion or prevarication. He can nonetheless make truth scream with pain.

For one thing, the statistician who interprets data is therefore argumentative and unscientific. Such, anyway, was what British scientists feared in the early nineteenth century when they were asked to admit statisticians to their professional society. They warned the candidates to eschew interpretation "lest we admit the foul demon of discord into the Eden of philosophy." That primness is antique now. Though some statisticians still limit themselves to offering bland data, the trend is toward the spiced.

How scientific is it? A reputable statistician professes to be neither soothsayer or doomsayer. He claims scientific method when he says "Let the facts speak." Yet some other things help do the talking. Among these are his opinions and, increasingly, his methods of sampling, which determine how "randomized" his data will be. Now assume that he has assumed too much, or overlooked too much, or knows too little. If statisticians cannot agree on the relatively simple, such as how many statisticians there are, how can they prescribe so positively for complexities like cancer or hardened arteries?

These two, the nation's most frightening diseases, in turn illustrate the distinctive laboratory problem of today's mass-produced science —the trend to favor the statistical over the experimental. This allows the counting and measuring of cigarette butts to become a high-speed, low-quality substitute for research on cancer. At first glance, of course, statistics seems to be doers at work. Then come disturbing doubts. As a science, whom does it teach? What can it build? What can it cure? If it cannot cure, how truly does it get down to the cause? Or is this simply Instant Science, a glib version that is overwhelming basic research rather than aiding it? For, obviously, the two methods should work together. They can and have done so. Like a useful theorist, the useful statistician ponders the data. If he values his reputation, he is also part experimenter: the data are his own; he tries better sampling methods to overcome bias; he carefully evaluates his probability of error. Likewise, the conventional experimenter is a statistician whenever he evaluates his sets of data; and he, too, must estimate probable error.

But these are overlaps. In fundamental approach the two methods remain a gulf apart. The experimenter creates and varies the test conditions so that he can get comparative, reproducible results. This control over causes is beyond the statistician. He can be only a spokesman for effects. Now apply the difference to something so challenging as cancer, which qualifies as Winston Churchill's riddle wrapped in a mystery inside an enigma. Cancer research also demonstrates how loud the voice of the statistician has become.

Here, comparison of The National Foundation with the American Cancer Society is helpful. The former was created in 1938 in response to a call by Franklin Roosevelt, the nation's best-known victim, for an organized voluntary fight against infantile paralysis. Patient research followed, and led through Nobelist John F. Ender's achievement, a tissue-culture method of growing the polio virus, to Jonas Salk's vaccine in 1955. Though overhaste and overpublicity led to trouble with it at first, the vaccine soon triumphed. So did the Sabin vaccine six years later. The foundation could claim, in italics: "Both were developed entirely out of March of Dimes funds." By virtually wiping out polio, this private organization might have put itself out of work, the more so because of "competitive philanthropy." But it moved quickly into the wide-open birth-defects field and has remained busy. Its research and clinics span the nation; it has opened a $1,600,000 Salk Institute for basic biological research; the cost of its programs, about $25 million a year, is raised mostly from those valuable marching dimes.

The American Cancer Society, too, appeals to the public for support. But there the similarities end. Unlike the independent National Foundation, this ACS is deeply involved with the government. It is also the louder crusader. This stems from its history. It was once the sedate American Society for the Control of Cancer. In 1945, this group was penetrated by such laymen as Albert D. Lasker, the advertising genius, and Elmer Bobst, now board chairman of Warner-Lambert Pharmaceutical Company—dynamic men who had sincere personal reasons for hating cancer. At first, the society recalls, "welding the medical men and laymen into a harmonious group came close to resembling Pier 6 brawls." But the weld held. And as a result of the takeover by advertising-minded men, ACS now raises about $40 million a year with the aid of two million volunteer fundraisers. Another result has been what George Crile, Jr., of the Cleveland Clinic deplores as national hysteria over cancer. Meanwhile, ACS has produced no basic causes, much less cures. It supports lab research but its notable achievement reflects the advertising man's reliance on statistics. Two dates are significant.

In 1956, Wendell M. Stanley gave his historic challenge to the National Cancer Conference: "The time has come when we should assume that viruses are responsible for most if not all kinds of cancer, including cancer in man. Acceptance of this idea will result in experiments that might otherwise be left undone, experiments that could result in the solving of this great problem." But Nobelist Stanley was two years behind a persuasive spokesman for non-laboratory "research"—E. Cuyler Hammond, head statistician of the American Cancer Society. The first of his announcements that blamed cancer on smoking was in 1954 at a convention of the American Medical Association. This gave statisticians a head start and they did not lose it.

Ten years later, while some experimenters still argued over Stanley's advice, and those who took it were finding themselves ever deeper in the mystery of life itself, statisticians made their great march. Their evidence dominated *Smoking and Health*. This report by an advisory committee to the United States Public Health Service made it officially correct to denounce cigarettes. But the report was a triumph for statistics rather than science, except in the indirect sense that such high-voltage prods seem necessary. The tobacco interests and others injured by the report now promised to respond with truly experimental research.

Perhaps, also, a worthwhile number of smokers saw the error of their self-polluting ways. Unquestionably, a prosperous but nonetheless tense nation was smoking immoderately—and the old rule is that excess, whether you eat, drink, or inhale it, can kill. So, figures for males (the data brushed past females) showed higher mortality among cigarette smokers. But the PHS document, the so-called "blockbuster" report, neither offered nor claimed to offer anything new. It was a review of statistics published through the years. It did not try to evaluate new smoke-filtering methods or the fresh Sloan-Kettering statistics showing filters were now twice as effective as they had been. Its biggest drawback scientifically, however, was its focus on effects and unconcern with causes—the really basic causes of, say, lung cancer, which was the report's proudest exhibit.

For if cancer in humans is indeed a viral disease, then the conventional counterattack is two-pronged: (1) basic research, to learn the why and how of the virus attack; (2) immediately practical research, to find vaccines. Merely stamping out the smoking habit could not help the nonsmokers who die from lung cancer or other kinds of cancer, each caused by a different virus and therefore perhaps requiring a different vaccine. And if cancer is not viral, if it is started somehow by chemicals, or radiation or whatever, nonsmokers again would receive no benefit from an anti-tobacco crusade. The same holds true if such environment causes the initial damage in some cancers and an infectious virus is the "mediator" that moves in to profit from it. At any rate, while the PHS report was making headlines, the Philadelphia Zoo was worrying about air pollution, and lung cancer in its nonsmoking animals. In twenty-eight years the death rate from this malignancy had risen six times higher than it had been. "It would seem," complained Herbert Ratcliffe, the zoo's research director, "that the outdoor life is not the healthy life, at least at Thirty-fourth and Girard Avenue." But this might not have impressed Dr. Hammond. The anti-cigarette crusader was even brushing aside the effects of California smog. Apparently, there was but the one outlaw worth hanging in effigy—demon tobacco.

Anyway, the government report was victory for statisticians, not the genuine scientists. It concerned an effect (cancer) and an intermediate agent (cigarette smoke) rather than a prime cause. The difference here between agent and cause can hardly be ignored. For instance, cancer-fighters have been driving hard to establish that at least one type, leukemia in humans, is "caused" by virus. Yet this blood malignancy is "caused" also by ionizing radiation; Hiroshima statistics, still being collected, demonstrate this beyond doubt. We seem, then, to mean "medium" when we say "cause." For the prime cause, science must solve deep mystery—how the metabolism of the body works normally, so we can then understand and do something about the outlaw growth called cancer. How do enzymes run the chemical processes of the living cell? How does a change in the cell's blueprint alter what the enzymes can do? How does an invading virus change the blueprint, and isn't this simply another version of mutation, also caused by a chemical or radiation? Manifestly, this takes us far beyond what is dreamed of in either Horatio's or the statistician's philosophy. Each question digs into the life process. Investigating one adds information for another. All require genuine research of the deepest kind.

The cholesterol story is another familiar example of the need for such research. The unlovely cholesterol phobia, however, is more seriocomic than the unlovely cancer phobia. And the terror here has come in fairly equal amounts from experimenter and statistician. It is debatable whether the pronouncements by some laboratory men about how this or that diet produces cholesterol deposits that harden arteries and cause heart attacks, and the risky drugs they have concocted to break into that chain of events, have been more or less fruitful than the statistical journeys to learn what the ancients ate and modern Seventh Day Adventists eat and Yemenite Jews eat and Trappist monks eat. Concerning the last-named, a *Medical World News* headline sighed "No Sanctuary from Serum Lipids."

Useful science operates in a quietly different way. It knows no proof that the amount of cholesterol in the blood is related to how much is deposited in the arteries. It seeks to learn how the deposits cause the dreaded blood clots and the perhaps thirteen steps by which a clot forms. It remembers that a normal liver manufactures more cholesterol than is obtained directly from food and that the normal body strikes a balance: through "feedback" controls, the liver produces less when the diet provides more. To cure the abnormal it closes in on the normal—in 1964, Harvard's Konrad Bloch received the Nobel Prize for the patient research with which he helped reveal the nature of the perhaps thirty-six chemical steps by which the body, with equal patience, starts with acetic acid and builds the cholesterol molecule.

Statistics helps too. It has provided a stopgap in the form of legal protection for cholesterol-fearing laymen who become victims of the fast-talking, fast-hawking P. T. Barnums of today. The Food and Drug Administration hired samplers who interviewed 780 statistically average householders. Their reports convinced FDA that the nation was badly misled by such suggestive labeling terms as "polyunsaturated" and "low in cholesterol." Whereupon FDA warned the food industry against such labeling, which it called "false and misleading and a misbranding under Federal law."

VI: *Of Life and Drugs*

"Why shouldest thou die before thy time?"
—*Ecclesiastes*

Biology was once modest. Lacking atom-smashers and such, it sometimes pleased its ego by regarding itself as "artistic," in contrast with "bleak" physics. Since then it has grown hugely into an assortment of biosciences tingling with excitement. For its hot pursuit of the genetic code and other molecular mysteries hidden in living cells it has absorbed many chemists and physicists, and claims to be cock of the roost: "The science most directly aimed at science's major goal."

Naturally, this offends rivals who think it is getting more than its fair share of R & D funds. Others compliment biology on the worthwhile portion of its research but deplore its association with rowdy companions ranging from outright quacks to some not always ethical members of the so-called "ethical-drug industry."

Furthermore, what is worthwhile research? Molecular biology happens to be on the higher plateaus of life science. Even so, a leader like René Dubos, of Rockefeller Institute, warns that enthusiasm for this specialty is a fad causing gross neglect of the total human organism and the modern hazards confronting it. This is another version of the complaint against specialists. If biology weren't so Big Businesslike today, and so paralyzed by lack of communication between specialist A and specialist B, the charge would be merely academic. It is inconceivable, for instance, that a real cure for cancer or real preventive of birth defects would not also help explain how the molecules of heredity work, and vice versa. There is indeed so much still to learn about the whole human in all his amazing complications

203

and surprising simplicities, so much still to come from creative researchers!

In this chapter on life science we will see what is being done about the body's basic functions of metabolism. A manufacturing process, from raw material to product, metabolism is the generalist's delight: in its broad sense it is a sum total of the chemical reactions within the body's cells. But those reactions do not always go as they should. So we will not overlook the desire to take medicine, which has been called the outstanding difference between men and animals. For despite intimations of immortality some day, man yearns to be a healthy animal today. And despite humble drugs and wonder drugs, his miseries remain, though perhaps under other names. The old-fashioned gout of the rich and "rheumatiz" of the poor have become part of a dozen or so of the more important capricious, tormenting inflammations called arthritis.

Nor are the mortality figures reassuring. True enough, the "germ" diseases tuberculosis, pneumonia, influenza, and syphilis are not the major killers they still were in the late 1930s; and the dollar value of government-sponsored medical research has soared. Unquestionably, with polio vaccines and the like, today's child has a much better chance to survive. And, in terms of longevity, we still have centenarians. But solid government statistics recently confirmed an "unexpected" but plain fact. The nation's mortality rate has stopped dropping. Despite chemical boons like antibiotics (and surgical ones, of course), the average American's life expectancy at birth has not gone past three-score-and-ten, a year or two more for women than men.

In view of the remarkable feats performed by the microbe-hunters, what has happened? A combination of things. Accidental deaths, like those on the highway, take their toll. But there is also the medical field. Some germs, like those causing tuberculosis, have mutated, developing resistance to wonder drugs. Some, like those causing syphilis, strike at an insouciant new generation of innocents who take liberty and safety for granted. Some, like staphylococcus, cause epidemics through carelessness at hospitals.

Mainly, however, the declining danger from infectious diseases has supplied potential victims for those that come with the degenerative years, or involve faulty metabolism in some other way.

There are the obvious cases—the nation's four million diabetics who, despite their insulin crutch, account for the seventh ranking killer. Looking at the broader picture, there are the uncounted millions afflicted with a variety of chemical disorders, digestive and glandular, caused by heredity or environment, including the one out of four American adults officially classified as obese. Then there are the hidden disorders that unquestionably go back to chemical mistakes in the genetic blueprint: blood diseases like hemophilia, and the dozens of metabolic errors that can interfere with the proper development of a baby's brain. But the best way to judge the new dangers, and need for research, is to compare the jostle of statistics from agencies, governmental and private, that keep us in worst fear for our lives.

Of course, a claim can be made for almost anything. Counting one suicide every twenty-six minutes, the mental-health people triumphantly name suicide as America's ninth (and Yale's second) "most prevalent fatal sickness." Also on the sideline of the main fight for research funds is malaria. Through the years it probably kills more people throughout the world than any other disease. But it lacks the personal interest of the Big Three that worry Americans.

One is heart disease (technically, nearly twenty cardiovascular ailments, with artery-hardening atherosclerosis far in the lead). It afflicts over 10 million living Americans to some degree, and the American Heart Association goes on to claim that the million fatalities a year are nearly twice the combined total for the next five causes of death. Next, of course, is cancer, with some 300,000 deaths a year. The third major contender is arthritis. Not a major killer, its claim is "the world's leading crippler"; and figures, depending on the source, range up to 12 million such cripples.

The point about all three is that each still awaits a cure, and that each is metabolic in origin. Atherosclerosis is obviously so. Arthritis fits nowhere else and has been delegated to the same NIH agency that researches diabetes, obesity, and the like. And cancer, whatever the triggering mechanism, is the body's metabolism gone wild.

Small wonder, then, that the broad field is tilled by many alarmists and quacks, the more so because in its narrower sense metabolism concerns what the body does with what it eats—and nutritional panaceas are an ancient and ever new approach to the wallet. Fat people, physical weaklings, and simply aging people are traditional targets for the sharper who promises to restore beauty, virility, youth; to protect against cancer, cholesterol, arthritis, and so on.

And what about the ethical-drug industry? It is candid. It seeks new pills for profit, a cause for resentment by "pure" researchers who stress the need for knowledge about life processes. But most such researchers are themselves vulnerable. They can hardly become excited over something so commonplace as exercise and a sane diet for a tense, affluent society that rides too much and eats unwisely. They, too, see new drugs at the end of the trail. And a prison inmate who volunteered for tests, when asked later, "What did you get out of it?" replied "Stomach trouble and a carton of cigarettes." But space does not allow more than passing references to the controversial economics of the medical field: the price of drugs, the wages of those who research them, the fees of those who prescribe them. Medical economics too easily becomes political economics.

Look closer at this creature that research has to deal with. If the "man on Mars" by some chance turns out to be an arthropod we will compare him with the lobster or an insect. These live inside their skeletons. He, in turn, will note the obvious and assign us to the vertebrates; skeleton and all, we live inside our skins. This includes man with the best athletes of the animal kingdom—highly developed muscles and efficient devices for oxygenating them. And we certainly are well balanced: not only male and female but also paired limbs, ribs, lungs, eyes; one nose but paired nostrils, one heart but paired ventricles and auricles, and so on down to the paired chromosomes with which we reproduce.

This is useful symmetry. And what a piece of work is man! exclaims the poet. But superb machine or not, and with all his bioelectricity, physical man reduces to a sum of chemical events. Some are simple enough, some can be imitated in the test tube. But the whole is a tantalizing complex of so many different reactions and buffered ones and equilibria, some in sequence, others simultaneous, that aside from other considerations, no chemist can duplicate man. To maintain these reactions requires a constant grinding and mixing and pumping as basic foods, additives, and fuels move through the body. It stores glycogen; on demand this variety of starch changes to sugar, which provides energy for the living cells. Simultaneously, the hormone insulin is ready to counter an excess of sugar. Meanwhile, the same blood that transports sugar and insulin carries much other cargo, including its own maintenance chemicals, and here again is a deft self-control—clotting agents to prevent hemorrhage, others to prevent deadly clotting.

The logic behind such reactions seems simple enough. But exactly how are the body's chemicals made? How does the body know when to make them? How, especially, can so many reactions go on in the same reactor? The biochemist can only shrug, admire evolution, and guess it all began with a simple reactor in the sea because the fluids inside our living cells and the bloodstream that bathes them, nourishing them and removing their wastes, are so remarkably like seawater in the kind of salts they contain and their relative concentration. In other words, the external environment became internal when we left the sea. Thus the cultist could glorify mighty mother salt, source of ions for the body's electricity and osmotic pressures. But on sea or land, the same rules remain. For instance, the concentration of salts inside a living cell must seek balance with the concentration outside. If the cell has relatively too much salt, water is taken in by osmosis, the cell swells and eventually is disrupted.

Chemical engineering can therefore look upon man as an ambulatory reactor, whether in the nude or loaded with furs; whether downing a morning cup of coffee to stimulate his juices, or returning to mother sea in a skindiver's suit. He has acquired a multilevel brain but in his adventures with weightlessness the liquids in his head don't sit right. He has acquired a heart-pump for pushing liquids but his artery-pipes become narrowed with deposits. However, man is not only a reactor, a vat of sorts. Falstaff was more than a tub of guts; above was a brainful of subtleties that could humorously contemplate both the vat and an abstraction called honor. This curiosity about himself is part of man's endowment. He combines sex with play, and the lure is said to be curiosity about another's body. If so, this is curiosity that leads also to scientific research.

One thing research has learned concerns new troubles it has given the reactor. It is not enough that the surgeon "prevent hair, with other contaminating accessories, from falling in the operative field" and remember to remove his sponges. It is against other carelessness that science has begun warning drug companies, doctors, and the public. Promiscuous use of hormones can change normal children into what pediatric researchers call "FLKs"—funny-looking kids. Promiscuous use of antibiotics leads to resistant varieties of bacteria against which the body is then helpless. Some years ago, an advisory report by the National Academy of Sciences stopped penicillin going into toothpastes, but the overdose of antibiotics continues in other forms. And a recent academy report warns that mild food poisoning has become common, thanks to a combination of faults: new food-packing methods and the cook's misplaced faith that boiling is no longer necessary.

The fact is that our bodies are under assault today, not only from malignant bacteria and viruses, but from a growing number of pollutants. Evidence is mounting that modern man lives in a state of chronic reactor-poisoning, ranging from stomach-and-head misery at work to hospitalization and worse. The chemist hunts down impurities in his flask because he knows how they upset the normal reactions and equilibria he desires. The body's reactor is treated less intelligently.

The same housewife alarmed over agricultural pesticides trudges upstairs with her aerosol bomb and, in the snug attic or closet, generously distributes the DDT between her own reactor and that of the little pests. Another reason why everybody should know more science? Then I remember the MIT-trained scientist who was hospitalized with hepatitis. A proper suburbanite, he had joined the war against ants on the lawn but had not bothered to read chlordane's warning label.

Obviously, then, there is no one villain. To begin with, the reactor has some congenital faults. A metabolic disorder helps explain, for example, why one person can "handle" alcohol and another cannot. Then come the pollutants. Alcohol can be a blessing. So can one of the safer sleeping pills. But taken in conjunction with sleeping pills, alcohol can be suicide—another metabolic upset. The trouble need not be that dramatic. It can be a chronic condition arising from a long list of direct effects, side-effects, and combined effects brought on by what we eat, drink, and breathe. Or it can be a transient condition: "I wasn't myself yesterday."

The shockingly careless driver is blamed for shocking carelessness.

But what is really the cause of the accident when a man quarrels with his wife, gets into his car whose tires have worn-out treads, stops at the bar for a couple of drinks, drives on through falling snow, doesn't reduce speed at a badly constructed curve on a road that has not been properly sanded, and crashes? And more "reckless- ness" than we can hope to guess is found in the rest of the driver population. The person at the wheel may be aging, with a correspond- ing decline in normal hormone activity; or he may have a headache from food he has eaten; or his acuity may be dulled by drugs, or perhaps a few whiffs of carbon monoxide from the car; or he may be bothered by his ulcer, diabetes, arthritis, bad circulation of blood, or a dozen other such ailments, singly or in combination, that dis- qualify him to cope with traffic. He can no longer rely upon his horse.

Some metabolic risks, like cigarette smoke or over-exuberant fluoridation, we are warned against and may try to control. Some seem unfair, like unsuspected arsenic in chicken livers and pesticides in food. Others, like polluted air (and polluted water), seem merely hopeless while the remedies offered by science await serious fulfill- ment. I have seen nothing more dismal than the usual anti-pollution conference, this despite a reason offered by the Public Health Service for why our life expectancy remains seventy: "The dramatic upward trend of the chronic bronchopulmonary disease mortality from middle age onward seems particularly significant." A dramatic enough ex- ample was the four-day fog, heavy with sulfur dioxide, that killed four thousand Londoners, most of whom already had "chest condi- tions." They were vulnerable; the heavy concentration of sulfur dioxide apparently pushed them over the edge. Or take benzpyrene, known to be a cancer-producer in experimental animals. It is in the "tar" of cigarette smoke. It is also in industrial smoke: "The amount of benzpyrene poured into the air on an industrial town," says Chairman David Radner of the Department of Thoracic Medicine at Chicago's Michael Reese Hospital, "results in every adult breathing in over a twenty-four-hour-period the equivalent of smoking fifty cigarettes." These are only a few of the "environmental" pollutants that beset us. For years there were hopes to set up a national research center that would find the truth and prescribe what should be done.

For years Congress and the White House remained uncertain which part of the country should be favored with the $70-million project and eventual $45-million-a-year payroll.

However, it is self-pollution, the chemicals we take voluntarily that interest us here—the kind that the Food and Drug Administration has for years been trying to police, blamed for high-handedness one day and laxity the next; and especially the kind that result in the "Dear Doctor" letter with which a drug company warns that side-effects have been discovered. For any drug is a two-edged sword. It should help considerably more than it harms. And rare indeed is something both as helpful and usually harmless as the package of 15 billion aspirin tablets we take annually. Troubles start even before life begins, with contraceptive pills accused of injuring a woman's liver, arteries, and so on. And if conception is allowed, there come the hazards of being a fetus. A classic example is the thalidomide tragedy. Thanks to this inadequately tested tranquilizer, European mothers were producing babies whose arms and legs were grotesquely deformed, and American mothers were running the same risk before Washington acted.

Soon the same William S. Merrell Company that distributed thalidomide pills in the United States was in trouble again, this time with a drug of its own. The FDA had allowed Merrell to put MER-29 on sale. Soon it was "the nation's most widely prescribed anticholesterol drug and the main reason for the company's 18-percent gain in profits," though complaints had already started—it was causing eye cataracts, loss of hair, impotence, and sterility. Eventually the company pleaded nolo contendere to having falsified research data concerning safety of the drug.

It goes without saying that there are many good drugs, as well as physicians who administer them properly. This is why an executive of another company said privately, "Our industry has to clean its own house. If it doesn't, then socialized medicine, or whatever you call it, will step in." But again, singling out villains isn't easy. Falsified data can explain only a small fraction of the prescription-drug industry's sales of over $3.6 billion a year. A drug company's four-color ad in medical journals urges the doctor to buy its new product, but also fulfills obligations in smaller print by obediently listing possible side-effects: "glossitis, stomatitis, proctitis, nausea, diarrhea, vaginitis, dermatitis, overgrowth of non-susceptible organisms." This reminds the physician that some patients may respond unhealthily to the drug, and to be selective. But the fact is that neither the industry, the government, the American Medical Association, nor spokesmen for science have been able to solve a complex situation—made worse by a very personal equation, the understandable craving for relief from pain and fear. If his physician is reluctant to prescribe, the patient goes elsewhere. But this isn't always necessary. In fact, some physicians, definitely not representative of their profession, have a sharp incentive to purvey drugs. Among these, some own pharmacies; and congressional investigators know of others who have averaged drug-testing fees of $100 per patient (while charging the patient, of course). If this is not conflict of interest, why not?

But let us return to research. To the extent that it is attracted by mystery and thirsts for knowledge, it need make no apology. To the extent that it turns technologist and seeks specific palliatives, it faces what might be called a matter of principle. While seeking relief for the ills of this generation, does it also dig deeper for answers that will benefit the next? The rest of this chapter concerns what is being done to solve mysteries of the vitamins, enzymes, hormones, and antibiotics. All four offer palliatives. They also are gateways of knowledge that invite man to get acquainted with himself.

Vitamins

When science knew much less about the body's reactor it concerned itself mainly with three major foodstuffs, the fats, carbohydrates, and proteins. Then biochemistry became increasingly interested in subtle organic chemicals that somehow operate the reactor—the trio called vitamins, enzymes, and hormones.

The first two are alike in that they enter directly into the processes, and in fact often function together as "co-enzymes." The hormones are considered the couriers that give production orders.

All three are vital, though needed only in very small amounts; all three still challenge the life scientist to prove exactly how they work. Though hundreds of natural enzymes are already known, none has yet been synthesized. A start has been made on synthetic hormones.

And synthetic vitamins to supplement those in food are, of course, no problem. Take your choice, multiple or single, in pills or chewing gum, for real benefits or something elusive like sexual vigor.

First, the vitamins. They are correctives for a wide variety of nutritional deficiencies. They are therefore needed by undernourished people, rich and poor alike. They are often removed by food-manufacturing processes, but chemistry can restore them in artificial form.

Scientifically, they exemplify many things, including the extent to which man has become dependent in the ecological scheme of things. Vitamins are not known to be homemade in the strict sense of the word. To make vitamin A the body first needs a "provitamin"—a precursor like the yellowish carotene supplied by carrots or egg-yolk. For "sunshine" vitamin D it needs sunlight and another provitamin, almost undistinguishable from cholesterol. For some others it turns the manufacturing over to intestinal bacteria—a mutual-aid arrangement. Still others come only in the proper food.

The classic example is the cure or prevention of scurvy with the juice from limes. Chemists later isolated the vitamin C and christened it ascorbic acid, which is now routinely synthesized from glucose sugar. Another concerns pellagra, a poor man's disease that somehow spared families with their own milch cow. Here the deficiency was in one of the B vitamins, which chemists found to be nicotinic acid—a harmless compound they could make from the dangerous alkaloid nicotine. But this brought a problem. The lay public might surmise that there were vitamins in tobacco. Hence the American Medical Association contrived the acronymic version "niacin."

Such was the research that led via usefulness to today's vitamin pills, and much nonsense. With some vitamins the overdosing is unquestionably harmful. Generally, however, it seems to hurt only the family budget, despite constant reminders that a balanced diet gives the ordinary adult all the vitamins needed. The intelligent housewife, for example, knows that milk and fruit juices are better than soda pop for her family, and that a sprig of parsley is fantastically rich in vitamin A. But even she might not know the extent to which some vitamins are oversold. A case in point is folic acid. This B vitamin is manufactured plentifully by intestinal bacteria, and the Food and Drug Administration says it has found deficiencies only by creating them with "antivitamins" in experimental animals. But it has been touted highly and priced highly too. Concerning his company's synthetic product, a chemist complained: "When the Pennsylvania Railroad built its tracks to Washington it didn't expect to get all its money back on the first train trip." At any rate, the production, advertising, and sale of vitamins helps keep the national economy healthy.

Science has been the worst sufferer. It cannot pretend to understand the body's mechanism until it knows how vitamins work. It can only guess that the vitamin is a catalyst, and it looks to familiar catalysts for guidance.

By definition a catalyst takes part in a chemical reaction, changing the rate of the reaction without itself being consumed—it can be reused. Platinum, for example. Far more important than its ornamental value is its service to industry. In finely divided form called platinum black it speeds the interaction of sulfur dioxide and oxygen that gives sulfuric acid, and of ammonia and oxygen that gives nitric acid. The method is believed to be that of a benevolent neutral. Sometimes the catalyst is deeply involved in the reaction. Other times it is thought merely to provide an electrically charged surface that crowds the atoms of chemical (a) and chemical (b) closely enough to stimulate their interaction. The vitamins, too, are considered matchmakers of a sort. Beyond that we know little about these precious additives.

However, in the heyday of vitamin research, they did provide insights into scientific method. The University of Wisconsin, for instance, fared nicely with its Steenbock patents on vitamin D. To exploit them, nine alumni each contributed $100 in 1925 to set up WARF (Wisconsin Alumni Research Foundation). Into the portfolio later went patents on the unique hydroxy-coumarins, useful either as a suave rat poison or as a blood anticoagulant for humans. In thirty years, WARF's patents and what it called its "aggressive investment policy" resulted in assets of over $30 million, plus another $18 million in grants to the university. Eventually, WARF's methods of licensing manufacture of the sunshine vitamin led to trouble with the antitrust laws and it lost the vitamin patents, which were due to expire soon anyway.

A more cheerful ending is furnished by the story of thiamin, the

B vitamin that shields against neuritis and other nerve troubles typical of beriberi. Our need to synthesize it doesn't speak well for American dietary habits, because it is overabundant in whole grains. We remove it by milling, then restore it as a flour-enricher. Anyway, Robert R. Williams, who had been a schoolteacher in the Philippines and seen the ravages of beriberi there, found the vitamin after twenty years of experimenting with extracts from untold tons of rice hulls, and synthesized it. He was then director of chemistry at Bell Labs. Vitamins, of course, weren't Bell's dish of tea and Williams assigned his patents to Research Corporation, the foundation that had itself been founded by a donation of patent rights, stipulating that half of the net proceeds flow into a special fund for fighting dietary diseases. In this way, royalties from thiamin were put to such uses as fighting pellagra in our South and beriberi in the Philippines.

Yet this is mainly philanthropy. The exciting days are gone; vitamins are orphans of biochemical research; the researchers did the immediately practical side of their work so well that vitamins became big business and science turned its curiosity elsewhere, leaving question marks. We still don't know just how vitamins operate in the metabolic scheme. Here advocates of basic research could complain legitimately but, strangely, do not.

Enzymes

Let us not make the faddist's mistake of worshiping one necessity and ignoring others. The body needs vitamins. But it would also be miserable, or die, without sufficient other additives. For example, it destroys over a million presumably shopworn red corpuscles every second. To escape anemia it must replace those cells, each containing perhaps 280 million molecules of hemoglobin, of which each comprises some 10,000 atoms, of which four atoms of iron are indispensable for the oxygen-delivery job. Hence the need for iron to replace what the body does not reuse. Likewise, respecting its ancestry, the body requires a "salt lick" of some kind to maintain the seawater-like composition of its fluids.

In contrast to such additives, the precious enzymes are home-grown. They require "raw material," of course, but are produced by the living cells. After that, their mission decides where one finds them. When chemistry was less sophisticated it thought of enzymes mainly in terms of food processes—fermenting agents, gastric juices, and the like. Since then they have been drawn into genetics: enzymes now participate in the excitement of molecular biology. In either field the enzyme molecules are catalysts in the sense that they themselves do not become flesh, blood, muscle, bone. Instead, they are thought to be the chemical reactor's main operating machinery, metabolic specialists that help with the hauling and assembling, each kind doing its one specific job.

To do this work, some enzymes leave the mother cell. For instance, a mouthful of food is met immediately by the amylase secreted by saliva. This enzyme splits the molecules of cooked starch into smaller, digestible components. More complex is the job of enzymes that remain in the cell. Picture the cell as a factory whose main job is to keep life going by building more cells. Here we meet a bootstrap operation. Obeying its genes, the cell constructs enzymes; they in turn help build cellular material. A rose, for example, is white if its cells lack a certain gene. Possessing the gene, it manufactures a specific type of enzyme whose job is to change a colorless substance in the rose petals into a red substance.

All enzymes are only chemical compounds, yet their work makes them seem lifelike or, at least, robotlike. Almost anything occurring in the body requires their help, presumably a different kind of enzyme for each mission.

Right at the start, an enzyme makes fertilization of the female's ovum possible. This egg is protected by a tough coating cemented with a substance called hyaluronic acid, but the male's sperm contains a corresponding enzyme that penetrates the coating, thereby allowing fertilization of the egg. It is by their "ase" ending that one usually knows the enzymes. Hyaluronidase works on the hyaluronic acid; maltase works on malt.

The enzymes are active in digesting food, building tissue, replacing blood cells—and clotting blood too. They change the chemical energy of food into electricity of a nerve and kinetic energy of a moving muscle. And the firefly's unique enzyme, lucerifase, catalyzes chemical energy into light. Parasites inside the termite supply a cellulose-splitting enzyme that keeps the termite race alive. When yeast cells convert glucose sugar to carbon dioxide and alcohol, each of the perhaps twenty small steps is catalyzed by a different enzyme. And, in the human, alcohol dehydrogenase helps oxidize the alcohol. If this enzyme is lacking—would this explain the alcoholic's trouble? Here is the concept that faulty metabolism is faulty enzyme reaction. It can be hereditary: in "maple syrup urine disease," cells lack the right gene to produce the right enzyme to control the right step in body chemistry. It can be heredity changed by environment: invasion by a virus, for example, substitutes the wrong genes, therefore the wrong enzymes, for the right ones.

But these are only bits of knowledge in a sea of deep mystery. Perhaps thousands of different chemical reactions occur in a single cell. The number of enzyme types known is less than a thousand. More important: though many have been crystallized in the pure form and some can be made to work in the test tube, their chemical structure—the arrangement of up to many thousands of atoms in an enzyme molecule—remained unknown until the British announcement in 1965 that it had been worked out for lysozyme, a mild antiseptic found in human tears.

In a way, however, they are more fortunate scientifically than the vitamins precisely because they have not yet become synthetics. To fortify oneself with digestion-aiding enzymes, for instance, one can only continue eating such things as natural yeast, yogurt, or perhaps an extract like pepsin from animal stomachs. And the hunt for synthetic substitutes helps in a modest way to keep enzyme chemistry alive.

Pills aside, enzymes offer a magnificent challenge. For one thing, all known enzymes have turned out, chemically, to be proteins. This means that their characteristic building blocks are what the chemist calls amino acids (as with nucleic acids and other such organic acids, "acid" refers, of course, to their structure rather than any corrosiveness). Other proteins abound in common foods. Plants manufacture them from simple substances. Like other animals, humans apparently cannot. Yet our diet requires them. So we eat plants, or other animals. When a steak is being digested, gastric enzymes, appropriately called proteinases, go to work splitting off the amino acids. These are then transported to the cells, where they form a reserve. From the reserve, a cell then recombines them to make those proteins that the body needs.

But more fascinating to today's science is the realization that all our life processes revolve around the chemistry and physics of the cell's protein chemistry. If we are to be mouse or man, or what kind of man, depends on the pattern transmitted genetically, whether by the genes of classic biology or by nucleic acids, the newer term favored by molecular biology. But in either case, the transmittal agent is part protein. Then the appropriate proteins called enzymes, singly or in combination, somehow build collagen, the major body-building protein (subsequently used as the basis of the gelatin, glue, and leather industries), and the others needed for flesh, skin, muscle, hair, and so on. They also build the vital functional proteins in the cells. Consequently, enzyme chemistry becomes protein chemistry and protein chemistry becomes life chemistry. In fact, as far as the cell's enzymes and proteins are concerned, science has begun using the terms interchangeably. The idea is that for every kind of gene there is a corresponding kind of enzyme (some theorists think that a gene may itself function as an enzyme), and for every enzyme the one chemical job it can do. The concept covers normal growth, and abnormal too. For the inborn errors of metabolism called birth defects, the enzyme chemist blames an enzyme condition and the geneticist reaches farther back to blame a genetic condition.

Or consider the parasites called viruses. They are one of the major groups that microbiology studies under the microscope, hence "microorganisms." Others include protozoa, bacteria, actinomycetes, molds, and other fungi. The viruses are too small to carry their own metabolic machinery, so their method is that of the hijacker. Their own genetic material moves in and takes over the enzyme machinery of the normal cell, or of a bacterium for that matter. The victim cell goes on reproducing, but not according to its own genetic code. It is being forced to reproduce virus material. This, of course, could explain some of the outlaw growths called cancer, each type according to its own virus.

Thus the ubiquitous enzymes offer a way to unwrap a single package containing riddles of life, reproduction, and disease; and, as G. D. Novelli, of Oak Ridge National Laboratory, puts it: "They open absolutely unlimited horizons in biochemistry." This also shows the pioneering importance of the step taken by the United States Public Health Service when it established at Tufts University the nation's first center for supplying the many special natural enzymes needed by basic researchers. Meanwhile, it hopes to synthesize enzymes. This cannot be easy.

True, protein chemists now string together amino acids routinely and often easily. One acid donates a hydrogen atom and the second donates a hydrogen and oxygen to give an H_2O molecule of water. At the bonds left open the remainder of each acid joins to form a peptide "linkage." Doing this repeatedly builds a polypeptide chain complete with its side chains—a primitive form of protein. But important proteins bring complications. The triumphant synthesis of insulin, announced by the University of Pittsburgh in 1964, required two chains linked by two bridges of sulfur atoms. Even this, claimed to be history's first laboratory synthesis of an important naturally occurring protein, concerns a relatively small molecule. There are twenty different kinds of common amino acids. And each kind can occupy a position anywhere along the chain. Which kinds are in the molecule, and where, determine the nature of the protein. And when hundreds of amino acids comprise the macromolecule, the combinations possible with twenty variables become astronomical. Worse, not all proteins are simple chain arrangements. Most—including all the enzymes—are globular. Their chains are coiled or folded in bewildering three-dimensional configurations. Evidence from X-ray diffraction is that these proteins resemble a badly tangled rope. The hemoglobin molecule, for instance, is deduced to be 574 amino acid units assembled in four strangely coiled chains, each enfolding one of the vital iron-containing groups of atoms.

Moreover, they are life chemicals that cannot stand rough treatment. Even mild heat affects them. In industry, a chemical factory can use high pressure, heat, and other violence to speed a reaction. But heat solidifies ("denatures") the protein in the white of an egg, and it destroys enzymes. This is sometimes beneficial; with frozen foods, for example. The first company to freeze peas was chagrined when they developed a foul odor and flavor, even in storage at zero temperature. The trouble was traced to enzyme action. The cure was scalding the vegetables before freezing them.

However, this is cookery, it does little to explain enzymes. Precisely how do they work? Science is convinced that the beginning of the answer lies in the specialization of each enzyme—its handling only one type of chemical, called its substrate. This introduces the most alluring field of today's chemistry, the relation of structure to function. For one thing, research is probing how the structure of a molecule allows it to associate with a molecule of a different kind. Formerly, these combinations were called "complexes" and bypassed as too difficult to understand. Today, chemistry has explaining concepts. In one, a large molecule is pictured as having a cavity of some sort that gives a resting place for a passenger molecule. Another concept is of the molecule that folds over the substrate. These comparisons with a bosom lead to the "lock and key" theory for understanding the specificity of an enzyme. The essential difference between two enzymes is the difference between their strings of amino acids; i.e., the length of the lineup and the arrangement of the units. Each kind of amino acid, in turn, differs in its own side chain. Some of these chemical groups are long, some short. They vary in chemical composition and electrical charge. Consequently, the surface of each enzyme provides its own pattern of an electrically suitable opening here and projection there. Such are thought to be enzyme "locks" into which substrate "keys" must fit before the enzyme can do its subtle work.

But locks can be tampered with. Like any other catalyst, an enzyme is poisoned—deactivated—when an interloper molecule is accepted at the so-called "active site" where the genuine substrate should go. When nerve gas does this, the enzyme cholinesterase no longer can function as a circuit-breaker for nerve electricity and the nervous system goes into convulsions. Similarly, but beneficially, sulfa drugs poison the enzyme machinery of hostile bacteria.

These come under the heading of environmental interference. But what of "inborn errors of metabolism"? In an enzyme of perhaps several hundred amino acids an important one may be chemically wrong, or lacking. The abnormality can be beneficial: mutated corn lost its ability to convert starch into sugar and man thereby discovered sweetcorn. But a sugar-metabolism abnormality can also be grievous: "Before you are born, you are prenatal; before you are diabetic, you are prediabetic." Many such gene-and-enzyme causes of physical and mental defects have already been discovered; undoubtedly there are many more.

One obvious attack upon the problem is the pill approach—to

synthesize the right enzyme somehow (Nobelist Pauling: "The only thing we lack to make an enzyme is the money"), and then incorporate it into the metabolism somehow. Another, more drastic and challenging, would be with the "genetic surgery" that life scientists discuss increasingly as a result of their successes with DNA. This would go deeper into heredity and change the genetic code. It would cause the cell to accept a section of a natural or perhaps synthetic molecule of DNA from elsewhere in place of a defective one, thereby bringing "the desired change at the right point in the right original chromosome." Nobody knows where this ambitious hope will lead scientifically, or socially. Less controversial and more immediately useful would be inspired research into the basic enzyme mysteries. While reducing abysmal ignorance about our bodies, it would likely produce more palliatives like the hormone insulin, which does not cure but does extend the useful life of diabetics.

Hormones

He was a popular physician, a specialist in internal medicine. Also, he had been testing a certain hormone treatment for many years as director of a clinical research program. He was enthusiastic over the results.

"No," he conceded, "I don't know definitely how it works in the body but I prescribe it. Just as I use such other crutches as aspirin and vitamins—we don't know how they work either. Take my own family, for example. My parents and grandparents were metabolic wrecks at the age of fifty. So I take the hormone myself and have been giving it to my children since they were a year old—why wait for degeneration before starting medication?"

Here was a pointed example of the difference in medical research between the basic and the clinical. Both have their usefulness. The one is dissatisfied until it knows the whys and hows of disease. The other, responsive to the needs of doctor and patient, wants relief quickly. And drug companies, of course, are eager to supply it.

In the pharmacopoeia of today, the hormones are the most alluring of the body's maintenance chemicals. The body makes its own, but some, like cortisone for the arthritis sufferer, can now be synthesized;

and industry is in hot pursuit of more such additives. The vitamins once had this glamour but are now available anywhere in 3-a-day and 5-in-1 pills. The enzymes are more basic but still too inscrutable. In contrast, the hormones are double-acting: they lure both the basic researcher and pill-maker. Nor is their glamour lessened by the sexy fact that many of them concern maleness and femaleness, beauty treatments, virility, and contraception too when, as in "the Pill," they produce a simulated pregnancy, thereby making actual conception impossible.

Truly wondrous is the potency of these regulators. In deficiency or excess, the thyroid hormones account for the difference between a torpid imbecile and high-keyed executive; likewise, HGH, the "growth hormone," makes the difference between circus dwarf and circus giant. With such potency goes a warning, of course, when hormones leave the research laboratory. The path of the pill-maker is strewn with possible side-effects. Medication with sex hormones can produce effeminate men and bearded ladies. Even the protein type of hormone called insulin, the effective metabolic drug for diabetics, must be in a three-way balance with sugar and exercise, lest there be convulsions followed by death.

And even the action of insulin, the best-known and longest-investigated of the hormones, remains a blank mystery—even now that it has been synthesized. Charles H. Best, the Canadian who co-discovered nature's insulin in 1921, recalls that "we were ignorant of the complexity of the situation then. Diabetes appeared to be a rather simple, straightforward disorder." Four decades later he was still researching eight possible basic causes for the sugar-insulin imbalance.

This much we know. Without sufficient vitamins the body is dangerously ill-fed. Without enzymes the biochemical reactions slow to a standstill. Without hormones the body loses its chemical sense of balance. These regulators keep inventory, decide when something is needed, send orders to the cells to produce more, order production to cease. They have been called masters of the living chemical plant. It is more realistic to call them monitors or simply warehouse clerks that the evolving body acquired as the number and interrelationships of its chemical reactions increased. This is figurative language but the best we can do until hormone chemistry fills in the broad picture with convincing facts. It is trying to do so, to the extent that the enthusiasm for quick cures will allow.

The broad picture starts with the body's glands. By definition a gland's function is to manufacture a chemical needed elsewhere in the body. All known hormones are produced by glands. But unlike salivary glands and others that provide their own transport for their secretions, the hormone glands are ductless. Their secretion seeps into the bloodstream, which then carries on, dropping off specific hormones where needed.

Physiology has discovered the important hormone-makers and, with its work eased by radioactive tracers, has been filling in the chart with the effects produced by their secretions. Meanwhile, biochemists tediously solve derivations and molecular structures. In brief, all known sex hormones have turned out to be fatlike substances called steroids; so is cortisone. The body's source of steroids is from its supply of complex alcohols called sterols, of which the principal member is well-known cholesterol: much used by the body, much abused by man, imperatively needed in moderation, a troublemaker when faulty metabolism deposits it in the form of gallstones or, of course, in the arteries.

But not all hormones are steroids. Others are protein, or proteinlike. Insulin, for example, is an assembly of our familiar amino acids. But the thyroid gland's thyroxine is a not-quite-protein. It is just one amino acid molecule, not a chain of them. However, like all amino acids except one—glycine, the simplest—it does have its own side-chain. And it is the side-chain that accounts for the difference in function. In thyroxine the side-chain adds up to twenty-eight atoms, including four of iodine. Inasmuch as iodine is a rarity in the body, those four atoms are the outstanding characteristic of this metabolism-regulator. How they work we do not know but it is an old story that iodine deficiency in the diet leads to the thyroid disorder called goiter, as well as a sluggish body if the thyroid is underactive, and a jittery body if the thyroid is overactive.

What, then, about the hormone glands themselves?

Elevated high in the body, protected by the skull and hanging just below the center of the brain, is one the size of a pea. Its location hints that the brain controls it somehow; its work indicates that it is the master gland. For this is the busy pituitary, whose front half secretes not only HGH (human growth hormone) but a half-dozen others at latest count. Among them are regulators whose job is to regulate other regulators. Alone or in combination they do such things as control output of sex hormones by the gonads; of thyroxine by the thyroid; of the abdomen's tiny adrenal glands which, among other duties, produce adrenalin, the emergency hormone that triggers a surge of energy for "flight or fight," when the brain calls for either. In sum, the pituitary is guessed to be a master console that receives messages via the bloodstream and nervous system and responds with the stimulators needed.

But whether controlling or itself controlled, any healthy hormone gland is best likened to a reliable adjuster that works on what engineering calls the feedback principle. A thermostat, turning the furnace on and off as needed, is such an adjuster. The insulin-sugar equilibrium is a familiar example of biological feedback. The popular theory is that when the concentration of glucose sugar in the bloodstream goes too high, the pancreas receives a message somehow to send in more insulin until the sugar level is reduced. When sugar is too low, a healthy pancreas responds by shutting down on insulin production.

The extent to which the brain operates the pituitary console, and exactly how the messages are translated into action, remain for fresh eager minds to discover. Nevertheless, knowledge about hormones has come far since the days when science was intrigued by the speed with which adrenalin from the adrenal glands responds to the body's energy needs, and guessed that this may be why the tiger's adrenals weigh three times as much as his thyroid while man's adrenals weigh only half as much as his thyroid. Eventually came World War II and its catalyzing rumors about Nazi radar and Nazi nucleonics—and also about Nazi airmen receiving an energizing extract from the adrenals. This spurred the hunt by the Mayo Foundation and Merck & Company that discovered cortisone in one of the two adrenal glands and later found that the pituitary's protein hormone called ACTH, which stimulated the adrenals, was as useful as cortisone for giving temporary relief to sufferers from rheumatoid arthritis and kindred miseries. Later, chemists synthesized derivatives that gave fewer undesirable and sometimes dangerous side-effects than cortisone.

This was practical-plus-pure research. Its main goal was new drugs; it also happened to develop today's picture of the body's hormone activity. As another byproduct ("hormone" comes from a Greek word meaning "rouse to activity"), the NIH added its Institute of Arthritis and Metabolic Diseases. And at some other important centers today, notably the University of California, some basic research accompanies the hunt for drugs.

There, Chinese-born Choh Hao Li has such trophies as these after a quarter-century of trail-blazing lab work: today's concept of the pituitary as the master gland; his isolation of its growth hormone; a structural picture of its ACTH molecule, a straight-chain assembly of 39 amino acids; the claim that his synthetic product, though containing only 19 of the acids, can do anything for the body that nature's complete 39-unit hormone does.

This assertion has produced one of the quiet controversies that stimulate useful research. The University of Pittsburgh, too, has a noted synthesizer, Swiss-born Klaus Hofmann. Doubting Li's method, he offered his own rival to nature's ACTH. But his version is a 23-unit molecule—four more amino acids than Li used. While the two labs jousted over which version is the "active core" of ACTH, one of Li's former students went ahead to synthesize the entire ACTH molecule. Li had not bothered to try. More alluring was the possibility of a better drug, and new questions intrigued him. Why would nature assemble 39 amino acids to do what 19, or even 23, can do? The rest of nature's molecule cannot be useless. It varies slightly from animal to animal. Why? And might the difference explain side-effects when animal ACTH is administered to humans?

Meanwhile, Li was pushing ahead with ACTH's companion, HGH, the growth hormone. "It's slow," he conceded. "Here I face a formidable chain of 256 amino acids. I have identified only the first six and the last three." Furthermore, animals cannot supply the specific hormone needed for research. It can be had only from humans—but a thousand pituitaries give only a gram of extract. And for the minuscule supply, Li's research must compete with clinical research. "But why develop clinical uses if the drug will be relatively unobtainable?" said Li. "It must be synthesized. And much of it is needed to learn how to synthesize it." He sighed. "I am a patient man when I assemble amino acids. But really I am impatient.

I wish for more of the hormone to work with." Thus does Li chide those more impatient than he, though the goal is the same. And the social responsibilities too. "The hormone has marvelous potential," said Li. "With it a dwarf girl begins to grow one inch per month."

Antibiotics

The antibiotics are in truth wonder drugs. Truly dazzling is the record of their cures. So is the record of their climb to fortune. Led by penicillin and streptomycin, in only twenty years they were selling to Americans at the rate of a billion dollars' worth a year. Though their price was cut somewhat by antimonopoly action at home and competition from aboard, they remain a star performer of the pharmaceuticals industry, along with their rivals, the so-called "mood drugs," the fast-growing hormones, and, of course, the faithful vitamins.

Scientifically, two counteractions face the antibiotics. One is nature's resistance. The wonder drugs must now struggle with wonder bugs. Bacteria have been fighting back, developing new varieties against which an antibiotic of yesteryear is helpless and needs repeated reinforcing.

The other is from human resistance. Inasmuch as antibiotics are avowed poisons—poisonous to bacteria—the warnings grow louder against using them so promiscuously. In varying degrees, all of them have direct side-effects. And, indirectly, they interfere with normal bodily functions. But warnings against the inpour of antibiotics have gone mainly to physicians, of whom far too many prescribe far too much antibiotic treatment. It may need a dramatic tragedy, followed by public uproar such as followed the thalidomide tragedies and careless use of pesticides, to translate the warnings into harsh action.

This would be a pity. The blast from a revival meeting against antibiotics would scorch the scientist along with the seller. Excessive regulations could kill off the discovery of another penicillin. More important than discovering another specific drug, however, is biology's bigger need: more knowledge about life processes. The antibiotics do thus and so, but we know next to nothing about how they do it. Yet, oddly, they have taught us much.

For one thing, they are reminders of earthly realities. These products of feculent, fecund earth do not spill from a dainty package. As drugs they do come in fastidious, purified form. But in its search for them among thousands of candidates, science had to rummage in barnyard soil and other such richness free of artificial fertilizer.

This back-to-nature movement fits into a vast ecology, a biological balance in which microorganisms prey upon or live parasitically with each other—living, procreating, then decaying to give nature room for further experiments with species. The human's intestinal tract teems with various bacteria, harmless if they do not escape into the bloodstream or abdominal cavity. The guess is that this is symbiosis: they live on undigested foods; in return they give such necessities as vitamins.

But there are less kindly microorganisms. Accordingly, the healthy body reacts with self-produced guardians in the blood, notably white corpuscles that devour bacteria, and with other agents more suitable against smaller invaders, the viruses. One agent is the protein called interferon, with which the invaded cell somehow blocks reproduction of the virus. The existence of this puzzling chemical has been known a long time. Only recently has research begun looking into it again. Better known are the antibodies, proteins which in some fashion immunize us against special germs as well as viruses by combining with them somehow.

The body's production of antibodies can, of course, be stimulated by vaccines. The need for such outside help varies. If the body hasn't met enough of a virus, and consequently hasn't been challenged to produce the specific antibody, it can be conquered by a mass invasion of that virus. This sheds more light on the mixed blessings of cleanliness. As far back as 1947, when Rockefeller Institute's famed Tom Rivers was still seeking a vaccine against poliomyelitis, he pointed out that sanitary conditions in backward nations were such that the population had encountered enough polio to produce antibodies and strike a truce with the virus; whereas in America, he mourned, "the cleaner our country becomes, the more polio cases we have." At any rate, the antibody tactic, with or without help from vaccines, would be wonderful if it worked against all varieties of invaders. It does not. Hence the wonder-drug antibiotics, a weapon primarily against bacteria.

Some researchers contend that plants produce their own defensive antibiotics. At any rate, man's body does not. For them he borrows from the soil's ecological system. A gram of rich earth may contain as many microbes as there are humans on earth. Some work together in a mutual aid system. Others compete for existence. Among the latter are humble microorganisms, popularly called bacteria and molds, that exude a substance poisonous to competitors. The spidery typhoid germ, for instance, thrives lustily in raw sewage until the sewage mixes with soil. There it quickly succumbs. How the exudations work, and how to synthesize them to any important extent, we do not know. The best guess is that they interfere somehow with the metabolic enzymes of the victim bacteria. The best way to get them is to hunt them down, then extract them in batch quantities from microorganisms grown in captivity.

Penicillin has remained king of antibiotics, though it led to a host of rivals. It is a classic example not only of the kind of accidental discovery called serendipity but of how we may need effective communication, and even war, before the discovery bears fruit.

The usual story overlooks Louis Pasteur: his puzzling over the fact that although infected men and animals deposit germs in the soil, it contains so few of the germs . . . his discovery in 1877 that bacteria from the air had wiped out a colony of deadly anthrax germs he was growing . . . his busyness with other projects but prediction that the antagonism of one microbe species for another could benefit man some day. In 1899, the first such drug, produced by the blue-pus bacillus, was found helpful against diphtheria. It suffered from wonder-drug claims and was abandoned. But the dream persisted. In America, in the 1920s, bacteriologist Paul de Kruif, whom Rockefeller Institute fired after he wrote *Our Medicine Men*, provided the scientific material for novelist Sinclair Lewis's *Arrowsmith*. Here, you are growing some bacteria in a dish. You leave the dish on the lab windowsill. Returning later, you find that the "soup" has turned clear. Its germs have been killed and devoured by something, a kind of mold. That mold supplies your drug for killing bacteria when you want to. Lewis called his germ-killer "phage" (using the short form of *bacteriophage*). In 1928, three years after Lewis's "postulation" and fifty-one after Pasteur's prediction, the English bacteriologist Alexander Fleming accidentally re-enacted the Lewis version, windowsill and all. His mold was a type of penicillium. He called its exudate penicillin. Its total destruction of staphylococci—probably the most universal germ—was sensational. But he could not extract it from the broth, and his unsuccessful paper on the subject led only to a short period of uninspired research by others. However, he did keep a culture of his mold alive.

Then came the war and its need for medicines. Teams of workers isolated the penicillin and rushed triumphant trials on human patients. And, as with her radar, England sent the Fleming mold over to America for large-scale R & D. One of our federal agricultural labs tried various other strains of the same mold and, from one that grew on a cantaloupe, extracted one hundred times the amount of penicillin that Fleming got from his fungus growing on bread, on cheese, and in the soil. The rest is history. Penicillin went on to destroy not only blood-poisoning staphylococci but venereal disease and much else. And America's mass-production method of growing the mold in deep tanks grew into our antibiotics industry.

The next of the major antibiotics is an all-American success story. "If anybody dies of TB today," Selman Waksman said, "though the medical people and societies for the eradication of TB won't like my saying so, it's the fault of the physician." Back in 1915, while a graduate student at Rutgers, he had studied some of the twisted fungus-like microorganisms called actinomycetes. Penicillin's success sent him back to them, with the aid of an initial $1500 research grant from Merck & Company. His first product, in 1940, was devastatingly toxic. George Merck was a chemist, not a microbiologist. When the drug killed ten thousand experimental animals, he exploded, "Either get those bugs to work or get them out of my plant." There was even thought of trying actinomycin as a rat poison.

Three years later, after trying other candidates, Waksman produced streptomycin from a strain he found growing both in a heavily manured field and in the throat of a chicken. Instead of killing, this one cured, and its dirt-to-riches saga began.

Other antibiotics followed, at Rutgers and elsewhere. Today, however, the bloom has gone off the field. Years pass without the discovery of a really important new antibiotic. Also, patents do expire —for streptomycin the year was 1965. This is why the Rutgers foundation set up to administer royalties has, like others of the type, squirreled away a "rainy-day fund." It has also used profits to set up the lab building for Waksman's people, and the hunt goes on. For more money-makers, of course ("How could I leave a field of diamonds?" said Waksman). But also for knowledge.

An example is Waksman's first antibiotic, the deadly actinomycin. It seems to work against some cancers, and dozens of strains have been explored to find out why, as well as to reduce the toxicity. Meanwhile, Waksman has dug deeper. He said his favorite problem is this: antibiotics work—but why does his beloved *Streptomyces griseus* devote one-third of its cellular activity to producing streptomycin? Why so much? For what purpose? Then, too, it turns out that an antibiotic can be victim as well as destroyer. An example is the microbe that eats streptomycin, thrives and multiplies on the diet, excreting urea and a vitamin-like substance.

Such are problems facing research. It now needs something more basic than Fleming's accidental discovery and the hit-or-miss technique that added new wonder drugs. Perhaps new seed will come from somebody who remembers that science specializes but nature works ecologically. Besides disagreeing with our concepts of antiseptic elegance, and bizarre hopes to produce germ-free man, nature does not recognize the cataloguing we do in attempts to understand.

. . . We set up a class called enzymes. Yeast is a notable enzyme-producer, but another fungus, penicillium, produces the leading antibiotic. Where, then, does enzyme chemistry end and antibiotic chemistry begin?

. . . We set up a class called vitamins. Yet vitamin D can also be classed as a hormone because of how the body uses and manufactures it. Furthermore, microorganisms produce not only antibiotics but B vitamins.

. . . We think of antibiotics as bacteria-killers. Yet research has raised hopes of using them against some viruses too.

. . . To such interplay, add this challenging example. We have growth vitamins, growth hormones, growth enzymes—and the same antibiotic that kills germs happens also to be a growth antibiotic. Here was another discovery that upset the cult of cleanliness. Modern farming is mechanized and conscious of consumer delicacies. It doesn't like hogs and hens rooting in dung piles. Cows go into stainless-steel milking parlors, and gutter cleaners hurry manure away as if it were a sexy secret. But the pampered livestock seem to need something besides a grain-and-vegetable diet. Accordingly, the rations were beefed up with APF—the puzzling "Animal Protein Factor" supplied by meat scraps and ground fish. Then it was found produced by bacteria in henhouse compost. Meanwhile vitamin B_{12} was discovered. Then the vitamin was found to be an ingredient of magical APF. But meanwhile, producers of antibiotics found this vitamin right in their vats, in the leftover mash. Furthermore, the mash caused faster growth than did the pure vitamin. Was this because of antibiotics in the mash? Soon enough someone had the bright idea of trying the antibiotics themselves as a food supplement. It worked, and meat-producers were jubilant. Press agents quickly noted that minute quantities of penicillin, aureomycin, and the like would mean two hundred more pork chops and five more chickens per American family per year. So antibiotics, too, were a growth factor. Fascinating, but also riddling. Do they poison harmful bacteria in the animal's digestive tract? Or do they serve as some new kind of vitamin, or hormone, or enzyme? At any rate, here was another boost for the farmer and the antibiotics industry. The drugs are now a common feed supplement. The animals, destined for slaughter anyway, do not complain.

For humans, however, the situation is different. Two serious challenges face the antibiotics.

One is the uprising by their intended victims. The drugs were still glisteny new when science began noticing that bacteria were becoming resistant to them. How could this be? The answer was cheerless. A successful antibiotic is effective against a target. It exterminates the normal bacteria it is intended for. But, as elsewhere in life, there are always mutations. For these different targets, the antibiotic must likewise be different. Furthermore, with competition destroyed by destroying the normal target bacteria, the mutant strains can flourish mightily.

This is why, despite Waksman's pride in his streptomycin, tuberculosis has been noticeably on the increase. (The first vaccines against influenza have faced the same trouble, though here it is viruses rather than bacteria that are agile in developing resistant strains.) As a result of the bacterial defense tactic, research is forced to continue hunting newer and newer antibiotics, and combinations of them.

This is why René Dubos, who went on from graduate work under Waksman to his own notable research, complains: "Nature always strikes back. It takes all the running we can do to remain in the same place."

The other challenge to antibiotics results from prescribing too many, too much, for too many people. Here, too, the complaints started when the drugs were still new. Today, the warnings to immoderate drug companies and immoderate physicians are louder. They are accused of ignoring side-effects. These can be direct— digestive ailments, birth defects, the killing of useful bacteria in the body. Indirect effects can be as harmful, or more so.

The antibiotic is a guardian only as long as it is being administered. When discontinued, it leaves the patient without sufficient natural immunity against new invaders. Meanwhile, as we have seen, promiscuous treatment gives mutant strains of bacteria their chance to increase; then, when the drug is critically needed, it is powerless against the virulent new targets. This explains why, in hospitals that drench patients with antibiotics, previously rare types of staphylococcus have erupted into "hospital staph." But that isn't all. The body may develop a kind of allergy to the drug. Cornell's noted pharmacologist, Walter Modell, puts it bluntly: "There have been many deaths directly due to sensitivity to penicillin—sensitivity acquired through needless exposure. In the course of a lifetime, 10 per cent of the population may, through contact with foods, drugs, cosmetics or other substances that contain penicillin or other antibiotic, become sensitized to it and unable to use it safely thereafter."

Yet a revival meeting against chemotherapy would be senseless. The point in all this is that antibiotics are very useful drugs, but common sense and research alike insist that they are two-edged weapons that must be used intelligently, with moderation. How to enforce this is another of the problems facing the massive medical establishment.

Common sense also reminds us that drugging the human reactor does no more than provide a crutch. Only by unriddling the body's secrets can useful science hope to help man live more healthily—and longer.

VII: *Toward Immortality?*

It is more obvious than ever before that our past has been prelude. Man has always refused to be another of Darwin's turtles dragging itself up a Galápagos beach to fulfill a manifest, weary destiny, but the ape's restless cousin is no longer merely testing the bars of his cage. He is breaking out to other planets. Equally adventurous, at least as important, and certainly more personal, he is rebelling against limitations of the genes he inherited.

With mutation experiments, with artificial insemination, with transplanting parts of the body, with daring manipulation of the heart that has stopped dead, with even more audacious attempts to substitute one gene for another, he hopes to escape the risks of random mating and postpone his appointment with death.

This rebel has long heard majestic organs, and siren calls too, urging his escape. Now, the bars of his cage are responding to his scientific twisting. What will happen to his weaknesses, and to his verities? To escape being the imprisoned ape, must he necessarily become that supposedly efficient organism, the ant—the automaton? And can we entirely banish the mystical? On a pinnacle was Albert Einstein. Yet all that he found confirmed his mysticism: "It is enough for me to reflect upon the marvelous structure of the universe which we can dimly perceive, and to try humbly to comprehend even an infinitesimal part of the intelligence manifested in nature." This is an intelligent man's humility. It neither challenges nor defends conventional theology.

About such matters, biology is too busy to philosophize. Fortified by the ingenious research methods of today's chemistry and physics, it is pursuing the discovery that leads to yet another discovery. This is especially true of efforts to master the genetic code. To the field that layman and scientist label sex in their relaxed moments has come the exciting specialty known as molecular biology. The words "gene" and "chromosome" remain, but mainly in association with the glamorous giant molecule of heredity called DNA (deoxyribonucleic acid) and its cooperator, RNA (ribonucleic acid).

As might be expected, there are predictions of tailor-made genetic material. The first experimental steps have been taken; the prospects for something practical are still vague. Furthermore, the DNA specialists are not so drug-minded as those who seek hormones and antibiotics. Here is more pursuit of knowledge for its own sake. Yet the DNA people do realize where they are heading. For all we know, this may follow the nuclear-energy pattern. Investigation of the atom brought hopes of tapping the power within its nucleus. Nobody knew precisely how it would be done. In fact, even in the late 1930s, England's great Sir Ernest Rutherford, pioneer in nuclear physics, still ridiculed the idea that man would ever tap this power. However, he had not anticipated a combination of two things. One was the announcement in 1939 that the uranium atom had been split. The other was America's vast A-bomb program in the coming war, which carried on what seed knowledge had started.

This is hindsight, of course. It does not answer when genetic manipulation will come. Meanwhile, there are indications of more foresight—the warnings by some leading biologists that it is time to think of the political and social problems that would result. Suffice to say for the present that the first steps in understanding and manipulating DNA and RNA have not yet brought them to the "genetic-surgery" stage. The work is still exploration, a paradigm of basic research in the modern manner: rich in budgets, thronging with incompetents, but also producing enough genuine research and healthy rivalry to show fascinating progress.

The excitement is so infectious that a college girl, catching it, writes home that she is no longer determined to become an actress. Instead: "I'd like to be a cytologist. I don't know whether I have the brains to be a cytologist but cells fascinate me. The boy I want to marry is working in cancer research but that is not why I want to be a cytologist. It is just something that fascinates me."

Possibly she has not heard of her fellow American, J. D. Watson. But cancer is part of the DNA story, and we can guess that somewhere, perhaps from the boy friend, she has been thrilled by what researchers like Watson are doing with the nucleic acids.

Unlike the young lady, Watson was a prodigy, a radio "Quiz Kid" who went on to college at fifteen. Ten years later, in 1953, he was one of the three men who composed our idea of the DNA molecule— the picturesque, mammoth assembly of atoms called a double helix by geometers, and the molecule of racial memory by geneticists.

As in the girl, though on a different plane, we detect in Watson the restless need for an outlet. It is revealed in the acceptance lecture he delivered in 1962 when he shared a Nobel Prize. Discontented with himself and the "classical" biology he was offered at Indiana University and later in postdoctoral work in Denmark, he had moved on, at twenty-three, to Cambridge, in England:

"I arrived in the fall of 1951. . . . I was becoming frustrated with phage experiments and wanted to learn more about the actual structures of the molecules which the geneticists talked about so passionately. . . . With Francis Crick to talk to, my fate was sealed. For we quickly discovered that we thought the same way. The center of biology was the gene and its control of cellular metabolism. The main challenge was to understand gene replication and the way in which genes control protein synthesis. . . .

"During the next eighteen months, until the double-helical structure became elucidated . . . we often worried that the correct structure might be dull—that is, that it would suggest absolutely nothing. . . . The finding of the double helix brought us not only joy but great relief. It was unbelievably interesting and immediately allowed us to make a serious proposal for the mechanism of gene duplication. Furthermore, this replication involved thoroughly conventional chemical forces. . . ."

In other words, what nature does with heredity, man can hope eventually to do also and even carry farther. He has synthesized diamonds and transmuted elements. Why not be bolder still? Hence the compulsive curiosity of molecular biology. Hence its attraction for so many outsiders (for instance, Robert Glaser, the Nobel physicist, and Linus Pauling, the Nobel chemist) that old-line biologists feel like picketing them with "Go Home" signs.

But the interdisciplinary attraction is two-way. To join the fun, biologist Watson migrated· to Cambridge, where he could work at the famed Cavendish Laboratory. Its world-wide reputation was in physics. Under Rutherford's leadership its neat combination of experiment and theory had pioneered the modern concept of the atom; then it had led in smashing that atom and transmuting one kind of atom to another—all this in the Rutherford tradition: the small, deft, imaginative experiment rather than the blockbuster. Then came the war, and America's transmutation of theory into the hardware of radar and A-bombs. After the war, America went deeper into nuclear physics with giant experimental machines that British science couldn't hope to match. So W. L. Bragg, then director of Cavendish and himself the Nobelist son of a Nobelist father, charted a radically new future in a hybrid field—physics crossed with biology. Here, he felt, England might again lead the world, and in the Rutherford tradition. The idea caught on with bright young men. At such centers as Cavendish and King's College, London, "biophysics" units were set up under such leaders as J. T. Randall, codiscoverer of radar's cavity magnetron, and the new adventure was under way. From working on the atomic code, though England didn't fully realize it yet, she was switching to the genetic code.

Again, as with America's young Watson, it is enlightening to hear in his own words the motivation of young British physicist M. H. F. Wilkins. The following is from the acceptance lecture he gave when he, Watson, and Crick became Nobelists:

". . . During the war I took part in making the atomic bomb. When the war was ending, I, like many others, cast around for a new field. Partly on account of the bomb, I had lost some interest in physics. I was therefore very much interested when I read Erwin Schrödinger's book *What Is Life?* and was struck by the concept of a highly complex molecular structure which controlled living processes. Research on such matters seemed more ambitious than solid-state physics. At that time many leading physicists . . . believed that physics would contribute significantly to biology; their advice encouraged me to move into biology. . . .

"Bill Seeds and I studied DNA, proteins, tobacco mosaic virus, vitamin B_{12} and so on. While examining DNA . . . I saw in the polarizing microscope extremely uniform fibers. . . . I found that they had been produced unwittingly while I was manipulating DNA gel. Each time that I touched the gel with a glass rod and removed the rod, a thin and almost invisible fiber of DNA was drawn out like a filament of spider's web. The perfection and uniformity of the fibers suggested that the molecules in them were regularly arranged. I immediately thought the fibers might be excellent objects to study by X-ray diffraction analysis. I took them to Raymond Gosling, who had our only X-ray equipment (made from war-surplus radiography parts). . . ."

So now, in the late 1940s, Wilkins concentrated on DNA's thin, very long, and strangely flexible molecule. His work performed no miracles. But it was painstaking. And it was opportune. Let us see why.

The Heredity Idea

. . . The time was ripe. Science was pondering one of the meanings of Hiroshima. The A-bomb not only produced stupendously more shock and blast and searing heat than a conventional bomb. These effects accounted for 85 per cent of the nuclear variety's energy. The rest was nuclear radiation, new in war. Some came within a minute or so after the explosion. Most was "residual radiation" produced almost entirely by radioactive atoms in the far-wandering debris called fallout. In this debris is notorious strontium-90, a product that can eventually find its way into the body skeleton and give such effects as bone cancer and leukemia. Its radiation is damaging mainly to the existing body. Other such isotopes, however, like cesium-137 and carbon-14, spread farther in the body and are the ones blamed for irradiating the sex glands. These cause mutations of genes in the female's egg cell and male's sperm. Mutations, of course, were not a new phenomenon. In his evolutionary history, man's genes have been subjected to many alterations. Some are "spontaneous"—mistakes made in the body's own chemistry. Others are caused by radiation: either the natural kind emitted by radioactive rock in the earth or arriving from outer space; or the manmade kind from fallout, X-ray equipment, and the like. Some mutations are beneficial, but Nobelist

Hermann Muller, dean of American geneticists, estimates that over 99 per cent are detrimental or even lethal. In sum, nuclear bombing and nuclear testing had introduced a new hazard to the security of the genes. Science was therefore acutely interested after the war in the makeup of the genes and reasons for their vulnerability.

... The time was ripe. DNA had been little more than another curiosity for many years, although biochemistry had accumulated a helter-skelter set of data about its habits and its molecule. Even finding it only in the nucleus of an organism's cells, localized in the cell's chromosomes—which, of course, carry the mysterious genes— caused no commotion. The rodlike chromosomes are composed of protein as well as DNA, and science had long been awed by the difficult proteins. So in its theorizing about heredity it pictured the genetic information carried by a combination of protein and DNA, with protein being the more important component of the so-called "nucleoprotein"; or perhaps by the protein alone. But much more was known now about proteins. And now, too, came this X-ray opportunity to probe the DNA molecule.

... It was 1946 and the time was also overdue. In that year, scientists found time to read and understand some research done in 1944, based upon an accidental discovery in 1928. This was the "transformation principle." To demonstrate it, you transfer pure DNA from one strain of germ into the cells of a different strain. For example, DNA from bacteria (a), a virulent type, into bacteria (b), its harmless relative. Not only does Type B now become virulent but its progeny turn out to be virulent too—they breed true to the new blueprint. The new DNA has taken control. In itself this is persuasive evidence that it isn't the chromosome's proteins or its nucleoproteins but its nucleic acid that does the work. It also indicates that when we speak of our genes we somehow mean the work of our DNA molecules. And if transformation, beneficial or otherwise, can be done with the DNA of plants, animals, and humans, the implications are obvious. They explain why science is already making its first fumbling experiments to substitute different instructions for the ones issued by defective human DNA.

At present, however, let us focus on truly pregnant tests with small, uncomplaining microorganisms. Many transformation experiments and the fact that viruses transform cells of their victims in similar fashion, producing a sort of death by transfiguration, have persuaded science that DNA, or in some viruses its close relative RNA, is the self-replicating material that governs heredity.

Consequently, genes are now usually pictured as potent groups of atoms that make up a nucleic acid's molecule.

How does this fit classical biology's chromosome theory of inheritance? One thing known very well is the internal convulsion during mitosis, when a cell splits to produce two replicas. At each such replication, chromosomes floating in the viscous fluid of the cell nucleus become easily visible under the microscope, first as a mass of thin, writhing threads. Next they shorten and thicken into an assortment of stubby rods. Then they line up and split lengthwise, each of the resulting two sets becoming the chromosomes of two replica cells. Thus like begets exactly alike. The theory is that when each chromosome splits, so does the collection of invisible genes that it is carrying, presumably arranged like beads along a string. If each splitting cell has 46 chromosomes, as in humans, then each replica also has 46, each with its full complement of genes—a total for which estimates run up to a million.

This nicely fits the DNA concept. Just as a cell has a characteristic number of chromosomes per cell, each is known to have its characteristic quantity of DNA. Just as chromosomes double, the replicating cell synthesizes more DNA just before it splits: the amount doubles, half going to each replica. Of course, in the special kind of cell division called meiosis, which produces only sex cells, each cell ends with half the normal number of chromosomes, so that when sperm fertilizes egg the normal number is restored. But, with either sex cells or replicating cells, the chromosome-DNA-gene basis is the same; and in the new language the DNA molecule becomes the chemical equivalent usually of a number of genes.

Now consider an abnormality different from transformation. Suppose that one kind of DNA molecule is not substituted for another. Instead, it is altered in some way—by chemical means perhaps, or by radiation. This, too, changes the blueprint and we have what classical biology calls a mutation.

However, transformation and mutation are gross approaches to understanding and manipulating the life process. They are like the savage who chews chincona bark for his malaria but doesn't know why it works. How to explain the gene action of this molecule that seems to make the germ-plasm of the parent potentially immortal, that is found in all living cells but varied enough to prescribe whether an organism will be flea or fly, and what kind of fly? In nonmystical words, what is the distinctive structure of DNA's molecule?

The Genetic Code

The time was therefore ripe for biology to get better acquainted with chemistry and physics. It had been easy enough to find the five kinds of atoms in the DNA molecule. These were carbon, hydrogen, oxygen, nitrogen, and phosphorus, already known to be vital for life processes. Also, DNA was recognized as a polymer—a macromolecule built up by a repetition of smaller units. When chemistry was more naïve, polymers were accidents that dirtied the glassware. [Modern instruments had opened chemistry's eyes to their possibilities.] In manmade polyethylene, for instance, small molecules of sweet-smelling ethylene gas are linked over and over again, like a string of sausages, to produce the valuable plastic. And nature's proteins, as seen in the preceding chapter, follow the same idea. They are characteristic assortments of amino acids forming a long chain. Further, two or more chains may themselves be joined in a three-dimensional network, and it is only because of rules of the game that the result, perhaps a million atoms, is considered a molecule at all.

At any rate, DNA's atoms were believed to operate in the form of a 3-D polymer whose molecular weight might run into the millions. Specifically, these atoms were arranged in repetitive units called nucleotides. These, chemists could already build up, tear down, and manipulate. Each nucleotide was a chemical group composed of a special sugar called deoxyribose; a phosphate unit; and one of four varieties of nitrogen-carrying units called bases. Somewhere in the interplay of these units was the answer to DNA's *modus operandi*.

Finding the answer was the problem that researchers like Wilkins set for themselves. As we have seen, the British physicist was using the X-ray diffraction method to get photos indicating the structure of the molecule. The ultraviolet microscope had shown DNA's home to be in the nucleus of the cell, in the chromosomes. The electron microscope had peered deeper and established the size of the DNA molecule. The X-ray method, which, appropriately enough, had been born at the Cavendish Laboratory, was chosen to show how atoms of the 3-D molecule were packed together.

This technique is a roundabout way of seeing that depends on statistical analysis, inferences, and imagination. It works with materials that can be crystallized, like DNA, because in the lattice pattern of a crystal the atoms are regularly spaced, much as trees are in an apple orchard. From some directions, the orchard looks like chaos. From others, the straight rows reveal themselves. This is the human eye seeing with ordinary light. Now, direct a beam of X-rays at a crystal. The extremely short-wave rays are reflected and show on photographic film the pattern of what they struck. For instance, when the distance is already known between the planes in a crystal, along which atoms are spaced, the wavelength of X-rays can be calculated accurately. But the converse is also true. Already knowing the wavelength of his rays, the experimenter can deduce the distance between layers of atoms.

Wilkins did get sharp enough X-ray diffraction to go on and confirm a helical structure in which some component groups of atoms lay in planes perpendicular to the length of the threadlike molecule. He could also calculate how far apart these planes were stacked. But how did DNA work, how did it replicate itself? The experimenter needed help from theoreticians. He got it from his friends Watson and Crick. The latter, like Wilkins, had been a radar physicist.

Indirectly, at Caltech in America, chemist Pauling was contributing too. He had done much to explain the bonding of atoms. With Robert Corey he had recently suggested that when a polypeptide chain assumes the curled-up shape, this is because it has taken the spiral form of a helix held in that shape by its hydrogen bonds. And the Americans were trying to make the same idea work with the DNA molecule, which, though chemically different, might be an arrangement of intertwined chains. To do this, they were assembling model after model, with small balls representing component atoms.

Wilkins' friends did likewise. And in 1953, their effort paid with a DNA explanation that still dominates genetic thinking. It was literally a flash of insight. Pauling had been on the right track. But to agree with theory and his experience with proteins, he had lined up

DNA's nitrogen-carrying "base" components along the outside of the molecule, like side chains of a protein molecule. Crick and Watson suggested swinging the bases inside, like rungs of a ladder. In short, they turned Pauling's model inside-out.

The concept begins this way. Picture a very long rope ladder: two parallel sides and thousands of runglike steps linking them. This is the beginning, the basic pattern. Now imagine twisting the flexible ladder, twisting it like a ribbon so that one side winds around the other. This is the now-famed double helix. The twisting has compressed the long DNA molecule but the two sides and the steps remain attached where they were. Each side remains a long line of the repetitive sugar-and-phosphate units. Each step, too, has been unchanged. But these steps are not all the same to begin with.

Each, to be sure, is like a cross-chain made up of only two links—a pair of those chemical groups called bases. And each base is joined to the other, inside the ladder, by hydrogen bonds. But remember that there are four kinds of bases. They are the chemicals adenine, thymine, cytosine, and guanine (in RNA, uracil substitutes for thymine), abbreviated simply to A, T, C, and G, respectively.

The crux of the entire concept is that when two of them link to form a rung of the ladder their hydrogen bonding is such that, to fit inside the double helix, an A can join only a T and a C can join only a G. If the left half of the rung is an A, the right half must be a T. Similarly, a rung can be either C–G or G–C. But this gives only an inkling of the many ways that one DNA molecule may differ slightly from another. There is no mandatory arrangement of the sequence going up the ladder. The rungs vary. The one above an A–T may be another A–T, or a C–G, or a G–C. Or there may be three A–Ts before reaching a G–C, and so on. Now we begin to see how large is the number of variations possible in a single DNA molecule containing several hundred thousand such pairs. And one mathematical exercise estimates that genetic variations possible from DNA in a human cell's complement of chromosomes is vastly larger than the number of all atoms in the universe.

How does the genetic blueprinting work? First, how does DNA ensure the continuity of life; how does it reproduce in its own image?

Here, the concept goes into a template analogy. To reproduce, the relatively weak hydrogen bonds open and the twisted helix unzips somehow, then splits lengthwise. Now it is two half-molecules —two straight half-ladders, each with a long row of half-rungs. And now, presumably through enzymes that muster the needed materials from the cell's store of chemicals, each half synthesizes its missing half: a side plus the complementary base needed to complete each rung. Through this copying mechanism, each half becomes a whole, and each whole now retwists into the familiar double helix. Then again the splitting, copying, and so on, each cycle giving replicas exactly like each other and the original template. This, of course, is the chromosome-gene theory in new dress. The idea is that when a chromosome reproduces this means that its DNA molecules are reproducing, with each gene representing a section up the DNA ladder.

But what about DNA's other function? Besides replicating, it must transfer its genetic instructions elsewhere in the cell so that amino acids will be chosen and assembled to become the specific enzymes and other proteins prescribed for that specific organism.

Here, theory is hazy and is constantly being refined to jibe with bothersome facts. However, science is confident now that DNA uses intermediaries for protein synthesis, and Watson agrees with others that these include three classes of the other nucleic acid, RNA. As he puts it wryly, "The involvement of RNA is very much more complicated than was imagined in 1953." And enzymes move enigmatically all through the picture.

Then there is the challenge of the genetic code itself.

When DNA only reproduces itself the code is simple. For each rung of the ladder it need choose among only the four base chemicals. But how to designate among the twenty common amino acids, so that they can be strung together in the multitudinous ways needed to build the different proteins that build life's different organisms, and variations among them?

The best guesses so far follow a suggestion by nuclear physicist George Gamow, a brilliant wanderer into several fields of science. He remembered that the letters in our ordinary alphabet can build many thousands of words. And he pointed out simply that even DNA's four molecular letters (the A, T, C, and G, standing for the four bases) can give many choices when one uses combinations— words instead of single letters. For example, if DNA uses three letters at a time—three-rung sequences up the ladder—this would give 4 times 4 times 4, or 64 words in the code dictionary, more than enough to designate the amino acids.

Such a code can work. In the past few years researchers have used simple combinations of the bases to direct the construction of simple protein-like chains of amino acids. They have even started a code dictionary. But it, too, is primitive. Jubilant claims of breaking "the code of life" have simmered down to "cracking" it.

The Concept of Life

How deep is the crack? Consider the twin mysteries of life and death. Skirting theology, researchers say they have no evidence that the life process, though forbiddingly complex, is mystical. And they bolster their biochemical view by pointing to findings in a new field that can be called primordial chemistry.

Among its leaders is the University of California's Melvin Calvin. In 1961, he won the Nobel Prize for working out the cycle of photosynthesis, showing how green plants convert water, carbon dioxide, and sunlight into sugars and other complex energy compounds that maintain life on earth. Meanwhile, he was speculating on which originated first, plant or animal life. And that led him into experiments to see how the simplest life could have developed after natural changes in the earth's first environment of some five billion years ago.

Our atmosphere then probably had no free oxygen. A favored theory is that it consisted of free hydrogen and such other simple gaseous building blocks as water vapor (hydrogen and oxygen), ammonia (hydrogen and nitrogen), methane (hydrogen and carbon), and perhaps carbon dioxide (carbon and oxygen).

Calvin wondered what might have happened when such raw material received energy of some kind—from cosmic rays, or the earth's radioactivity, or ultraviolet light from the sun, or flashes of lightning. Did this build somewhat more complicated molecules? In his first try, in 1950, alpha particles from a cyclotron bombarded a primordial mixture of carbon dioxide, ammonia, and water. He got something in the way of more interesting molecules: formaldehyde and formic acid. They were not very complex but they were a beginning. Others, like Harold Urey, joined in the adventure, and in 1953 his student, Stanley Miller, with an electrical discharge for energy, produced simple amino acids from methane, ammonia, hydrogen, and water. Eventually, in 1961, Calvin's people tried bombarding the same mixture, but now with a beam of electrons, and thought they produced some adenine. Two years later, with electrons again, a Calvin team led by Cyril Ponnamperuma, a Ceylonese, repeated the experiment and proved the product was adenine.

Here was indeed a trophy. Adenine is a double-ring organic compound with the formula $C_5H_5N_5$; consequently, it is fairly complex. But much more: it is a versatile building block. Remember that adenine is one of those four base chemicals in DNA's code. Accordingly, Calvin's group went ahead to mix it with a simple organic phosphate and ribose sugar (which irradiation can now synthesize from formaldehyde) and send ultraviolet light into the solution. There were intensely interesting products. One was adenylic acid. This happens to be one of the nucleotide subunits that comprise DNA's associate molecule RNA. Another was DNA's chemical cousin, adenosine triphosphate (ATP). As the master molecule of heredity, DNA is today's glamour child. But ATP is the living cell's energy bank. Instead of storing and transferring hereditary information, ATP stores and transfers energy obtained from food. For everything it does—building proteins, contracting a muscle, transmitting a nerve impulse—the cell must spend some ATP. Meanwhile, the work of Calvin's group has progressed. The five nucleotides that characterize DNA and RNA have been created, and without need of an organic phosphate as one of the ingredients—inorganic phosphates sufficed.

All this synthesis of major life chemicals is highly promising. But it isn't quite creating life. And it brings up a trio of questions. Scientifically speaking, what is life? How did it begin? What is aging?

Science can do little with the first question. Biologist Norman Anderson of Oak Ridge National Laboratory asks if life is "the embodiment of self-maintaining chemical processes within a certain volume" or, more simply, "the ability to metabolize, grow, and divide—to produce two living cells where only one existed before." He concludes that we know only that "unless molecules can duplicate

themselves directly or indirectly there is little chance that cells can."
And life certainly is cell duplication.

Beyond that is the fact that science cannot define life, simply or
otherwise; it is even baffled by the difference between living and non-
living matter. Movement? A car moves under its own power.
Response to a stimulus? A bubble does that when you touch it.
Definite life span? A radioactive isotope has that. Growth? A crystal
grows, so does a river. Reproduction? A virus reproduces—but until
it kidnaps the enzyme machinery of a living cell, it is as inert as a
stone. And so on.

Very well, how did life as we can only know it begin? Tracing
evolution backward has its limits. Very primitive forms—microbes—
left no fossils. Furthermore, science has been re-examining its dogma.
For a century, it was certain that damp earth cannot create earthworms and bread cannot create mold any more than a slightly soiled
shirt, placed in a dark corner and sprinkled with nutrient chemicals,
will produce mice in twenty-one days. Such notions of abiogenesis—
spontaneous generation—were overthrown by Pasteur's "like begets
like" concept. Hermaphroditic earthworms reproduce worms, spores
reproduce mold, parents reproduce mice. But today, says Harvard
biologist George Wald, "the only tenable scientific view is that life did
originally arise by spontaneous generation."

He is referring, of course, to the clues supplied by primordial
chemistry—how it all started—rather than to any prospects that
science will perform abiogenesis in the test tube. But the work by
the chemists does indicate something, the track anyway, that could
have led to life's beginning. Visualize a warm ocean in which it is
estimated that as much at 3.6 million cubic miles of amino acids
and other organic compounds might have accumulated via primordial
chemical reactions. They mingle in that warm soup for over a billion
years. In such an incubator, molecules would be absorbing more
energy, colliding, and interacting at times to form still more complex
molecules like proteins, ATP, and DNA. But a virus is considered
mainly a nucleic acid within a coat of protein. Could not simple,
virus-like systems have resulted? Then evolution would take care of
the rest. Somewhere here, of course, a detail is still lacking. Just how
did the reproductive process start?

Inasmuch as life's definition and origin remain elusive, what of aging? Here is something visible. And the question arises: why is our life expectancy only seventy; why do we have only twelve thousand living people who have passed their hundredth birthday?

True enough, for evolution there must first be reproduction, and both require the old to make living room for the new. In this way emerged man, climbing over the dead cells of his ancestors. But perhaps man is satisfied with himself now, or perhaps there can be a compromise with death?

Pills and other palliatives soften the ravages of aging; modern society provides comforts for the helpless, confused second childhood of man; it also sanctions a grisly series of surgical operations to prevent the dying, like General Douglas MacArthur, from simply fading away. But astonishingly little has been done to research the technical causes of aging. Calling it the cumulative effect of a lifetime of traumas isn't enough.

Hubert Humphrey stressed this when he was senator. Castigating the NIH for "merely handing out money," he conceded that death remains man's lot but called for research to investigate ways to postpone it: "No man can foresee what a greatly enlarged scientific drive could achieve. But a decade or two from now, we may look back to present-day attitudes toward death as primitive and medieval."

What do we know about aging? The organism "runs down." Why? A common explanation is that the body—its cells—becomes increasingly susceptible to disease. Why? Here, theories diverge. Two interest us here in the context of what has been said about the big molecules and about the hazards of radiation. Both, of course, can offer some experimental evidence.

1. As the body ages, the large vital molecules like enzymes and nucleic acids are increasingly put out of commission by "cross-linkage." The binding agent here is a chemically active smaller group of atoms. Notoriously active are the "free radical" molecular fragments produced by radiation; industry, in fact, uses them as polymerizing agents to join molecules together. But there are many others, including the unstable and therefore active products of unsaturated fats. In any case, the result seems simple enough. Two DNA molecules, for example, are tied together so firmly that they cannot perform their functions. With several cross-linkages, neither

DNA can go through its own splitting process of mitosis. With only one cross-linkage, they may rupture in the reproduction attempt, and mutations are the result.

2. The liveliest theory about aging goes beyond cross-linkage. It holds that DNA molecules are changed by mutations, whatever their cause. And the harm done depends on the kind of cell. Some, like blood cells, are constantly dying and being replaced. Hence the small risk in being a blood donor. At the other extreme are brain cells. The human, for example, is believed to start with a complement of billions and later lose about ten thousand a day without replacing them to any noticeable extent. Mutations, this theory goes, are relatively harmless to the organ in which cells are busily subdividing. The damaged cell here is either killed outright or unable to compete with its normal neighbors. But in the brain, the damaged cell—therefore its damaged DNA—would likely remain indefinitely as an impediment. Would this explain why mental ability decreases after some decades and, similarly, why muscular weakness is one of the first signs of advancing years? The theory is backed by considerable experimental evidence. For instance, irradiated animals contract the same fatal illnesses as normal ones, but do so sooner. Does this mean that mutations "aged" some of their organs and these dragged the rest to the grave?

At any rate, we are back with DNA. Its blueprint builds the new body, then keeps it alive. The DNA may be defective to start with, through inheritance, or it may be changed environmentally by one of several causes. How to overcome the defects, whatever their origin? How to live more healthily and longer?

Genetic Surgery

One way is to alter the DNA. As I have said, molecular biology is seeking knowledge as a goal in itself, but can hardly ignore the practical implications, any more than could the physicists who started with the atomic nucleus and went on to release its energy.

Space science has its "big question": Is there life on Mars? But nearer home is the other big one: Can we alter the life process on earth?

The thought of using manmade nucleic acids for assembly-line methods that will synthesize manikins according to man's specifications, not nature's, is still too remote for anything but philosophical discussion or the kind of science fiction that reaches far into the bizarre. The thought of *altering* a germ cell, or an already existing human, is no longer far-fetched.

Like Pauling, his fellow Nobelist, Edward Tatum of Rockefeller Institute suggests changing abnormal DNA "by replacement or correction and substitution. You might inject new DNA into a person. Or you might take some of his cells, make them grow in the laboratory, and expose them to new DNA—then select out the rare cell that is favorably affected and put it back in the patient to grow." Such versions of the transformation principle—changing the blueprint—are wrapped up in the term "genetic surgery." Its purpose is manipulating the genetic code to give healthier humans, and eventually perhaps fulfill intimations of immortality by stimulating the body to go on producing healthy young replacement cells, including those of the brain.

Either prospect is tempting, and industry is already looking ahead. For example, Syntex, the hormone manufacturer, set up an Institute for Molecular Biology and hired Nobelist Lederberg as scientific adviser "in anticipation that the nucleic acids and related compounds must ultimately play a highly important role in medicine." Stanford Research Institute is bolder: "The future citizen stands to gain in the most spectacular way. At his birth he will be free from congenital defects—this from deciphering the genetic code." More specific is geneticist H. Warner Kloepfer of Tulane, who says DNA may "open the door to the mass production of genes, just as the discovery of vitamins and hormones paved the way for large-scale production of those items. They may be used to replace or counteract the effects of the harmful, mutated genes responsible for cancer, muscular dystrophy, and certain neurological, psychiatric, and cardiovascular diseases."

But the master-molecule concept of DNA makes even that prophecy much too modest. The brunette could be changed to a natural blonde. Or, going back to the germ cells, the child could be coded to be male or female, tall or short, white-skinned or dark.

How far has all this already gone?

First, the laboratory problems. Here are a few:

. . . Many embarrassing challenges to DNA dogma need explanation. One of the first was the accidental discovery of virus DNA that worked efficiently in the form of a single-stranded molecule, rather than as a pair of twisted strands; this was like finding a unicorn in a herd of steers. Also, there are many viruses whose genetic material is RNA rather than DNA.

. . . Learning nature's code is considerably more than cryptanalysis of manmade ones. The code seems to flower with ambiguities and redundancies. And, as already indicated, biologists have been baffled by the sequence of letters in a DNA word. For example, reading up the ladder, is a three-letter word G-A-C, or A-G-C, or C-A-G, or G-C-A, or A-C-G, or C-G-A? Which combination prescribes a certain amino acid? Even assembling a protein chain only one hundred amino acids long requires a hundred such decisions. Moreover, the three-letter-word idea itself needs confirmation, despite evidence for it at the University of Wisconsin and elsewhere. Suppose, for instance, some words are two, and others are four letters long. Then would even a DNA fragment like AGCTCCATCGT stand for AGC-TC-CATC-GT, or AG-CTC-CA-TCGT, and so on?

. . . Claims to having synthesized DNA that reproduces itself have bolstered DNA theory but not entirely overthrown Pasteur's dictum that all life comes from life. It all depends on the definition of "synthesis." Pioneering researchers have made DNA in test tubes; but they used crucial ingredients not made by man: for instance, natural DNA served as a "primer"; and DNA polymerase, a natural enzyme, promoted the reaction. Somehow, to call this synthesis doesn't sound quite cricket.

. . . The excitement over genes, and now over DNA, overlooks one of the arguments by mystics who still have faith in an *élan vital*. They point to the apparently driving force called differentiation. The newly fertilized egg has divided and gone on replicating, each new cell containing an identical package of DNA. But soon comes specialization. Now, some instructions are obeyed, others ignored. At a mysteriously appointed time, each human cell's metabolism has begun responding only to those genes calling for "eyes—blue" or "nose—snub," as the case may be. And the still unhatched chick has begun sprouting feathers. This may be only responding to a pattern acquired during evolution, but how to specify differentiation in a synthetic DNA molecule, no matter how cleverly its gene components have been contrived? How to combine the blueprint with a push-button operator and timetable?

... On the other hand, what of environment's perplexing effects? Again, consider a chick embryo. When it is farther along in its development, transplant some of its eye-making tissue to the area that is becoming a leg, and the transplant faithfully tries to become an eye. But transplant eye tissue when the embryo is only a few hours old, and it becomes leg tissue. And what about other alterations (disregarding, of course, those that come under the heading of mutations)? Working with mice and suitable environment, biologists have induced the female gonad to begin the production of sperm, thereby disobeying its blueprint.

But the most immediate technical problem remains that of deci-phering the code. I asked Robley Williams for an appraisal. He heads the University of California's new Department of Molecular Biology (where younger talent can work with Nobelists Calvin, Glaser, and Stanley). "We're still a long way from the answers," he warned. But he also pointed to growing evidence that the central doctrine of the DNA concept is essentially correct. Soon came an-other big step forward. A trail-blazing team of Cornell and Agri-culture Department biochemists worked out a map showing the sequence of the 77 nucleotides that comprise one of the "transfer" types of RNA molecule. These RNAs are exceedingly small nucleic acids; but the announcement raised hopes for eventually learning the chemical structure of DNA molecules, and going on to genuine synthesis.

This brings back the inevitable question. To what extent can present knowledge help man live more healthily, longer—and how?

DNA theory owes much, of course, not only to transformation experiments but to clear evidence that genetic defects result from gene errors, another way of saying DNA errors. For instance, the classic work with the usually fatal disease called sickle-cell anemia. Here, the blood trouble was traced to wrong coding for the hemo-globin molecule. All 574 amino acids in its four chains were correct except at a place in two chains where one kind was substituted for another.

More recently, an outpour of research shows the directions being taken with the new knowledge. Here are some:

... Though the decoding is slow, there is indeed a code and we know its components. After producing simple test-tube versions of RNA with an enzyme's aid, Marshall Nirenberg and his NIH colleague J. H. Matthaei built short chains of amino acids with them— in other words, primitive proteins. This is how they made their start on a dictionary of the code. It is also reminiscent of the patience with which science learned how to construct the smaller proteins from amino acids.

... Research need not wait for synthetic nucleic acids. It can mutate existing ones; as nature makes her changes, but faster. This is not entirely new. Science has been doing it a long time with plants, bacteria, and test animals. Certain chemicals, for instance, will affect either the DNA blueprint directly or the work it does. One of the latest tried, streptomycin, indicates how the antibiotic combats bacteria. It apparently causes the bacterial cell's protein-making machinery to accept a "wrong" amino acid. But irradiation has broadened the possibilities of changing the DNA itself. Brookhaven, for instance, has a 10-acre "gamma garden" where plants are mutated by cobalt-60's gamma rays. There are difficulties, of course. Since biology doesn't know where each "gene" is located on the DNA molecule, it cannot prescribe the change desired. So, a Brookhaven biologist told me, "Ours is still a shotgun approach, not sharpshooting." Then, after irradiation, comes tedious identification of those targets that have been changed in a way that produces interesting mutants. Finally comes conventional genetics—the inbreeding and outbreeding to see what can be done with the mutants. Yet there is already a beginning of significant results, and practical ones too— new types of beans and oats that give heavier crops and resist diseases; a shrub that endures climates a thousand miles farther north than previously; and a square pineapple that canners wanted— but it didn't catch the public's fancy.

... The vital role of DNA also indicates directions that curative medical science can take. At Oak Ridge National Laboratory,

X-rayed bacteria lost their ability to synthesize a certain enzyme, therefore to synthesize a needed protein. Fresh DNA from cells able to make that enzyme was added and the defect disappeared.

. . . Researchers have already reported first attempts to alter human metabolism this way. For example, nutrient was mixed with DNA from two types of hemoglobin-producing cells: one from a victim of pernicious anemia, the other from a victim of sickle-cell anemia. The result was a strange, third type of hemoglobin, presumably an attempt by one DNA to transform the other.

. . . A start has been made on transforming a cell, not with complete molecules of DNA, but by separating the gene portions believed to constitute a DNA molecule in bacteria, then introducing them into bacteria that lacked such genes. This changed the characteristics of the recipient bacteria.

Such examples indicate a major hope for genetic surgery, which would alter the human's DNA rather than try to supply him with a lab-made kit of it. This hope has been aroused by finding that the evolutionary process has produced different species but many of their genes remain identical and therefore theoretically interchangeable. Even mice and men share about one-fourth of the nucleotide sequences that indicate a similarity of their genes. Researchers learned this by making composite DNA molecules out of portions from different species.

But, to begin with, this business of genetic grafting, of replacing an undesirable section of DNA with a section improved in the lab or found elsewhere—and doing it intelligently—calls for methods of microsurgery we still do not know. Secondly, it will require deciphering the genetic code, then classifying the traits represented by the billions of different genes that now make up mankind. Despite future aid from automated scanning methods, Nobelist Muller calls this an "incredibly titanic job for many lifetimes on the part of successive hosts of investigators," and he goes on to suggest that there may eventually be a race between genetic surgery and the manufacture of robots.

In the long meantime, where may attempts at genetic surgery lead? At present, it can be only the shotgun approach—trying something, then seeing what happens. The fact that we still know so little is a warning. So is the fact that here is the old problem of not knowing what *in vitro* research will give. Even something simpler, like the test-tube method of growing an already formed human egg cell fertilized by human sperm, led an Italian researcher to destroy the embryo after twenty-nine days because it became deformed as it grew and "I did not go further because this monstrosity blocked me" (the Roman Catholic Church helped him decide).

To what extent is that different from the "tampering with life" that Nobelist Tiselius warned against while discussing the prospects of DNA science? In the hands of brilliant, responsible researchers, DNA technique can lead to advances beyond our imagination. For with knowledge, man elevates himself still higher above beasts; and the antidote for the dangerous thing called a little learning is more learning.

But what of the irresponsibles—not only the Frankensteins but the dolts? And what of the less respectable elements of the drug industry? A panicky public reaction to "tampering" could paralyze the new biology and cripple all other research. Calling himself a professional pessimist, Erwin Chargaff, the Columbia biochemist, puts it simply: "It is possible we will put a wrong base into the DNA, which will make the wrong RNA, which will make wrong protein, which will make wrong everything."

Apparently, here is one more self-control problem facing science and, if it is not solved, a control problem facing government.

Meanwhile, are there not other ways to a healthier human? And is death inevitable? The aged reconcile themselves to it; chronic sufferers from physical and mental ills even welcome its enveloping wings; and adventurers, the young in heart, dare wrestle with it. All wonder about living forever.

Until science can manipulate the body's chemistry at will, it can only toy with thoughts of true physical immortality. Meanwhile, it skirmishes with the challenge in several indirect ways overlooked by those who would alter the genes.

Reversing Death

Consider two ways of helping the heart. One is with basic research. "In 1947," says Lewis E. January, professor of internal medicine, "only a dozen scientists in the nation were doing full-time research on cardiovascular diseases. Why, right now we have half that many at the University of Iowa alone." Typical projects there are the effects of cholesterol and the effects of counteracting drugs.

The other approach deals with emergency relief. At Western Reserve University, Claude Beck, professor of cardiovascular surgery, agrees that research has been laggard: "Only fifty years ago the fatal heart attack was still lost in the abdomen. It was called acute indigestion." But Beck hasn't waited for basic research on causes. He crusades on behalf of resuscitation—the reversal of death in hearts still too good to die.

Let us take fibrillation as an example. It is common. This attack stops an apparently sound heart in an accident or during violent exercise. It is a hazard in surgery, in childbirth. It brings death that fulfills the traditional definition: the heart no longer beats.

For the cause of fibrillation, Beck has a theory that is controversial. This is understandable because it concerns ions and membranes. Electrochemistry deals with them much, but has much to learn. Concerning ions, it isn't yet sure how ordinary rusting occurs. And the public, of course, knows less. Often enough, a householder buys a water-softener when he needs a water-hardener.

At any rate, the rhythm of the beating heart is controlled by an electrical impulse originating in its sino-atrial node, better known as the "pacemaker" region. Moving through the heart muscle, this impulse normally causes pump action—contraction followed by relaxation. In the fibrillating heart, the impulse short-circuits in various directions, giving a random twitching. Instead of beating, the heart is in convulsion and goes on to electrocute itself. Here is a fatal attack.

But it can be reversed by defibrillation, a method discovered in 1898 and then lost in the literature for thirty-five years. As late as 1937 it was still a laboratory curiosity. Beck first performed it successfully on a human in 1947, and industry went ahead to devise routine equipment. Today's standard instrument, smaller than a portable TV set, deliberately shocks the heart with a superseding electric current (in emergency, even a pair of lead wires torn from a lighting fixture has done the job). The shock makes all muscle fibers contract uniformly. This restores the rhythm; the heart resumes beating normally. Some of the resuscitated persons send a card annually to their doctor "on the anniversary of my death."

The method is constantly being refined. In the original "open chest" procedure, the electrodes were inserted into the heart itself. With higher voltage, defibrillation can now be done from outside the chest. Or if the heart needs surgery for some other reason, it can be deliberately stopped by a low-voltage shock, then restarted with higher voltage. Thus it is no exaggeration that life can be stopped and started almost at will.

There are problems, of course. Following the attack, a defibrillator must be used quickly, hence the introduction of smaller, portable models. Haste is required because, a surgeon told me with a grimace, "When the heart stops we must do something, and have only three minutes to do it in." The patient's brain is to blame. It starts deteriorating within three to five minutes after its oxygen supply stops. Contrasted with the merely "clinical" death of the heart, the brain's organic death is not reversible. So, unless defibrillation can begin immediately, the heart must be massaged—pumped by squeezing it with the hand. During an operation the surgeon can switch to this emergency procedure in a hurry. But elsewhere?

Beck found himself in new controversy when he insisted that a physician carry a pocket knife and know what to do with it if, for example, his golfing companion's heart stops at the eighteenth hole. Cutting through to the heart and squeezing it under such conditions seemed outrageously crude. But Beck continued his crusade and several victims have been restored in this fashion. Meanwhile, Johns Hopkins researchers perfected a way, somewhat like artificial respiration, whereby "anyone, anywhere" can pump the heart from outside the chest; and Beck, among others, has been teaching classes of laymen how to do it without cracking a victim's ribs or doing other harm.

Another important aid, this one pioneered in the USSR, is hypothermia. In experimental animals it has extended to an hour the usual few minutes after which death cannot be reversed. Here, for lengthy surgery, the body is cooled by one of several refrigeration methods. The possibilities for such suspended animation do not belong entirely to science fiction. Not only has nature preserved the frozen bodies of mammoths for thousands of years; Soviet researchers have gone so far as to claim reviving an ancient lizard estimated to have lain dormant in frozen Siberia for five thousand years.

Here, if immortality is the goal, seems an approach no more bizarre than genetic surgery.

Spare Parts

Or why not merely substitute a sound piece of vitalistic machinery for the one that is hopelessly diseased or senescent? Medical engineering is certainly not abashed by this challenge. In little more than a decade it has learned how to replace a faulty valve in the heart with either a transplanted one or a plastic one. It can also implant a transistorized pacemaker that keeps the faulty heart beating regularly and has even devised a pacemaker that needs no batteries. Somewhat like a self-winding watch, it borrows energy from a pulsating artery or the breathing motions of the diaphragm. But valves and pacemakers are only components. Complete hearts, made of plastic, operated by compressed air, implanted like a pacemaker, have also been tried. One leading researcher foresees success with such devices in the coming decade; another adds details: "Patients will walk around with artificial hearts inside their chests, and we had better be prepared to recognize complications that might result from such unnatural conditions."

But plastics still have drawbacks for such purposes, and many surgeons as well as biologists prefer "living" things anyway. So Nobelist André Cournand makes the equally bold prediction: "The next big step will be the substitution of a young heart for an old one."

The success of any such spare part, human or artificial, predicates, of course, that the patient isn't already a hopeless emergency case or will not die from something else while under surgery. Moreover, transplanting a human organ presents a unique problem. The chemistry of the body is notoriously antagonistic to an intruder, whether virus or transplanted tissue. It sets about quickly to resist and destroy the foreigner. This "rejection" is combated with drugs and radiation but awaits a genuine breakthrough.

However, there is increasing infiltration of the forbidden territory.

By definition, both blood and flesh are tissue, and the transplantation of compatible blood—transfusion—is so common that medical science now condemns its overuse as it does needless surgery and over-indulgence in antibiotics. Even fantastically difficult transplantation holds no terror for Vladimir Demikov, Russia's leading surgeon in this field. He contends that successful grafting depends mainly on swift, skillful technique. To prove it he added a second head to one dog and a second heart to another. The two-headed creature survived for a month; the other, for four months.

Where would donors be found? Chiefly among healthy young people who die accidentally. The USSR, which leads in the technique, routinely uses cadaver blood. The USA prefers live donors for its blood banks but is willing to use "eye banks" for spare corneas. These methods would have seemed black magic in ancient days but they work. So does transplanting the heart's aortic valve, and England has accordingly set up a "heart valve bank." The liver and kidney are much more troublesome, but even here a start has been made, though hardly measuring up to sensational news stories.

Many problems do remain, and not all are technical. Ethical questions have arisen over where to get enough transplants. However, in the careful words of Surgeon General Terry of the United States Public Health Service, "We are beginning to look forward to a time when healthy organs may be substituted routinely for diseased ones."

Sperm Banks

Mankind already possesses immortality of a sort. It is carried on by reproducing the hereditary genes now considered synonymous with DNA. But this is very haphazard. Though theoretically immortal, genes are not immutable. And the vagaries of ordinary mating bring unexpected, often undesirable, combinations. Furthermore, some mating is unreproductive. Also, mating cannot satisfy the purist among immortality-seekers—only the "virgin birth" of parthenogenesis could do that. So the idea of "sperm banks," of ultimately storing male and female cells alike, is offered as an answer for people who want to specify genetic material for their descendants.

Looking at the prospect less personally, some scientists also see in the banks possibilities for controlled breeding, therefore a way to delay their growing fears of an exploding population, especially among genetic "inferiors." This, of course, brings up many questions. Was the rustic an inferior because, as his mother recalls, he "was conceived after a Friday night fish supper"? Is the physician referring only to boors when he states: "The sight of two normally placed testicles in a newborn male brings pride to the heart of the paternal parent"?

At any rate, geneticists estimate that one person in five carries a seriously detrimental gene that arose in the preceding generation. Normally, persons with this mutation would die before reproducing it. But modern medical methods allow most of these people to survive, at least long enough to breed. Thus the idea that natural selection no longer works. Geneticist Muller calls this "biological decadence of the species."

For this problem, the growing vigor of the birth-control movement in many parts of the world is considered an insufficient answer. Insufficient, too, is Bernard Shaw's ironic suggestion to skip a generation. Such controls reduce quantity without necessarily improving quality. If the atheist's son becomes a clergyman, and the clergyman's son a drunkard, this may be attributed to a combination of heredity and rebellion against environment. But in conventional mating, the careless joining of genes alone is enough to produce embarrassments. There are too many hidden genes in the lifestream. The beauty's daughter may turn out to be a fright. The Phi Beta Kappa's son may be a congenital dullard.

If birth control isn't enough, then what of another eugenic approach—a long, supervised program of inbreeding for desired traits? This is done regularly with plants and animals. But with humans, there would be technical problems. True, both a cow and a human mother "carry the calf" nine months. But a heifer can be bred when only two years old. This promises fast turnover of generations, impossible for human inbreeding. Furthermore, the human dislikes being treated as a plant or animal.

But eugenics hopes that mankind might respond to something more godlike. Whatever we call it, accidental evolution or Bergson's *élan vital*, the cells and their genes go on scorning death. This they do by reproduction. Then why not a more personal version of immortality, in which an individual's own unique assembly of genes do not die when he dies? Narcissism or not, he dislikes vanishing entirely. Even the juke box wails "I woant th' wurl' ta kno-o-ow th' sto-ary of mah life." And in an era of parents and children striving to be look-alikes we see the same vague hope for continuity.

The height of narcissism would be parthenogenesis. And though the prospects remain remote, it should be mentioned. It does away with impregnation—bizarre but far from incredible. Nature has experimented much; and certainly the mating method, by allowing continuous variations, has enabled creatures like man to adjust to changing environment and climb high on the evolutionary ladder. But sexual fusion isn't a fixed law. There was apparently a period when nature couldn't decide whether sex is necessary. Parthenogenesis is one example. It is still found among some males far back in the evolutionary scheme but we know more about it as a female feat. The favored explanation is that in bisexual reproduction the sperm serves two purposes. It supplies one set of genes. It also "activates" the egg cell. In female parthenogenesis, too, the egg cell is produced, apparently for bisexual reproduction. But then the cell activates itself. Thus it relies on its own genes and, except for mutations, the parent truly lives on in its child, and that child's child.

It is found in many simple aquatic creatures, insects, and some plants. An attempt at it is seen in the occasional partial development of an unfertilized egg in the human ovary. In Martin Luther's day such abnormal growths, composed mainly of hair and teeth, were called "Offspring of the Devil." The best successful example of it in a familiar creature occurred spontaneously in 1952, in the turkey pens of the USDA's Beltsville research station. Several unfertilized eggs hatched into young turkeys. Some lived to maturity and in turn produced fatherless turkeys that became useful for other research.

Meanwhile, biologists have learned how to activate an unfertilized egg cell and produce such offspring. They can do it many ways, such as by warming or shaking the egg of the starfish or pricking the eggs of frogs with a needle. Among mammals, a special saline solution has given parthenogenetic offspring from rabbits. There is no record of comparable attempts with the human egg cell, but science is understandably fascinated with the thought of producing offspring whose genetic material would be so predictable.

Doing such a thing would require some version of the sperm bank for storing desirable cells and using them when desired. In Muller's words, "This would bring back to life outstanding individuals long since dead, perpetuating for future generations large numbers of men and women of genius in all fields of endeavor. This would, in a sense, represent a form of physical immortality. It does not seem at all far-fetched."

However, like most other geneticists, he prefers parental selection that can become practical sooner. Where he differs is in being less dogmatic than old-style race-improvers. He realizes too well the difficulties in prescribing who shall and shall not mate. Geneticists offered many congratulations in 1964 when a great-grandson of Charles Darwin married a great-granddaughter of Thomas H. Huxley. But Muller will settle for less—for storing genetic material from outstanding people. This would be augmented with sex cells from other pioneers, those who wish to protect their heredity against damage from radiation, or against their inability to reproduce in later life; or perhaps wish for use of their cells even after death. Classifying the material would then build a supply representing various traits considered desirable. This would give germinal choice to parents who have genetic defects or desire a child of unusual promise.

There is already considerable experience with such storage. Freezing the male sperm for use later is merely another version of hypothermia. Any day in cattle country one can see the technician driving with his kit of refrigerated sperm from a choice of prize bulls. He is responding to the telephone call that announces a cow is "in heat." Even after seven years' storage, the semen has been found viable enough to produce normal calves.

Artificial insemination of humans is less common and definitely not a subject discussed among gentlefolk. The practice of using sperm from the husband, or another donor if the husband is sterile, is endorsed by leading medical groups but some physicians perform it furtively "as if everyone concerned were guilty of something." Further, there have been technical doubts about the value of frozen, stored semen from a "bank."

However, Jerome K. Sherman, University of Arkansas, has improved the dry-ice method by fast deep-freezing and storage in liquid nitrogen at temperatures under 300 degrees below zero Fahrenheit.

Normal children have resulted. And Sherman has found the sperm still active after three years.

Medically, the method answers a variety of parental deficiencies, and Sherman envisions storing female cells also, for subsequent implantation in recipient females. Theoretically, this is entirely possible, an experimental start has been made, and it allows science to look farther into the future. Both parents would contribute to the bank. Their cells would then be classified and matched—to produce a son or daughter, and other desired genetic characteristics as well.

Eventually, if mankind consented to live with the ectogenesis of Aldous Huxley's controlled *Brave New World*, reproduction as we know it could be eliminated entirely. The USDA runs a national storage laboratory where essential plant seeds are kept for the needs of crop breeders in generations to come. Projecting from this idea, human cells would be chosen from desirable donors, stored, grown in culture, matched for specific characteristics, then united and fed to reproduce outside the mother.

But again, what of the meantime and the question of who speaks for science? Using the entire sex cell is incomparably easier than going to genetic surgery. Nevertheless, much research is necessary before cells can be classified and matched. For instance, a start has been made on growing human tissue artificially in laboratory flasks. This will lead to putting an artificially grown sperm and egg together, to start an embryo. And then? Who takes responsibility for the abnormal growth that may result, or for aborting it? From Johns Hopkins, H. Bentley Glass has warned fellow biologists that all this is possible before the end of the century, and it is now time to begin considering the moral problems.

VIII: *The Computer's Rival*

> "Man is but a reed, the weakest in
> nature, but he is a thinking reed."
> —Blaise Pascal

About a hundred thousand years ago, man as we know him is believed to have made his debut on earth. Since then, zoologists tell us, the size of his brain has stopped growing, hence his thinking capacity hasn't increased. This is humbling but, progress or not, there is change. Among other things, the brain has invented ways to count faster: with pebbles, and on through the abacus to the modern digital computer.

This electronic assembly not only counts in a flash, handles numbers and equations that numb the brain, remembers variables the brain cannot. It is also a symbol. It epitomizes hopes that automation will banish all labor—and the fears that this will somehow throw the computer's creator upon the discard heap. And, ironically, the computer's own needs spur researchers to turn truly introvert and examine the marvels of man's own brain.

The methods of automation can come later. Here we will first scan the relationship between brain and computer, which forms a natural bridge between the life sciences already discussed and the physical sciences that are coming; a bridge because the nervous system is biological, yet highly electrical, and the computer is electrical, yet highly robotlike. This intimacy is forever making trouble because of the inevitable, often silly comparisons between brain and computer—another reminder that analogy, though common and necessary in science, is risky. The computer has no psyche, mind, consciousness, or soul (whatever these associates of the brain may be). Even mechanistically, it is no brain. To think that it is, is one of many errors that the brain is capable of.

262

It is the anthropocentric fault of picturing even gods as we are. And with computers the temptation is strong to go beyond safe limits when comparing electrical impulses along a nerve with electrical impulses along a computer wire, or comparing the memory within a computer's ferrite cores with the memory within brain cells, or comparing the computer's either-or method of response with a nerve circuit's all-or-none refusal to heed any impulse that isn't strong enough to meet a "threshold" requirement.

The differences are better understood now. Not long ago, when the computer was very, very young, though this was only in the 1950s, there was much enthusiastic balderdash from some writers and technical folk, too, about the computer's capability and future —as there was also about prospects for fusion power, for weather-making, for answering ultimate questions about the inanimate atom and animate body. Since then, science has sobered and gone back to the laboratory for more of the kind of knowledge we call facts.

It is not the electronic system built into a computer but the brain housed in the skull that has changed its thinking. A few years ago, an article about computers, written by a respectable engineer, declared comfortably that "we will eventually be able to construct systems which, we will agree, 'think' in every sense of the word." He could be forgiven. Computers were being christened Oracle and Aldous (Huxley). And the noted physicist-engineer Vannevar Bush, who had found time to help pioneer with computers, foresaw the machines thinking "creatively"—composing music, writing poetry, and so on. And why not? The merely repetitive they can reproduce. And when creativity becomes abstract enough, even a finger-painting hominoid like a chimpanzee is hailed as an artist.

It was mathematician von Neumann who accurately put his finger on the main point. At an informal discussion a woman kept challenging him to prove that a machine could really think. He finally retorted, "If you will tell me precisely what it is that a machine cannot do, then I can always make a machine that will do just that." The embarrassing fact is that nobody has accepted the challenge because nobody yet can satisfactorily explain how our basic five senses work, much less tell us what thinking is; and the concept of consciousness remains as incomprehensible as the infinitude of time.

Meanwhile, International Business Machines Corporation, leader of an industry that does not want to risk clouding a glowing future, has practiced its preachment to "THINK." It is thoughtful about public relations, even more so than another giant, the Bell System. Telephones may be a nuisance; they are not a menace. The computer is an ogre that symbolizes automation. Accordingly, IBM advertises how its data-processing "helps science save protein-starved children." It retains its own jobless on the payroll. It discourages its departments from using the word "memory" for the computer's accumulation of data and operating instructions. The preferred word is "storage." The official IBM view is that a computer should not be likened to humans, even if this means robbing it of a memory,˙ which the computer does happen to have.

Memory and the ability to use it amount to a great deal. It is pointless for the other of the "two cultures" to scurry up a tree and make rude noises at the flashy stranger: to call it only a flashy moron; to jibe that it cannot parse a sentence; to ask who needs the value of pi beyond four decimal places, or at most eight; to predict that it will put only logarithm tables, slide rules, and ordinary desk calculators out of business. To sneer that it can count on only two fingers brings the fair retort that a Heifetz only drags horsehair over catgut.

In number of cells, to be sure, the computer remains a dolt compared with the human brain. And in associative ability it remains a primitive. The human infant comes equipped with genetic instructions and what we call instincts; it can and does go on to add circuitry through life. The computer can do only what its programer can arrange.

And yet, when an experimental computer can respond to the voice of a stranger as Stanford University's "Madaline" responded to mine, we realize how far computer robotry may go. This was pattern recognition, a method simulating the one with which science now believes we hear and see.

But again, comparisons are risky, if for no other reason than because our ignorance about the brain remains so abysmal. Why? For one thing, research here faces an inherited mystery and must use extremely delicate probing methods. The computer engineer, by contrast, understands his machine and can treat it cavalierly. After all, he built it.

Also, the computer enjoys a kind of favoritism. It is sparkling hardware that speeds the operations of industry and operates the nation's defense networks. Also, science itself buys multimillion-dollar computers for its increasingly massive research in biology, physics, meteorology, space exploration, and so forth. As a result there is no lack of men, money, and facilities for the race to develop still newer computers.

By contrast, the basic research needed for the nervous system has been untouched by glamour and appeals only to a relatively few dedicated people. Conventional mental-health programs find it more attractive to seek new tranquilizers and provide better care for the growing number in modern society who seem unable to tranquilize themselves. The mind, viewed in mystic apartheid from the rest of the body, is a favorite conversation piece; its very real associate, the brain, is overlooked. Yet until we know more about it, the rest can be only palliatives; and any discussion about the "mental endowment" of this group or that race is another statistical flight of fancy that invites rabble-rousing.

The brightest part of the picture is that computer research produces feedback in the form of curiosity about man's own system for gathering information, retrieving data, and making decisions. This has led several scientific disciplines—biology, chemistry, physics, electronics, experimental psychology, mathematics—to investigate various aspects of the nervous system, ranging from the simple enigma called the nerve cell to the complex one called the mind.

Animal Electricity

Working backward, any attempt to understand the mind immediately calls for understanding the brain. And the brain is very real. Literally, figuratively, it crowns the human's nervous system. But through the evolutionary process it came later than the rest and nobody denies that it is more complicated. Consequently, much of what we know about the brain, as a mechanical thing, has come from what we have learned about the rest of the nervous system. And there is no longer anything revolutionary about the idea that the basic components of this system, the nerve cells, work electrically rather than mystically. And inasmuch as electricity is familiar, the comparison follows easily: electricity along a wire to or from the computer message center; electricity along a nerve to or from the spinal cord or brain. Electricity, yes, but certainly not the kind from a wall outlet.

In 1780, twenty-eight years after Ben Franklin flew the kite that discharged "static" electricity from a thundercloud, Italy's Luigi Galvani found another version in the nerve of a frog's twitching leg. There is something odd about such "animal electricity." Signals sent along a wire by conventional electricity travel thousands of miles per second. Nerve impulses move less than four hundred feet per second in man and only one-third as fast in a frog.

The biochemist doesn't quarrel with this fact of electrochemistry. He tries to explain it, without departing from the faithful concepts with which the electrochemist builds better batteries, or frees a stubborn metal like aluminum from its bauxite ore, or struggles with perennial problems of corrosion. He recognizes that ionization is at work here, as it is in the auto storage battery. The source of its current is a two-way traffic of ions supplied by the sulfuric acid. But there are many types of batteries. The nerve cell is an unusual version suited to the body's delicacy. Here, a leading role is played by ions from ordinary salt.

In this compound the molecule is an atom of sodium joined to an atom of chlorine. To begin with, each atom is electrically neutral. Here is our old picture of the planetary atom, which has as many orbiting negative electrons as it needs to balance the number of positive protons in its nucleus. This simplest version, as we saw in Chapter V, evolved into a picture of concentric "shells" around the nucleus, with each shell able to hold a specific number of the electrons. It is with the easily reached, electrically potent outermost shell of each kind of atom that chemists usually work. Here are the bonds that can join atom to atom; likewise the bonds that can be broken to separate atom from atom. How are these bonds formed?

For maximum stability of the atom, this outermost shell should have a certain number of electrons. The need can be met by trading or sharing electrons. Sodium chloride happens to be a simple example. The chlorine atom, with seven electrons in its outer shell, needs one more to total a required eight. Under the right conditions, this comes from the sodium atom, which has a very incomplete outer shell containing only one electron. Thus the two atoms join through that linking electron. And the molecule exists as a molecule as long as this condition lasts.

Now put this salt in water. Though the exact nature of the process is still debated, most of the molecules split. This does not occur violently, nor does it produce the original two components, a normal sodium and normal chlorine atom. The split is such that the chlorine atom carries away its extra electron and is therefore a negatively charged ion; similarly, the sodium atom, now lacking an electron, is a positive ion. And unless something occurs to disturb the equilibrium, the salt solution is now, for all practical purposes, a mingling in definite proportions of free ions, plus molecules of water, plus whatever molecules of salt have not ionized.

The fluid around cells in the body contains such dissolved salt. And the uniqueness of nerve cells is their ability to use it for generating small electric currents.

These are the cells also called neurons (with confidence that they will not be confused with the physicist's neutrons). Neurons vary. Those doing the actual brainwork we know least about, but their electrochemistry is considered the same as that of the more familiar sensory and motor neurons. And the essential difference between these two is that they transmit signals in reverse directions. For example, a sensory neuron is stimulated by an impulse of some kind. —a smell, temperature of the skin, sight of a written word. (There is practically no evidence to explain how the stimulus works.) At the other end of the sensory line is the center in the brain, or a shortcut through the spinal cord, that does something about the signal, perhaps stimulates a motor neuron to carry back another signal—this one to twitch a muscle.

In any case, the neuron has three main parts. Its compact "body" looks like other kinds of cells and is located in or near the brain or spine. Its twiglike dendrites serve as bridges for incoming stimuli. And growing out of the other side of the cell body is the message-transmitting fiber called an axon. In the brain neuron it may be so short that the cell resembles a bramble patch of dendrites. In the sensory or motor neuron it is a strange appendage for so tiny a cell. It is microscopically thin but may be several feet long in man. Though it is thought that a completely destroyed neuron is not replaced, a damaged one can repair itself and must continue feeding itself. We now have sequential motion pictures showing that it may take a year for nutrients to creep from the cell body down to its axon terminal in a toe.

In sum, a nerve is a bundle of axons, sometimes thousands. And it is the axon that interests us here.

A closer look at it shows several layers. One or two may be outer coverings, of which one, the myelin sheath, speeds the nerve impulse in some unknown way. Farther in is the fiber proper with an outer layer of its own. This is a remarkable membrane. It is both a "wire" for transmitting the signals and a battery for generating the electricity needed.

By now we are down to really fine measurements. The thickness of this membrane in man is between 50 and 100 angstroms—less than a half-millionth of an inch. The researcher's need to probe for voltages across the membrane requires microelectrodes and explains a preference to experiment with the "giant axon" of the squid, which dwarfs that of man.

The researcher is also fond of electric fish of various sorts. They carry the strongest bioelectric generators known. Swimmers fear these creatures, but, two centuries ago, researchers began respecting them for other reasons. Their weapon is what Volta in 1800 christened the "electric organ": an assembly of many plates called electroplax, each a thin tissue of modified muscle that builds up electric potential the way a neuron does, and the same amount—a little over one-tenth of a volt. But the function differs: a nerve fiber is for signaling; the electric organ is for war. Celebrated *Electrophorus electricus*, the electric eel from South America, with a battery of over 6000 electroplax connected in series, electrocutes prey with its 600 volts.

The membrane that makes such things possible is semipermeable, which is characteristic of the outer layer of a cell in the living body. That is, it is selective. Some barriers of this kind allow only water molecules to go through, others permit passage of salts but not sugars, and so on. Science has never been certain what causes semipermeability but is increasingly eager to find out because here is a field with growing lure for applied as well as basic research. Engineers have designed rival membrane methods, for example, to remove salt from seawater. Here, too, biology seeks better explanations for such phenomena as cellular osmosis and virus action.

This we know now about the axon membrane. It is not only selective but changeable. For each "firing"—for each bioelectrical discharge that moves the nerve impulse farther on—it allows sodium ions, normally concentrated outside, to come through; and a similar number of potassium ions to go out. Then, after this discharge, during preparation for the next, the original condition is restored by some unknown kind of pumping action that reverses the traffic: now, potassium ions come back and sodium ions return to their normal location outside the axon.

Though this tells what the membrane does, it doesn't explain the mechanism. For perhaps the best educated guess, let us visit the laboratory of David Nachmansohn, professor of biochemistry at Columbia's College of Physicians and Surgeons. I found him a vigorous scientist of the old school, disdainful of research "from nine to five." His own earlier days, at Kaiser Wilhelm Institute in Germany, were with such mentors as Nobelists Otto Meyerhof and Fritz Haber.

It was at the University of Paris, in 1937, as a refugee from Hitler, that he began his classic work on the nerve system. Remembering Meyerhof's creed—nature doesn't complicate things unnecessarily— he refused to believe that the nerve impulse depends entirely on "neurohumoral" secretions to carry it across the small gap ("synapse") from neuron to neuron, or neuron to muscle cell, and doesn't have the same chemical basis when it moves electrically along the axon. One of the secretions was thought to be the chemical called acetylcholine. And the enzyme that inactivates it is cholinesterase. Because of this enzyme's abundance all along the neurons, rather than just at their synapses, Nachmansohn suspected that it might point to a universal answer for nerve action. Adding enzyme chemistry to electrochemistry, and turning to electric fish for aid, he started probing the axon membrane.

In the following years he cemented facts with sufficient guesswork to demonstrate that acetylcholine is the leading actor in a series of events fascinating enough to delight any theoretical scientist:

1. Consider only one section along the membrane, which is made up of acetylcholine, various proteins, enzymes, and other chemicals. This place has not yet been reached by a stimulus. Sodium ions are

waiting outside. Acetylcholine within the membrane is in the resting condition, linked to a "storage protein."

2. Now a stimulus arrives and if it is strong enough the protein molecules release the acetylcholine molecules. However, some acetylcholine molecules immediately lose their new freedom. Each is seized by a large molecule of another kind called a "receptor protein."

3. The receptor molecule is thereby changed in some fashion; possibly a section of its long chains folds partly around the acetylcholine.

4. The change in shape of the protein molecules shifts electrical charges. One way or another, this shift changes the makeup of the membrane so as to let the electrically charged sodium ions through. The barrier is temporarily removed.

5. The result is a small electric current, the flare called a nerve impulse. Truly electrical, it shows as a spike on the oscilloscope. Most important, it is the electric current that then stimulates the adjoining section along the membrane to repeat the same sequence . . . and so on along the entire axon.

6. Meanwhile, the acetylcholine molecules that remained free in Step 2 are being hydrolyzed by the enzyme cholinesterase. This upsets the equilibrium: as fast as the acetylcholine is broken up, more is freed by "receptor protein" and is hydrolyzed, until all of this protein's molecules have resumed their original, unfolded shape. Thus the enzyme has acted as a circuit-breaker, ending the flare of current. The membrane is again a gate closed to sodium at this region.

The entire sequence at each point of activity has happened in about one-thousandth of a second. During the recovery, this section has had its acetylcholine rebuilt by another enzyme, sodium ions are again waiting to come through; this region is ready to accept and transmit another impulse that is strong enough. Thus the current splutters along the axon like current from a series of tiny batteries, each triggering the next; rapid enough, but slow compared with the single flash along an electric wire.

We can now see some reasons why normal nerve action is so effective, not only for sending signals but for controlling them.

. . . Because the original impulse must be intense enough and last long enough, neuron circuits are protected by an "all-or-none" filter. They can ignore the inpour of thousands of weak background stimuli and save themselves for important signals. Otherwise the entire nervous system, especially parts of the brain, would be jammed. The typist in a busy office, for example, can be oblivious to the sound of all other typewriters, or even ignore her own when she is concentrating on words.

. . . Because of the circuit-breaking enzyme, a new original impulse is required to start each signal. This, too, prevents chaos. Otherwise, the eye wouldn't stop blinking after blinking once.

. . . Because the enzyme can inactivate acetylcholine in less than a thousandth of a second, the efficiency of the entire electrochemical sequence allows the membrane to propagate a thousand or more useful signals per second.

There is also the fact that Nachmansohn's concept not only works, but works so neatly. Though a "pure" researcher, he experienced a very practical interlude.

Early in World War II, intelligence reports reached Washington that the Nazis had developed and were stockpiling sinister nerve gases that made other poison gases obsolete. The danger from these organic phosphates was twofold. They could completely upset normal nerve action. And masks were useless because these poisons need not be swallowed or inhaled; they penetrate a victim's skin easily.

So Nachmansohn left his ivory tower in the science world. When the Army's Chemical Corps asked if he needed any special materials, he replied: "Yes, please, a hundred electric eels from the Amazon River." Thus began Operation Eel. It was their cholinesterase enzyme that he wanted. Working with it, he first overthrew the prevailing idea that the organophosphates actually destroy this circuit-breaking enzyme. But this was no antidote.

Nachmansohn's research group set out to learn precisely how the gases block the enzyme's action. The suspicion was that this might be the kind of enzyme poisoning mentioned on page 219. It turned out to be so. The organophosphate molecule contains a subassembly called the phosphoryl group. By attaching itself to the enzyme molecule, barnacle-fashion, it leaves the enzyme unable to do its job of breaking up molecules of acetylcholine. The membrane's neat sequence is ruined, the nervous system goes into uncontrolled twitching, then convulsions, and death follows.

Result of the research was PAM, a synthetic chemical that interferes with the interferer by removing the phosphoryl group from the organophosphate molecule. The antidote proved effective in research animals. By this time, however, the war had ended. Germany had not used her nerve gases, because she feared either retaliation or that a shifting wind might poison her own troops. But the research was not wasted. Not only because the victorious USA and USSR were now able to make nerve gases themselves, for possible use against each other. Also, these chemicals, under such names as parathion, soon began reaching farmers in the form of powerful insecticides. Various woes ensued. For some reason, many farmers handle parathion as many householders use DDT. They are too careless or impatient to read and heed the warning labels. The result is a procession of parathion deaths. Some victims triple the strength of poison called for, others ignore the protective measures recommended. I have seen some slopping the chemical over themselves as casually as they might the safer DDT or arsenate of lead. And there are truly innocent victims, like fruit-pickers poisoned by spray residues. However, even in desperate cases, PAM may save the victim if used soon enough.

The last time I visited Nachmansohn he was more mellow toward researchers who still wouldn't see things his way, and resignedly quoted physicist Max Planck, the original quantum theorist: "A new scientific truth does not triumph by convincing its opponents and making them see the light. The opposition dies only with the death of the opponents." His research team was now concentrating on the problem of just how protein molecules work in his theoretical sequence of ion activities. And he prophesied that increasing knowledge about proteins, enzymes, and membrane structure will in the next ten years clear away much of the fog concerning how the nerve cell does its bioelectrical work.

Mind and Body

There is much fog to clear away, despite the work by Nachmansohn's group and others. And it is significant that by far the largest number of Nobel Prizes in life science have been going to researchers working with DNA and the like. Work on the nervous system has been much neglected; and dependent on "spill-over" from other fields. Yet man has no research tool more important. Is there life on Mars? Can man alter his heredity? Because mental man's thrust of curiosity is probing such questions, if for no other reason, the overshadowing big question becomes: How do the brain and mind work?

Taken together, these two have given him great power, joy, sorrow. With his brain, man discovered science. With it, too, he found even earlier that he had a unique mind. For there is more than having "a mind of one's own." The pestiferous mosquito has that. We may assume the brain is mechanistic, nonmystical, a vast network of interconnected, electrochemically active cells. Conceivably the mind, including judgment, consciousness, instincts perhaps, can eventually be explained mechanistically. But at present it is the biggest riddle facing the brain of man. Even while trying to define the problem, science can refer only to the brain "and its contained mind."

Semantics aside, what do we know in general about this supposed combination? Though the brain is itself discouraging enough, it is less so when we consider it merely a physical organ whose job is perception. To it, the eye sends messages for analysis, interpretation, registry, action. Through a matching of patterns, or a playback of memory, it can also see what the eyes do not. And to help understand its mechanics we remember that physically and figuratively it crowns the central nervous system. Originally it was a swelling of nerve tissue atop the spinal cord. During evolution it extended into the skull and went on enlarging. Today, it is the supreme appendage that wags dog and man alike. But beyond this, the picture becomes blurry because the "mental" mind intrudes upon the physical brain. It is with both, his brain's large neuron capacity and his facile mind, that man rules the world.

The brain-mind, for example, provides consciousness: a person "sees" that he is seeing. But more. With the brain-mind a Bach composes a passacaglia, then by way of their own sensing fingers, eyes, and ears, the performers and audience somehow share the wonders. With it, too, man steals the eggs laid by a hen, then contemplates her stupid insistence on trying to hatch chicks from an empty nest; he blunders into unnecessary wars that other creatures don't fight, then seeks to divert his "animal spirits" into a "moral equivalent of war" such as driving himself to run an unnecessary 4-minute mile.

With it, gamblers figure odds, but also Rodin sculptured "The Thinker"—and thinkers ponder over the mind of man. It is so versatile that it can regard itself quizzically, as in the psychologist's story about conditioning animals. One laboratory rat to another: "It works—every time I go through the maze, he drops in food."

Anatomically, disregarding the elusive mind, today's essentials about the brain are these:

. . . Besides being served by ordinary sensory and motor neurons, it has its private "connector" and "associative" neurons for the processes of memory, correlation, decision. As the child matures, the number of neuron connections multiplies enormously.

. . . Modern *Homo sapiens* has a reassuringly large number of brain cells to begin with, 10 billion or so. A 1500-pound cow's brain weighs one-third that of a 150-pound man; so, roughly, does the brain of the most advanced apes. But actual weight isn't all, nor is ratio of brain weight or size to total weight of the body. The ratio of brain weight to weight of the spinal cord seems more reliable. It shows how much the "brainy" part of the nervous system has developed beyond that of the lower levels.

. . . The most significant progress in the two million years or so that saw man presumably evolving from apelike ancestors was the tripling of his brain size. It is therefore not reassuring to hear from Harvard's noted evolutionist Ernst Mayr that man's brain has grown no larger since he emerged triumphantly as a new species superior to Neanderthal Man some hundred thousand years ago. Others add that its size is now decreasing from generation to generation. The explanation suggested by Mayr is that humans now control the earth securely enough, that they lack the drastic conflict and toughening that weeds out the unfit while stimulating mechanical and social inventiveness. For stress is not necessarily a bad word. Howard A. Rusk, a medical leader of rehabilitation programs, points out that it is an integral part of life: "We set our whole pattern of life by our stress endpoint. If we hit it exactly we live dynamic, purposeful, useful, happy lives. If we go over, we break. If we stay too far under, we vegetate." For instance, Mayr adds that enlargement of man's brain was catalyzed most by the need for neuron connections to handle communication. This was stress, but more profitable than the "commuter's syndrome" and others blamed for today's peptic ulcers; more profitable, too, than the purposeless hardship, also called stress, with which manmade radiation strikes directly at the genetic makeup.

. . . In the course of enlargement, from the time of the simplest vertebrates, the brain has been adding new pathways and relay centers for its cells. While the simpler "animal" needs were being left for the hindbrain and midbrain to handle, the forebrain was expanding remarkably in its portion called the cerebrum—the decision-maker, the organ of the mind. Needing a network of more nerve cells, it expanded the coating over its roof. This, too, wasn't enough, and more cranial space was lacking. So, as the coating grew, it began tucking itself into folds—the familiar convolutions called the cerebral cortex. This abnormal, grayish massing of cell bodies in man accounts for his superior intelligence. But even when healthy organically and when well informed—able to correlate and "reason"—it is not in complete control. For example, the hindbrain ("medulla oblongata") still supervises internal organs and involuntary muscles. And in the forebrain itself, dwarfed and hidden by the cerebral structure, is the anarchistic hypothalamus, a control center for such instincts as feeding and mating. To learn the functions of each part of the brain, and of the cortex areas called lobes, there has been much laying on of hands by surgeon and biologist (as well as phrenologist). Such mapping continues and, as with astronomy's mapping regions of the moon, much has been learned. The difference is that man expects to know the moon's exact geography within a few years; when we will have a comparable atlas of the mind, or even the physical nervous system, is unpredictable. In this respect we remain primitive primates.

. . . This ignorance is reflected not only in our musing about the *modus operandi* of intellectual processes. It paralyzes the routine of caring for the body. Take pain, for example. It is the alarm signal that something is wrong. A fire siren can be built, can be repaired, is entirely understood. But, to start with, we often don't even know what starts the pain signal. This may be dismissed as something for theoreticians to ponder; less important than remedies for pain. But what needs remedying? A homely example is the physician's trouble when diagnosing "stomach-ache." Unlike an obvious gunshot wound, it is often buried in abdominal mystery. What maps we have are utterly confusing, hence the "exploratory operation." Consider the upsets that lead to visceral pain. It is risky to assume that the conscious, elegant part of the brain stands aside, leaving the gut and other internal organs to the more primitive nerve centers. There is too much interplay; mental stresses do intrude upon the viscera. So, for the wretch suffering from "emotional overlay"—formerly "nervous stomach"—the physician prescribes an antacid to counter excessive stimulation of the stomach's gastric glands; or an antispasmodic to relax overstimulated digestive muscles; or an anti-anxiety tranquilizer; or a combined potion for the "psycho-visceral who has everything." This assumes a trustworthy diagnosis, a syndrome of associated symptoms that makes sense. But making sense isn't easy. First, the problem of communication between two brains—patient's and physician's; too few doctors are good interviewers, too few patients can localize their trouble. Second, the three so-called "zones" of visceral pain are vague makeshifts: pathways taken by pain sensations remain uncertain; deceptive cross-over circuits "refer" a pain to a blameless part of the body. Consequently, it need not be surprising that a simple "intestinal blockage" turns out to be really a heart attack, or gall-bladder trouble, or cancer. In the meantime, the physician faces cruel dilemmas. Such is the price we pay for ignorance.

And what of the burgeoning, prospering psychic drugs that aim at deep reaches of the brain and have become the drug industry's leading source of revenue? Whether or not they will lead to Huxley's brave new world, stupefied with "soma," is for others to prophesy. Already, there are numerous reservations about them. Many are bootlegged and the FDA keeps busy running down quacks and peddlers. Others, when improperly used, are like illegal narcotics in that the user can become an addict. Accordingly, the World Health Organization has suggested international control and there have been moves in Congress for tighter domestic control. And yet, properly used, they have contributed much to the decline since 1955 in the number of resident patients at our mental hospitals.

The point here, however, is that even the respectable tranquilizers, sedatives, and energizers, despite the lavish research money spent to find them, are hardly scientific. Because the nervous system is so badly mapped, they are necessarily shots in the dark and can give more results than bargained for. The physician is warned that the reputable quietener Librax may give such "paradoxical reactions" as excitement and "acute rage"; that the meprobamate Miltown, king of tranquilizers, is a habit-former, is unsafe with too much alcohol, and: "Use with care in patients with suicidal tendencies."

Consequently, medical practice must rely upon its art rather than on sure-footed science. If the stomach sufferer does get relief for his intestines he may be willing to risk what the muscle-relaxing drug does to his bladder, just as a mental patient's family will approve drugging him with chlorpromazine, though its benefits are accompanied by a long warning-list of side-effects, from "autonomic reactions" through "reversed epinephrine" to "seizures." Interestingly, it is the Defense Department rather than a health agency that has made a sizable start on the problem: a $3-million contract to the Arthur D. Little research laboratory for an independent, careful study on how human behavior is modified by organic chemicals like the tranquilizers and such other mood-changers as marijuana.

The psychic drugs are unscientific also because of their origin. They are products of serendipity. This is the word that Horace Walpole coined for a kind of accidental discovery after reading a fairy tale about the three alert Princes of Serendip (modern Ceylon).

Now there is nothing in itself reprehensible about serendipity. In science, it is the kind of sagacity that turns the unexpected to profit, certainly superior to not believing what is in front of one's eyes, such as was the first evidence of uranium fission. But the point is that serendipity is not blind man's buff, not a glib synonym for luck. It requires what Pasteur called an already prepared mind, seeking something, able to spot something different, alert enough to change course. Dexterous minds have made many such discoveries. Charles Goodyear, wearily trying one method after another, accidentally spilled a mixture of rubber and sulfur on a hot stove and found the way to vulcanize rubber. Albert Taylor and Leo Young of the Office of Naval Research, radioing each other across the Potomac, noted that a passing ship interfered with reception and with this anomaly discovered radar. Unable to make a heat equation balance any other way, Max Planck veered off and fathered the quantum theory. If the tale about Isaac Newton be true, then the apple that fell upon his noggin, thereby stimulating his brain to formulate the universal law of gravitation, was serendipity too. Serendipity comes in many types and the results are often dramatic.

But research can hardly be called science when it depends almost entirely upon serendipity. This has been true with the mood drugs. Notorious thalidomide was such a discovery. So was Benzedrine. A pharmacologist had recommended against it after it ruined a carefully designed experiment to test its effect on the blood pressure of an anesthetized cat. Given the chemical, the cat promptly awoke and ran away. Then an imaginative physician suggested such a drug might help patients who complain of an uncontrollable desire to sleep. And when the drug was found also to discourage eating, a virtue was made of that side-effect too.

Or take chlorpromazine, first developed in France as a hypothermic drug to prepare patients for surgery. A respectable American pharmaceutical firm, Smith Kline & French Laboratories, which had evolved far from its earlier days as a seller of sassafras and cod-liver oil, began experimenting with this drug. In 1954, its researchers announced that chlorpromazine was also a powerful antiemetic that would stop vomiting in dogs and affect the nervous system in a variety of other ways. Then they found something unusual. The drug would quieten a laboratory rat but, unlike the rat sedated with barbiturates, this one would scamper off when touched. Further research led to what might be called a breakthrough. Certainly it became chlorpromazine's big selling point—a new type of calming agent now called tranquilizer. Unlike shock treatment it could "slow down" a patient without crushing mental awareness. From interviews recorded at a mental hospital I heard a previously violent patient explain quietly, "She deserted the children." A schizophrenic spoke retrospectively, "It began when I was twelve after another kid said I was a Negro and couldn't have a soul." The psychotic may not be permanently cured, and the drug does have its side-effects. These limitations, and the serendipity approach, are understandable enough—results of our ignorance about the nervous system. Chlorpromazine seems to do its work in the subcortical region, somewhere in the area of the thalamus, where anxieties transmit their plaguing fears to the cortex. But this is very loose talk. Exactly where and how the disturbances arise, and what pathways the stimuli take, remain dim guesswork.

Telepathy, Electronically

An entirely different field, applied electronics, meets similar secrets of the nervous system but is better able to detour them. For here is practical engineering, which sets up a definite problem and attacks it with the "can do" rather than serendipity attitude. It does this by reducing the nervous system to an electrical system. The electronics man can consequently amplify its signals, can connect it to other electrical systems, can dream up hardware, often with dramatic results.

Mental energy of the physical kind, for example, helps explain brain waves, whose reason for existence is still baffling, but whose patterns the brain specialist can record with an electroencephalograph, then study the EEG for resulting clues to abnormalities, just as the heart specialist's ECG displays the electrical impulses, faulty or otherwise, developed with each beat in the cardiac cycle.

It is significant, too, that engineering is finding ways to feed such signals through sophisticated communication systems. A demonstration EEG, for instance, went from England over land line to a radio transmitter; then it hitchhiked on microwaves to a satellite, which was meanwhile charging its batteries with solar energy. The signals were amplified and retransmitted to a receiving station in New Jersey, thence by land line again to a Mayo Clinic neurologist in Minneapolis. There they were fed into a computer that printed out data from which a diagnosis was made and flashed back to England by the same route.

That is pretty much straight engineering. Still more fascinating is the progress by Case Institute of Technology and others in interdisciplinary work by electronic engineers and medical scientists. A paralytic, without use of arms or legs, wants a cup of coffee from a nearby table. A flick of his eyebrow turns on the source of infrared light built into the frame of his eyeglasses. Now, he looks at the desired cup. This action throws the invisible light upon a photoelectric cell beside the cup, and a self-powered brace then moves his arm to the cup and helps him bring it to his lips.

A more direct hookup between mind and machine seems at first glance merely an overgrown wonder toy. Actually, here is master-slave ingenuity that allows a human to perform tasks in an inhuman environment. He may be on a surface ship controlling a research vehicle at bottom of the sea. Or he may wish to stay in the spaceship that has landed on the moon, and send out an exploratory crawler. He—and his precious brain—remain safely, comfortably at a control console and operate an articulated arm equipped with electro-mechanical shoulder, elbow, hand, fingers. Some experimental versions send back a sense of feel. With others, the operator has closed-circuit TV with which to monitor what is occurring.

An odd assortment of companies have been lured into this robot field. It is logical that General Electric would be. But even General Mills got into it, by way of its electronics division, and became a leader, though with soul-searching as to whether such diversification strayed too far from the Wheaties business.

All this was an unforeseen byproduct from the nuclear field, where the need for such remote control soon became urgent. Near MIT's reactor, for instance, is a lab room to which "rabbit tubes"—pneumatic carriers analogous to those in old-time department stores—bring materials irradiated at the reactor. The "rabbit" goes directly into a sealed, glass-enclosed case. Here, the researcher working with, say, cancer tissue, operates safely from outside the case. A simple $1500 robot arm manipulates the specimen for him.

It was at Brookhaven that I saw the most splendid master-slave manipulator, a $40,000 product of General Mills. This was in one of the two "hot cells" constructed to show industry the way for "cold sterilization" of foods, etc. The cell was a large room that has radiation-shielding walls of extra-heavy "Brookhaven concrete," and an observation window of glass 54 inches thick; it bristles with fail-safe mechanisms, such as the one that allows escape if you are caught on the wrong side when the massive doors of lead lock shut.

This cell's function is to prepare radioactive materials. For instance, the dangerous fuel assemblies removed from nuclear reactors are submerged and guided in through a protective water-filled canal, removed from their encapsulation, cut into smaller pieces, then encased in protective capsules of their own for irradiation tasks elsewhere.

Obviously, this work must be governed from the outside, and Otto Kuhl, head of the High Intensity Radiation Development Laboratory, was proud of the robot that had just been installed to make this possible. Here was no ordinary manipulation of control buttons. Instead, you move your own arm, grasp with your own hand—and in the cell the arm of the massive manipulator mimics every motion. With its own fingers it picks up several hundreds of pounds, or performs an operation as gentle as handling an egg.

But what about something more direct, more daring—no human hand at all? No, not actual telepathy, or extrasensory perception. This is the field of sensory perception called cybernetic medicine. Here, again, the human brain makes its decision and a nerve message travels down the arm, for example. But now the human hand is dispensed with. The human nerve impulses operate the electro-mechanical hand—a direct form of thought control of machine by man.

This seemed another fantasy of the Russians when they began talking about it in the 1950s. However, they have become leaders in the field, as they did in the transplantation of human organs and other surgical triumphs, and for the same reason. The last war gave them many wrecked bodies to repair.

As with radar, however, the pioneering had been done in America. At MIT, I visited the late, world-famous Norbert Wiener, father of cybernetics and coiner of the word. It was he who led America's theoretical mathematicians into the nervous system—its feedback controls, its storage of information; and from there, in collaboration with computer technologists, into futuristic automation. I found him disgusted, however, with the common idea that cybernetics simply means automation. He conceived it as cooperation between what the human calls thinking and the engineer calls control and communications. "The word 'machine' has bamboozled us," said he.

A truly remarkable man, quick yet profound. A stocky little man with a wild splash of mustache and a smudge of chin whiskers, eyes twinkling and cigar puffing; an aging child prodigy who became a Harvard Ph.D. at eighteen when, his autobiography says, he had "an aggressive unlovable naïveté." Since then he had learned to be a man, and had also become a mocker of the science establishment: "Our techniques are running ahead of new, fresh ideas . . . There is no physics today, only pieces of physics . . . crash programs are rash programs . . . scientists are becoming intellectual lackeys and clock-punchers."

He was now emeritus, an MIT "Institute Professor" free to do as he pleased. What pleased him was working in the infant field of cybernetic medicine with Joseph Barr, of Massachusetts General Hospital. Behind this research is the fact that electrical impulses generated in the brain or heart can be picked up by electrodes on the skin and fed to recording instruments, providing the familiar EEG or ECG. Wiener's own interest was roused by the insistence of some amputees that they had a "phantom limb." The leg was gone, for instance, but they still felt leglike sensations there. Wiener reasoned that nerve messages trying to reach the phantom muscles were real enough. Why not, then, relay the signals to something real, an artificial limb operating as if it were part of the body?

In essence, the idea is simple enough. Usable signals could be obtained from just above the amputation by inserting electrodes that make contact with appropriate nerve circuits. The signals could then be strengthened by conventional electronics and made to manipulate the prosthetic device. Or, instead of inserting bothersome electrodes, a tiny radio could be implanted to transmit the signals to the skin surface, and the rest would go on from there.

Using the conventional term, I asked Wiener if this project had reached the "feasibility" stage. He listed the technical and psychological questions that still needed answering, then reverted to the man who never quite belonged to the establishment: "At this stage, for work of the quality we want, the project is deliberately being kept small. A crash program would wreck it. We would become administrators, doling out the work to too many incompetents."

How far might the man-machine coupling go? I talked with Director Robert M. Page of Naval Research Laboratory about it. Here, contemplating the human brain, was an outstanding one at work within the framework of what we call personality. For, like any scientist, Page is unlike any other. Professionally, he is best known for pioneering paths to modern radar. Privately, he is a devout Methodist. In all, a courtly man with a gentle smile and occasional tartness: "Too much technical literature since the war is trash that should be fed to the strawpile."

Projecting into the twenty-first century, he foresees a body bristling with pickup electrodes or wireless transmitters. In a few minutes, these would supply for machine storage and decision-making more information from the brain and elsewhere than is now possible in a lifetime of man struggling to communicate accurately with man. Such hookups would solve problems of ordinary life and prescribe appropriate action; they would diagnose psychological and physical abnormalities and prescribe cures. And eventually, Page suggests philosophically, when the secrets of tight coupling between brain and machine are mastered, the machine might be eliminated as middleman, and the coupling occur directly between human minds: "a group of people tightly coupled together and highly organized to concentrate all minds on a single purpose—could we perhaps call such an organization of people an all-human machine?"

Of Mind and Memory

Science goes on pondering. When is the mechanistic brain attended by "personality"; together, do they comprise what we call the human mind? Research quickly finds here that its biggest problem is defining the problem, so that it can seek something more than lucky accidents.

Shall the researcher examine the concept of consciousness? But consciousness quickly broadens into more than the difference between awake and asleep. Capable scientists have believed in ghosts and more so in "life after death." And what of the border area called dreaming? Or that acute form of consciousness called pain? Some wonder if a tree experiences pain when it is being cut, though without an outcry. And are we only being anthropocentric again when the playful dog exhibits a canine sense of humor—and what is humor?

Closer to things we know, the ecstatic reaction of a cat to catnip is now attributed to a gene in the cat's makeup. This involves procreation, which handed down that gene, and eating, which satisfies the prescribed desire. Then how account for the poet's ecstatic reaction when he views the Parthenon at moonlight though no slim huntress Diana is there, or for the hunter's transports of glee beside his slain buck though he doesn't need meat? Or take music. A guess, so often repeated that it now masquerades as a truism, is that in enough time a computer, its fingers wandering idly, might produce not only "The Lost Chord" but a Beethoven-like quartet. Whether the music is by Beethoven or IBM, what is our pleasure from these harmonies? Is it analogous to the satisfaction of the catnip cat? Or is the cat responding as we do to an excruciatingly lovely dissonance?

Or take the voice of the dolphin. Until recent years, almost all we knew scientifically about these remarkable creatures was written by Aristotle. Navy now wants to borrow from the dolphin: not its intelligence but the efficiency of its hydrodynamics and, of course, its sonar-like ability to communicate. At foggy Point Mugu, California, Louis R. Padberg, Jr., an acoustics engineer specializing in antisubmarine warfare, showed me the Naval Missile Center's test dolphins. Then he played back five minutes of the three hundred thousand feet he had recorded for studying their ability to locate food and obstacles by means of their wide range of sound frequencies, a choice unequaled by any other creature. As the tape moved, he announced the striking similarities: "barnyard cackle . . . baby crying . . . human laughing . . . burps . . . canary whistling," and so on.

But again, analogies can be an easy trap. Shunning them, what can the genuine human mind reveal about itself? When it is possessed by devils we go less frequently to preachers to cast them out; we go to psychiatrists. And scorned now is the concept that studying algebra teaches us to think. Instead, science has caught up with John Dewey's learn-by-doing and makes its students "discover" a theory for themselves rather than memorize it. This, theoretically, builds a nation of bright researchers. It also brings a growing number of charges that students are wheedled and pushed into worthless and even fraudulent Science Fair projects. In any event, it creates creativity about as much as algebra creates thinking. Similarly, there is little enthusiasm for physicist I. I. Rabi's recommendation that "judgment" be taught.

Then what of raw knowledge—the accumulation of facts—which might presumably aid creativity and bolster judgment? This quickly introduces questions about the memory process. It should be comprehendible, in view of the mechanistic way we can build it into a computer and what we know of the nerve system.

As the system matures, it adds inter-neuron connections to satisfy communication requirements of the maturing body. A simple example is how it can elaborate upon the hereditary reflex with which, for instance, the spinal cord jerks the knee. Evolution has provided the brain also with some short circuits for automatic response, such as the one that winks the eyelid. But a big difference is that reflexes through the brain can be altered, notably by the conditioned-reflex method with which Russia's Pavlov founded experimental psychology.

Consequently, the temptation is strong to compare such changes with learning and memory because these, too, depend upon "reinforcement" of neuron response along a certain pathway. The child learns a few times that two and two are four. Thereafter, the question brings a quick answer. Similarly, a neuron connection formed strongly in the adult brings vivid memories thereafter. Conversely, in senility enough neurons have died to leave only fragments of circuits, pieces of memory.

But such explanations remain empty. We just do not know how memory works: how the brain cell stores information, how the cells join their bioelectric circuits, how the pathway for an impulse is chosen, how pathways remain permanent, and so on. The computer cannot tell us. Can the tantalizing planarian do so?

At first glance it is merely a half-inch freshwater flatworm that looks cross-eyed. But it is a primitive creature long famed for several distinctions. One is its reproductive versatility. It reminds us of a period in evolution when nature could not decide whether sexual union is necessary. This left the flatworm confused too. It is a hermaphrodite in its odd fashion. When young it functions as a male, when older as an egg-laying female. Then there is the other way, which makes the flatworm a favorite of experimental psychologists. It easily replicates by fission. Researchers bring this about at will by cutting the worm in half. The head portion then grows a new tail and the tail portion grows a new head—though a vertebrate, the planarian has a nervous system so rudimentary that it easily grows the new brain.

In 1952, young biologist Jeffrey J. W. Baker started careful tests at the University of Virginia of the planarian's learning ability. This was followed by the Pavlov-like experiments of Robert Thompson and James V. McConnell at the University of Texas. They "educated" the creature by conditioning. A light was flashed at it, then it was jolted by an electrical shock. The result was a contraction of its body. After about 150 such experiences the flashing light alone was enough to make the worm contract; it had "learned."

That was the starter. Since then, at the University of Michigan and elsewhere, McConnell, an unorthodox psychologist, has gone farther

—even farther than Russia's Lysenko, whom science scorned for his claim that acquired characteristics can be inherited. First, McConnell and his associates found that when the learned planarian was cut in two and proceeded to grow into two worms, the one with the original brain retained memory, as might be expected, but there was also recall in the worm with the newly grown head. Then the testers tried a simple enough but bold experiment. They chopped learned planarians into pieces and fed them to unlearned planarians. And the cannibals thereupon demonstrated that they had acquired some of the learning. It is understandable that the research report about this sent shock waves through the science world—the more so after Arthur Koestler spread the word with a brilliant article about the results.

The research has continued, by McConnell and others. The theory is that RNA is at work here, partly because nerve cells are known to contain a rich supply of this nucleic acid, partly because of the nature of RNA. It is commonly believed to be various versions of a messenger molecule that receives DNA's coded genetic instructions and carries them to the cell's chemical reactor, where the designated compounds are manufactured. Why, then, so the theory goes, cannot RNA also receive, store, and transmit environmental information—the stuff of memory?

The conjectures on how this may work are too varied to examine here. So are the possibilities of what can be done with the idea. Suffice to say that nobody yet has proposed another fad for already many-fadded education—turning college students into witty dramatists or brilliant scientists by feeding them hamburgers enriched with the RNA of a Bernard Shaw and Charles Darwin. But there have been stirrings elsewhere. Already, for example, researchers at McGill University have reported improvement in the memory of senile men who were simply injected with RNA from yeast. And from Japan a rayon manufacturer has written McConnell that his company also produces RNA.

To put it mildly, many other scientists reserve opinions about much of this. Though they prefer the "rat men" of experimental psychology, and now the flatworm researchers, to the educationist and industrial-counselor varieties of psychologist who write such books as *30 Days to a Higher I.Q., Psycho-Cybernetics*, and *The*

Strategy of Creative Thinking, they have inherited a mistrust of behavioral scientists. This is not surprising. Many rat men themselves remain modest about their methods and accuracy, though they cannot quite agree that animals studied by Americans rush about with bustle and pep, achieving the desired result by chance, while German animals sit still and think, finally reaching a solution out of their inner consciousness. Specifically, the scientific fraternity is touchy about taking seriously what might turn out to be more Lamarckism, or, worse, more Lysenkoism. Yet it realizes that today's Lysenkoism might become the approved creed of tomorrow, just as some concepts of spontaneous generation are now respectable. So it proceeds with caution, going no farther than the blithe psychologist who said, "A theory is like a woman. It's more important that it be fertile than good." At any rate, I was told by a biochemist that after a year's work with planarians his group could not confirm the McConnell claim and was retooling for more experiments. "We're thinking over," he said politely, "what errors we might have committed."

Unlike psychologists, psychiatrists do have medical training, and class war follows when psychiatry challenges psychology's right to practice psychotherapy. Psychiatry does what it can for mental illness. It may recommend shock treatments with insulin or electricity, or even drastic lobotomy to remove part of the forebrain. But these smack of the shotgun approach. So psychiatry is becoming increasingly addicted to the use of paralyzing drugs that will "block off" troublesome nerve centers in the brain.

But what of the many mental troubles this side of insanity, of neuroses instead of psychoses, of the "know thyself" art that Shakespeare illustrated when he dramatized tragic characters, that clergymen practice when they invite a member of the flock to unburden himself?

This approach, Sigmund Freud built into a helpful new therapy. And the inadequacies of today's psychoanalysis are not entirely Freud's. His doctrine cannot be boiled down simply to "everything is sex," such as the speculation that an ulcer patient is raging against the mother figure when he "bites" his gastric mucosa. And in Freud's native Austria today, psychiatrists are taught to regard flirtation by Americans with existentialism as an attempted escape from toughening realities into a vacuum.

Freud apparently would have preferred the mechanistic approach. But he was discouraged by the still shrouded secret of what is mental: "We assume, as the other natural sciences have taught us to expect, that in mental life some kind of energy is at work; but we have no data enabling us to compare it with other forms of energy." So, turning inward where only art, philosophy, and religion had explored, he began probing the mind's response to environment's pressure upon instincts. An instinct he pictured as a relentless energy drive of some sort. When pent up it becomes troublesome undischarged energy. Hence the need for catharsis—a vomiting out of repressions.

"After long doubts and vacillations," Freud reduced the instincts to two. Eros corresponds to the biologist's creative instinct; it demands food and sex for perpetuating the species. When interfered with in some way, Eros may find "creative outlets"—art, science, and the like. Opposed to Eros is all-consuming Thanatos, the death instinct. It seeks to undo what Eros built, to return the body to the inorganic condition from which life emerged with futile defiance. Neither concept is transparently clear, of course. Yet neither is without parallels of a sort. Biologists, too, say that, for the race to evolve, the old must make way for the Bible's "those that shall come after." And physicists are resigned to something worse—the second law of thermodynamics, which says the total quantity of useful energy will go on decreasing and the corresponding increase of entropy will bring the entire universe to the standstill of death.

But all this is sticky ground and certainly Freud's *id* and *ego* cannot be defined as easily as chromosome, neuron, erg, and watt. Freudians do not try. Doctrinal wars involved Freud and the disciples who broke away to set up rival schools of treatment, but today's nonmechanistic psychiatry—except, of course, for its quacks —is more modest. In this, it has been unlike the behavioristic branch of psychology, which tried to scorn the mind and consciousness. In Russia, and in America under dogmatic John B. Watson, this branch acknowledged only what instruments could reveal about the nervous system and insisted that human behavior could be changed, unchanged, and rechanged by conditioning alone. But behaviorism has become uncertain of itself in the past generation and is better typified today by Harvard's brilliantly reasonable B. F. Skinner, while the nonmechanistic concepts, in one version or other, have gone on being useful. They add a basic though vague approach to the puzzling mind. And with other branches of psychiatry they bring sympathetic understanding to the subtle problems that bedevil the ape's cousin. Prosperous mental-health programs have become a virtually unchallenged part of the prosperous new American scene.

But here again we face questions. And the one most important discovery about brainwork—its electrical basis—is now two centuries old. Despite what science has learned about the bioelectric nervous system, about ways to link this system to robot outlets, about ways to alleviate troubles of this system by cutting, burning, shocking, drugging, and psychoanalyzing them, the sum is gossamer.

The brain remains a frustrating mystery and the mind a will-o'-the-wisp. And until science concentrates on solving the mechanics of the brain, comparing it with a computer is worse than comparing apples and oranges. It is comparing apples with question marks. For the computer, though its wiring may seem impossibly tangled spaghetti, is a factory product. Man builds it. Then man prescribes how it shall do one task after another, just as the nonautomatic delivery man is given his truck and his route. In short, the computer has no secrets, mechanical or psychic. What, then, of this machine and of the automation it promises, or threatens, depending on one's outlook?

IX: *The Automaters*

Computers can search their memories and then speak, after a fashion.
But if you ask an all-electronic high-speed digital machine to classify
itself more simply, do not be surprised if it replies crisply, "Engine
of war." Born in World War II, it grew through years of cold war,
and Pentagon funds continue trying to overcome its weaknesses as a
master component of automated national policy.

The continuing R & D is not unusual. As in other glamour fields,
computer realities do not easily overtake the projected dream. If
success is measured by costliness, then the computer is sensationally
successful. As a military brain, however, it needs much more schooling; and as the symbol and spearhead of automation, much more
reliability. In the early 1950s it proved that an H-bomb was possible
and also became the fast calculator in our complicated air-defense
systems. Prospects seemed unlimited.

A dozen years later there were many second thoughts, and the
Air Force chief of missile planning was writing an article for *Fortune*
magazine: "Security Is Too Important to Be Left to Computers."
Also, though the Pentagon's complicated economics were being
handled well enough by computers and their civilian associates, the
"technipols" and "whiz kids" mistrusted by old-line brass, actual
war was something else. Defense Secretary McNamara was commuting often between Washington and Vietnam. The computer apparently could not be programed for judgment. Or, for that matter,
for courage. It would have coolly counseled the outrageously out-

numbered Greeks to surrender at Thermopylae; twenty-four centuries later, it would have coolly ridiculed the resistance of battered England to the Nazi wave of the future.

But what of automation elsewhere? Has not the computer begun to wear several nonmilitary caps—master accountant, head librarian, chief secretary, and if not the executive himself, at least his surrogate? Journalism chronicles such progress daily, and the better journalists do not exaggerate. In fact, there is little need to do so. The computer commands the sequence that operates spaceship and oil refinery. It is the cool big-business head that runs various operations in a modern university, advertising agency, automobile factory. It grades people for the census-taker, tabulates lungs for the American Cancer Society, counts votes even before the polls have opened.

And, human enthusiasms being what they are, it becomes the Wizard of Duz who can do anything. Two easier electronic devices, the lie-detector and hidden microphone, have not put the human sleuth out of business any more than they have cured criminality itself. Yet the computer is offered as the eye that will recognize, then watch, potential assassins of the nation's President.

All this, and mammoth science too. Its hunger for automation is insatiable. Researchers now routinely bring their nebulous or tedious problems to the electronic circuits that are unruffled either by ghastly equations or endless data; circuits that work three shifts a day, uncomplainingly except for breakdowns, and accurately, except for human and machine errors. They calculate chromosomes for the biologist, "strange particles" for the nuclear physicist, new stars and new breeds of stars for the astronomer.

This constantly brings up the problem: Who in the insistent queue of researchers should have time on the computers? No computer could decide. It might handle questions of pecking order; it could not distinguish between brilliant research and humdrum, humdrum and bad. One result is a version of Gresham's Law—the bad smothers the good. Hence Vannevar Bush's fear that research will become "inhibited like a colony of bacteria by its own exudations." Hence a NASA official's pessimism: "For Project Apollo, we will probably generate so much paper that, if we piled it up, it would get to the moon before Apollo."

Business offices, too, now question the obedience with which computer systems spew more and ever more paper. "It's worse than ticker tape," sighed an efficiency expert, looking out over New York from his office in the Empire State Building. "Data processing is a tool for those who can use it, and a prestige symbol for those who cannot. More and more reports, copies of reports, and copies of copies. Communication will be buried in a new carboniferous era." To all of which the computer would reply with the stock defense, "I only work here."

Similar evasion of responsibility underlies another built-in limitation: the computer's blind reliance upon the raw data, and upon the program for homogenizing the data. This explains why computers can assemble medical symptoms into somewhat of a diagnosis but cannot unriddle the complexities of nonmedical human behavior. For this task, satisfactory input does not exist. Even "hardware" assignments bring trouble. Jet Propulsion Laboratory forgot to insert a hyphen in the punch-card instructions fed to a computer. For want of that hyphen, an $18.5-million project, our first exploratory spacecraft to Venus, went off course and had to be destroyed a few minutes after launching.

The nervousness increases with manned spacecraft. At MIT, "Doc" Draper showed me what would become the miniaturized computer for the guidance system that his laboratory was designing for Apollo. Then he gave one of his earthy appraisals: "We need them but there is too much malarky about computers. If it doesn't check out with what I can figure on the back of an envelope, I recommend checking the computer. It can only put out what goes in." In their own lingo, those who program computers put it this way: "Garbage in, garbage out."

However, the computer does have an unchallengeable claim. Though it cannot think, it can relieve humans of staggering amounts of mental drudgery. And if it encounters a problem too vast for even its capability, it unashamedly allows humans to simplify the problem. The answer may stray from the ideal but if this is to err, it is human —and practical.

Also human: the computer can suffer its own version of nervous breakdown. Despite "debugging" by the manufacturer, it remains a network of vulnerable electronic components. An example is a standard massive machine demanded by massive science, IBM's 7094, which has been priced at around $3 million off the line, and $5 million with needed accessories. Three were working for GOD ("Goddard Operations Director") when I visited the big center that NASA has in Maryland for tracking spacecraft. Cape Kennedy was getting the publicity but Goddard was receiving and interpreting the crucial data. For instance, it compared where the computer said a Mercury spaceship should be with where radar told the computer it actually was. To ensure against breakdowns, GOD was practicing redundancy: two of the computers were installed back to back, one ready to take over for the other. Moral: the flesh is weak, so is hardware.

There is no need for further examples to introduce a realistic examination of what the computer does, its prospects for doing better, and the effects all this will have on the rising tide of "hands-off" operations called automation. For besides offering the console from which automation is controlled, the computer is itself the shiny, blinking epitome of automation. Whatever its specific task, its over-all function is to eliminate human labor, by the white-collar as well as blue-collar worker.

Viewed mechanically, its memory capacity is far smaller than that of the human brain, but neither does it forget so easily. Also, its step-by-step procedure cannot match the brain's agility and associative powers (the housewife, whether washing a breakfast glass or a red shirt, is reminded to jot "tomato juice" on her shopping list); but the computer compensates by working at dazzling high speeds.

Consequently, it offers many abilities as a lightning calculator and processor of data. But the computer need not be so prosaic. It is able to imagine in the sense that it can feign. Whether it simulates with mathematical models or real hardware, the result is valuable trial-and-error at high speed. Example: a company wants the best location for a new branch plant. It feeds requirements into the computer, then introduces variables until it gets the choice that best meets the objectives. Another example: the need to test a new kind of spacecraft. At Grumman Aircraft, I saw OAO, the orbiting astronomical observatory. Instructed by a computer and reporting back to the computer, it was a performance model that would never be launched. Its mission was inside an aluminum vacuum chamber. Here it was going through the sequence that imitated launching, tumbling, and eventually "locking" on to simulated stars—all this while maneuvering its telescope away from the simulated bothersome "sunshine" of eighteen 6,000-watt xenon arc lamps.

And now a computer's greatest charm. Without it, the assembly would be little more than a glorified adding machine, or filing system, or comparator. With it, the computer becomes an adviser able to balance many variables, left against right, pro against con. To have this ability, it is designed to include more than "and" circuits for adding everything that comes its way. For instance, it also has "or" and "neither" capabilities for choice and rejection. Now, it becomes a worthy servant, even rival, of the brain, because man's biggest intellectual trouble is his inability to handle a number of variables. But now, too, it runs the risk of any earthly oracle. It must have reliable input, whether it is advising the racetrack gambler or the Secretary of Defense.

A homely example might be the economics of apples. Simply as tabulator, the computer would be fed data from various sources and told to reckon how many apples are produced by all nations. Or, more worthy of its potential, it might be told to choose data concerning only apples, McIntosh variety, of a certain size, produced in Massachusetts, in a year when apples brought a specified price. Or, as an orchardist's "think tank," it might decide how many seedling trees should be planted next spring—this from data on production and prices of the past twenty years, the rate at which our population is growing, the rate at which we are eating fewer apples, weather forecasts; also the tax situation and hosts of other statistics and predictions, including any prospects that the nation's next President will be kind enough to munch on publicity apples in public.

A human, unless he were Sherlock Holmes's dazzling brother, Mycroft, will soon wilt under so many data and variables, or resort to his hunches and intuition. The computer patiently works the problem. And the result is accurate enough if the machine is being serviced dependably; if it isn't being hoodwinked by errors and propaganda; if data are weighed properly; and if the orange-grower's computer isn't preparing to report that the rosy apple a day reeks with metabolic risks.

Buying the Computer

Stand up to the computer, or bow to it, here is America's most glamorous machine, product of an EDP (Electronic Data Processing) industry growing so fast technically that the year 1950 is already ancient. It has moved equally fast financially. By 1963, it was doing a $4-billion business in computers, a figure expected to double by 1970. Almost half this income is from "software," notably from programing the machines with instructions according to the users' needs. And the hardware half includes the extra called rentals, all the more juicy for IBM because it dominates the computer field.

An example is the machine called Stretch. Only seven others were in existence, doing secret work elsewhere in the government, when I visited the eighth soon after it began masticating data for Weather Bureau researchers. With Stretch doing ten billion calculations daily, they hoped to learn eventually how to provide reliable forecasts.

Here was the biggest, fastest computer in IBM's line—twice as fast as the 7094, just as 7094's speed was twice that of the older favorite of scientists, IBM's 7090. However, Stretch was spending part of its time checking for its mistakes. It could correct a single error itself; when there was a bunching of errors, the machine had to stop for help from human attendants. It also had electronic slaves, like the satellite computer that prechewed data from punch cards, then provided it in gulps so the speedier giant need not be idling meanwhile. Stretch time was precious, understandably so. This was a $7.5-million system, for which the government was paying $160,000 rent per month, plus extra for overtime. Nor does the rent go down as the computer ages.

On the 7090, for instance, the Comptroller General's investigators found that purchase would save up to $3.7 million over five years, and $1.5 million yearly after that. And, of course, leasing eludes requirements for competitive bidding. It is also habit-forming; the customer is conditioned against shopping around. There are other supplementary details, pro leasing as well as con. For example, computers have improved so rapidly that, as an NASA policy-maker explained to Congress, "We would be foolish to buy one, then be stuck with it."

Bypassing details, however, the sum total goes beyond IBM and beyond leasing. It is a situation unparalleled in R & D history. The United States Government pays for its computers twice. On the one hand, it is the world's biggest market for the machines, including smaller ones and the monsters required by its science agencies. On the other, the computer is something that industry cannot claim as reward for conventional free enterprise. It was mainly government money, combined with university talent, that invented and developed the modern computer. For instance, the only important patent squabble in the industry centered around rivalry between IBM and RCA to profit from an MIT "breakthrough"—Professor Jay Forrester's now standard magnetic-core memory. It was financed by Navy and Air Force.

For similar R & D dependence on government one might go to radar, better yet to nuclear power. Neither computer nor nuclear power plant can ignore its ancestry. Both were war babies born of (1) a military need; (2) government's calling on university brain-power to meet that need. The difference is that the power plants are still in a subsidized hazy area between commercial and experimental while computers are commercial indeed. At any rate, computer manufacturers charge the government full price. And since 1948, when it ordered its first general-purpose computer, a Univac for the Census Bureau, government has been the industry's best customer, also its fattest victim when there is monopoly or price-gouging.

Noteworthy, too, is how IBM took control of the EDP industry with financial rather than R & D acumen. Today, the company has research facilities that befit its prestige but, like would-be rivals, it cannot boast a portfolio of basic computer patents. Rather, it was with punch cards, developed by a census expert, that Thomas J. Watson Sr. originally built IBM's data-processing reputation. Later, its first computer clung to then conventional business-machine technology rather than thrust daringly through to electronic methods. This Mark I was a wartime project undertaken with the Navy; the necessary inventiveness for its cumbersome assembly of electric relays and adding wheels was provided by Howard Aiken at Harvard.

Even the first Univac—a commercial outgrowth of University of Pennsylvania research sponsored by Army—didn't excite IBM at first. Such misguessing about computer prospects was common back around 1950. The difference was that IBM detected its danger sooner. Thomas J. Watson Jr. was imaginative, and as a wartime bomber pilot had caught a glimpse of how superior the electronics approach could be to cogs, gears, and wheels. Furthermore, he was acquiring enough responsibility in monolithic IBM to oppose even his father. He noted many things: Univac's successful debut at the Census Bureau; the speed with which National Bureau of Standards built valuable Seac for the Air Force and was pioneering elsewhere; forward leaps such as Forrester's new memory at MIT, mathematician von Neumann's Maniac that decided the H-bomb was feasible. Watson needed only pencil and paper to add all this to the computer's possibilities for automating office work and manufacturing processes. He computed IBM's future, hired von Neumann as consultant, and started a program to snatch leadership before competitors could know what was happening to them. By 1956, when IBM signed a consent decree agreeing to stop various practices that the government called antitrust violations, the company dominated computers as well as the rest of EDP.

Since then, the best that a half-dozen competitors have done is fight for second place. When a count showed that three-fourths of all the nation's computers, including two-thirds of the government's, were IBM's, Representative Joseph E. Karth could only say plaintively, "I am not saying that IBM is not good, but I know there are others who might want to get in on this gravy."

Among the "others" were two of Karth's fellow Minnesotans, Minneapolis-Honeywell and Control Data Corporation. Honeywell resembled sprawling RCA, GE, Sperry-Rand, and others in that it could apply losses from one product against profits from another. Youthful Control Data was truly independent. It was also the sensational dark horse not being overlooked by those Wall Street insiders lucky enough to have knowledgeable scientists as consultants. It was focusing strongly on the big science–big government market for elaborate machines. It welcomed purchaser as well as renter. Altogether it was a fresh breeze in the computer world and a lesson to industry in general: there was still opportunity for an alert new-comer to catch the Sperry-Rands asleep. And there is room for others because today's digital computer is by no means a finished product.

Meanwhile, what of its older cousin, the analog computer, which is likewise useful and electronic? This type differs in several important details but mainly in that it needs no memory and does not count. It measures. Many tasks can be performed by either type. Often, both can be geared together for a complex assignment. Digitals, however, are far in the lead, for big research jobs as well as general-purpose clerical work. Of NASA's large computers, for example, 95 per cent are digitals.

To see the directions that the digital may take under pressure from the forces of automation, let us first see what it is now.

Inside the Machine

At first glance it is easy for the layman, and the scientist who isn't a computerman, to mistake the whole for a part. The whole is a data-processing system, more awkward than engineers like. Actually, the computer itself isn't that big and complicated. Its console, with the blinking lights so attractive to cameramen, is an auxiliary of sorts; it betrays the fact that the machine needs someone to command and monitor it. And much of what you see crowding the corners of the room, perhaps overflowing into other rooms, is peripheral equipment. Of this, much is the result of unbalanced technology. In exchange for high speed the computer had to sacrifice efficiency elsewhere. For example, Control Data's giant 3600 at Argonne National Laboratory is part of a system including four slave or desk-size computers that feed the big one. Two dozen other satellites are tape units for additional memory—a usual trouble is that the computer cannot have both high speed and big memory. Tape also serves as a "gear-reducer." Output from the computer would pour into its printing machines faster than they can handle it, even at their thousand lines per minute. So the output first goes to one reel of tape after another. Then, at their slower pace, they take turns feeding the printers.

Probing deeper, to see how a computer itself cerebrates, we find two main elements, the internal control system and the memory. They add up to an electronic network. And, like any other versatile wiring system, this one looks complicated only until one notices the variation on a single theme.

1—The Code

Everything that occurs in the conventional computer, and all information stored in its memory—mathematical tables; prose and poetry; telemetry signals from a satellite, the stuff of photographs—is governed by a rigid code whose only two symbols are 1 and 0. This matches the fact that components of the computer know only two electrical situations. For example, its transistors are either conducting or not conducting, its memory materials are magnetized in either one direction or the other. In short, the computer resembles the ordinary light bulb that can be only switched on or off, or the damsel who chants, "He loves me . . . he loves me not," as she plucks her daisy.

A code so simple becomes troublesome only if we forget that the 1 and 0 are symbols, not quantities. In arithmetic, where the distinction is especially important, computers leave familiar decimals and use the binary numbering system. So, when a careless scientist says that computers cannot count to ten, the humanist pricks up his ears and says, "I told you so—an idiot." This overlooks the computer's ability to count so fast with the only two fingers it has that it may indeed dance on our graves after burying us under its outpour of statistics. At any rate, binary's two symbols are as sensible for this machine as is the human's counting on his ten fingers, a symbolic device that led to the decimal system.

Admittedly, binary seems awkward at first, but less so when we remember that in the decimal system, for instance, 35 is represented by three 10s and five 1s. Binary's two-finger system has to break 35 down into powers of 2. That is, it considers 4 as 2^2, which is the second power of 2, therefore 2×2; it considers 32 as 2^5, which is the fifth power of 2, therefore $2 \times 2 \times 2 \times 2 \times 2$; and so on. Then, to encode 35, we would get:

```
1—a Yes for 2⁵, which is ............... 32
0—a No for 2⁴, which would have been 16
0—a No for 2³, which would have been  8
0—a No for 2², which would have been  4
1—a Yes for 2¹, which is ...............  2
1—a Yes for 2⁰, which is ...............  1
100011                                    35
```

That bizarre 100011 obviously does not mean one hundred thousand and eleven. And it represents 35 only indirectly. It is the computer's way of transmitting a specified arrangement of Yes and No signals—a packet of six so-called "bits" that allow manipulating the number 35. Like other technical fields, computer engineering has a jargon alarming to laymen. Some is sheer uniquack, like naming a computer Brainiac. There are also hardware terms like pixie lights and flip-flop circuits. And from ordinary English, computerese twists into puzzlers such ordinary words as "logic" and even the word "word." But anybody can see the aptness of the word "bit." It is a condensation of "binary digit," which, in turn, is the computer's smallest piece of information; in other words, the Yes or No represented by 1 or 0.

The rest is a matter of "how many bits for a buck." For example, the computer can be made to handle entire "words" as a unit, the "word" being a packet of up to perhaps 50 bits representing a real word, a number, and so on; or a routine instruction programed into the machine: "Get three prices for wheat—average them—store the answer." And among them may be bits that do nothing more than try to keep the data honest. Simplest is the redundancy bit—a repetition of the same bit. Others are check bits. Trickiest of these are the intentional errors, monitors that automatically slow down the system when necessary.

2—The Control System

Speed is the computer's big selling point, whether it is solving strictly mathematical problems, translating languages, or doing something more urbane like checking its own errors or advising the Pentagon on a best choice. Its speed depends partly on how fast it can operate its network of switching mechanisms, the gates that, by opening or shutting to appropriate signals, control operation of the computer. It was because of their slowness that the first computers did little more than rouse hopes for something radically different. Then, in 1946, came Army's Eniac, the first electronic computer. For electromechanical relays and adding wheels it substituted the speed of vacuum tubes, thousands of them. It made the computer a thousand times faster. Here was indeed a breakthrough, even though in a few short years the Eniac idea has become more obsolete than the airplane that the Wright brothers built at Kitty Hawk. In the 1950s, ordinary electronics expanded into solid-state physics: transistors, faster, smaller, began replacing tubes. Now, we are well into the third generation—thin-film circuits need only one-hundredth as much space and offer switching speeds measured not in millionths of a second but in the billionths called nanoseconds.

3—The Memory

Here, as in the control system—and like the human brain too—the computer had to evolve from primitive beginnings. Both the punch card and the cathode-ray tube could speak in the computer's binary language of bits. But they were bulky and slow. Magnetism opened another avenue. Bits could be stored in the Yes-No form of magnetized spots on reels of special tape, on rotating drums, or on disks. This was a faster, less sprawling way to store and move information. But the computer still wasn't a brain depending on its own memory; it was more like a brain visiting a library. Needed was something compact and fast enough to act as efficient internal storage.

Then came Whirlwind I. Like Eniac, it emerged from a university lab working on a military problem—how to convert radar warning data into defense against Soviet bombers, and do it in "real time," as fast as the situation changes instead of chewing on data a half-hour or so. Whirlwind, on which Forrester of MIT had been working, answered the need as far as a fast, internal memory was concerned. Each "core" in this computer was a memory cell—a ferromagnetic ring only a few hundredths of an inch in diameter. Each could be magnetized in a few millionths of a second.

The technical details are many; the principle is simple enough.

Each core has an address because the cores are arranged in planes, or "layers," and laced together by hair-thin conductive wires. Each layer may be, say, 50 cores wide, 80 cores long. So, if stood on edge, its 4000 cores would be analogous to an array of numbered mailboxes at the post office. And the computer code allows each core a binary choice. If given one magnetic condition, it can represent the 1; if the other, the 0. In this way, electrical signals obeying a program already stored in the memory can instantly store each "bit" of input information at its own address; likewise, electrical signals can then instantly find each bit needed, and send it on for processing, with the ultimate result perhaps appearing as real words on a typewriter, or as data on punched tape that runs other automated equipment.

Efficiency of the memory depends on crowding the cores as much as possible without the magnetization of one affecting its neighbors. MIT's Lincoln Laboratory carried the idea farther for itself, the government, and computer manufacturers (IBM later settled with MIT by giving a lump sum of $13 million for a paid-up license to use the magnetic-core memory). By the 1960s, Lincoln Lab had a core memory that could store 2,500,000 bits; the first Whirlwind's capacity was 16,000. Eventually, progressing from one development to another—faster transistors for switching, and a memory that substituted magnetic thin film for cores—Lincoln introduced a working model called FX-1. Compared with Whirlwind, this pioneer averaged seventy times more operations per second and its memory, though small, worked thirty times faster.

Other such advances are being tried experimentally throughout the computer world. Most interesting is the hope for a speedy miniaturized machine using the thin-film device called cryotron for switching and memory units. It exemplifies growing interest in the pregnant field of cryogenics. Both its memory and controls would profit from the alluring phenomenon called superconductivity: at deep-freeze temperatures of around −270 centigrade, electrical resistance in some metals vanishes and current goes right on flowing through them until quenched by the magnetic field of another current. Here obviously is a way to speak the computer's code—in terms of which cryotrons are superconducting and which are not. But although an experimental memory of, say, 16,000 bits can be stored in an area smaller than that of a common playing card and only 120 millionths of an inch thick, the practical problems are many. For instance, a liquid-helium bath is needed to keep the equipment cooled sufficiently and, for all its virtues, helium has freakish habits. It will leak through holes so small that no other substance can follow; defying gravity, it even leaks upward and out of an open container.

The Better Computer

As with man, the future of computers holds many enigmas. But some projection from the present is possible. How much farther need these machines go to satisfy the foreseeable requirements of automation? One of the experts I consulted was R. R. Everett, head of technical operations at Mitre, the company organized to relieve MIT of such embarrassingly unacademic projects as computerized SAGE, the radar protection system against Soviet surprise attack.

He foresaw sophisticated systems built around these goals:

1. Speedier computers: "We're never satisfied. We want them from ten to a hundred times faster." (They already can handle letters and numbers over a million times faster than man can with pencil and paper.)

2. Cheaper, larger storage capacity: "Here, too, our desire is unlimited." (The largest computers have reached three million bits; guesses for the human brain run into many thousands of millions.)

3. Large, transportable systems for far-out space projects: "Such, literally, don't exist yet." (The human carries his brain wherever he goes.)

4. Better "software" to answer the most acute need—programing. The machine can be taught to modify some of the instructions. Other shortcuts are reducing the need for changing from one program to another. But the initial need for a human instructor remains the bottleneck: "In a large system, programing costs more than the computer. And it takes too long. We race to build the computer and, say, the airplane that goes with it. Then the programing takes two years."

To those requirements can be added a variety of modest ones, such as the office manager's dream of microminiaturization that will place a telephone-size computer on his desk; and the urgent need to end what David Sarnoff of RCA calls a "technological Tower of Babel." For instance, computers work happily enough with their binary code but neither manufacturers nor users have worked out a simplified universal vocabulary for telling the machine what to do.

Such developments, however, promise no surprises. They would continue a series of begats, just as today's automobile, though faster and more automatic, remains essentially the horseless carriage propelled by a chugging engine. Even the time-sharing method, though it eliminates the queue of people waiting for computer time, offers nothing radical. A large computer, controlled from many consoles, becomes a statistical mill that serves many customers simultaneously. Versions of this were introduced at such places as MIT and Dartmouth, and IBM followed two years later. But the method requires nothing more bizarre than reprograming so that questions from one user will not interfere with work being done for somebody else.

Cannot computers be taught something really new? Well, there is the flirtation with machines like Madaline. If Madaline works out, it would free the computer from its most noticeable defect, which is not the limitations of its hardware or software, but its innate infantilism. Immediately after birth, before formal schooling, the normal human begins self-education. Its brain starts blank but immediately begins storing memories, programing automatic reactions, adapting itself to new conditions. Once bitten becomes twice shy; once gratified becomes twice desiring. Furthermore, the human is a discoverer who takes shortcuts to learning. He forms a first impression; the accurate details can come later.

Compare this with the conventional computer, which cannot leap to wrong conclusions but neither can it learn from experience. And, unlike the human, of course, it does not investigate a surprise. Instructed to trail rabbits, it is the beagle that ignores the scent of what might be a unicorn, thereby overlooking what science calls a precious anomaly. It meets the statistician's requirement: "If you can't count it, it doesn't count." Even this ability is seriously restricted. The infant eventually digests raw material. The computer must continue with prechewed data. Suppose it is being taught to recognize letters of the ordinary alphabet. Into its memory goes the letter A—a black-and-white pattern of dots supplied by a photo scanner and translated into the Yes-No code. Thereafter the machine should recognize other A's by comparison. But variations—in typography, in handwriting—are many. To store a sample of every possible A, even the human memory would soon become a gruesome example of specialization. So the brain generalizes; it learns to recognize at a glance the "A-ness" of an A. This is the practical kind of pattern-recognition imitated to a surprising degree by Madaline, an example of a self-adaptive computer. Its name is the inventor's roundabout way of giving credit to the human neuron. This is because Madaline depends on small electrochemical memistors, "resistors with memory." So the acronym Adaline stands for Adaptive Linear Neuron, an adaptive threshold element having a number of memistors; and Madaline is a team—Multiple Adalines.

Its success story is the usual one, university brains and Pentagon support. The researcher here is Bernard Widrow, an MIT graduate who migrated from that institute's computer colony to Stanford. His Madaline is a transplant too. Into the usual realm of digital computers he and his first doctoral student, Marcian Hoff, introduced the Adaline, a vital organ of the analogue type, to serve as a trainable decision-maker. Each of its memistors, a weighting element, is basically a variable resistor. In pioneer form, it is a sealed small tube containing an electrolyte—a bath of copper sulfate and sulfuric acid. Inside are also two rods. One is copper. When fed electricity, it deposits electroplated copper upon the other, which is in its own electrical circuit. This other, the resistance element, was at first simply a short length of pencil lead. The input that trains the Adaline determines the amount of current through the copper electrode. This current then governs the amount of conductive copper plated on the resistance element; and the thicker the copper coating, the less resistant it becomes to passage of electricity along its own circuit. This variable response allows training the memistors to recognize a generalized pattern. The human's main job is to provide sample inputs until the computer gets the idea, after which it stores the result in its memory for reference.

Madaline's feats are many. One day, for instance, some of Widrow's graduate students wanted conversation with the computer. Their experiment had become a routine method when I visited the lab.

After the usual exchange of instructional courtesies with Madaline, my companion typed a sequence of test words into the machine, an adaptive system added to an ordinary digital computer. Then he talked the same words in through a microphone. Next, he varied the pattern—transposing the words, barking some, drawling others. This ended the input phase. The machine now had several versions of a sound wave pattern for each word. It was at this point that the samples were routed through the equipment, and it went through its adjustments until responses for each sample word were established. After this, the operator switched to the output circuit and began repeating the words over the microphone, again with challenging variations.

Now it was Madaline who worked the typewriter, repeating each word. Then the microphone was passed to me. My voice has oddities of its own, but the typewriter faithfully chattered my words back at me. Occasional errors did occur—but to err is human too. And Madaline is still experimental. Says Widrow: "This is a wide-open field of Ph.D. thesis topics."

How far might pattern-recognition go? Electronics engineers are nimble. Obviously, a Madaline could be wired to repeat words, not by typewriter, but by reproducing sound frequencies. That would be speaking as the telephone does. More difficult, but of keen interest to computermen, is the possibility that such a machine will go beyond mimicry to a version of actual conversation. It would understand and act upon instructions given in ordinary English rather than via the makeshifts of machine language. It might even reply with enough ability to choose, say, between "I help myself" and "I help me." If so, it might no longer sound foolish when translating a foreign word that has perhaps a half-dozen meanings in English. Like any worthwhile translator, it would appraise the word in terms of pattern—that is, context.

In the future, too, a complex enough Madaline could conceivably learn to drive a car, fly a plane—perhaps ride an unmanned spaceship and choose the best landing site on Mars, depending on the conditions it finds. Similarly, a war missile could be given a main mission and alternate missions.

All this, and yet—the human is still needed to invent, build, and supervise computers. Some of the machines already read cardiograms and map chromosomes. In the life-science field it will be possible to build a computer whose electronic input will be entirely from parts of the body. For instance, it would "ask" the patient the usual questions, then give a diagnosis of, say, stomach cancer. But the human can ask questions too. How far would a patient with any choice in the matter trust a machine that lacks not only a bedside manner but the curiosity to pursue an anomaly—the obstruction that turns out to be a swallowed button?

Nor is the machine creative in any sense but a tortured one. And its judgment is highly suspect. The human's judgment may be swayed by prejudice, but the human can also seek more data when a clean decision is imperative. The computer's judgment depends entirely on whatever data the operator cares to supply. Undoubtedly all this helps explain the suspicions and even terrors aroused by automation. But there is more.

Next, Joblessness?

A consoling thought or not, we are entering the Age of the Console. I found everywhere the blinking monitors that herald this age. These switchboards have their eyes on electronic equipment that counts neutrons and calculates payrolls, forecasts weather and translates Russian, scans the heavens and scans bank checks. Occasionally, there is excitement, as when a nuclear power plant or a spaceship signals it is in trouble—but when all operates smoothly, the attendant sits there casually enough, perhaps also glancing at closed-circuit TV while he presides over the console's banks of buttons and occasionally pushes one. Or, because automation is not yet complete, he may respond to a computer's call for its nurse: Its typewriter is requesting a fresh ribbon. In any case it is not this technician's job to answer the growing questions about automation.

They range across the board. At one extreme is the ever-fascinating one: Can a machine be given the genetic ability to reproduce itself? At the other is the nagging worry that Americans forget when they flagellate themselves with sharper fears—of war, of cancer, and the like—and which they remember again when such dreads subside: "Will automation throw people like *me* out of work?"

This homely worry is not new. But in the past it has concerned mechanization, a favorite target for humanists like John Ruskin and

Herman Melville (who likened the working girls in Massachusetts mills to so many mares haltered to the rack); and eventually for comedians such as Charlie Chaplin, who pilloried the mechanized human condition in his movie *Modern Times* (anything is comic, wrote the Nobelist philosopher Henri Bergson, that seems human enough but betrays mechanical manipulation—a puppet, for example).

Automation is different, a fad word that has engulfed the older "mechanization." With this we cannot quarrel; language changes. However, automation is more easily understood when we realize that the two words are not synonymous. For one thing, automation burst upon us much faster. Eighteen centuries were needed before the steam-engine idea became practical; transistors needed only six years.

But the main difference is between mechanizing brawn and brain. Mechanization substitutes the cranes that build great skyscrapers for the human backs that built the Great Pyramids. It is also the machine tool, guided by a human operator, that eliminates the blacksmith and other hand laborers. By contrast, automation is the machine tool guided by punched tape. And even this machine isn't fully automated until it is taught to make worthwhile decisions. Possibly this is why automation sometimes arouses a feeling of *déjà vu.* Watching a jetliner's automatic guidance system, we recall the horse who could be depended on to bring us home safely through darkness and storm. But again, automation is more than another mechanized step beyond horse-and-buggy days. It carries the Industrial Revolution into an entirely new dimension, the mechanization of the mental.

This is only one reason, of course, why automation rouses latent fears. For example, there is mistrust of anything that might reduce the rights and privacy of the individual. In itself Fosdic is no threat to liberty. This optical scanning device took microfilms of the 1960 census returns and turned them into electronic data for the Census Bureau's statistical computers. Meanwhile, the 837 tons of original returns were mutilated under careful supervision before the wastepaper buyer was allowed to take them away. But electronics means a growing amount of personal information committed to the memory of computers—not only from the Census Bureau, but from Selective Service, Social Security, Internal Revenue, insurance companies, medical services, even airline companies. Richard W. Hamming of

Bell Labs asks: "How do we know that this is always being used for the benefit of the individual? How can we be sure that this information will not be used against a person?"

Nor does government always trust automation. The problem of how to police an atom-test ban brought Moscow's willingness to allow electronic "black boxes" on her soil. But Washington balked. The United States preferred on-site inspections by teams of humans less vulnerable to electronic trickery. And along with our automatic fail-safe methods to prevent an accidental nuclear holocaust, Washington recognizes that it would be madly irrational to assume that an electronic system will always function reliably and that its human attendants will always be goof-proof. Hence the emergency "hot line" for teletyped apologies between Moscow and Washington.

None of these fears, however, match those of the wage-earner. That he has done little about them indicates how benumbing, even ingratiating, automation can be. In its early days at least, there has been no mounting the barricades, no Luddite rioting. Rare is the Cleveland clerk who tore out the brains of the data-handling computer he accused of threatening his job. Resentment against automation burst out more typically in a *Washington Star* editorial flaying the telephone people for "this rush toward a dehumanized, all-number world." The title of the editorial was "Block Those Digits."

Even organized labor, though strong, has preferred delaying tactics while it ponders how to handle the future. In 1961, the appearance of the first feedback-controlled subway train in New York City resulted in immediate threats of a city-wide transit strike. But the train went ahead with its experimental runs. The Transit Authority reserved its right to automate. The union reserved its right to strike. And intellectuals, traditional defenders of the laborer, are also resigned to what seems inevitable. Serious writers of our day shun as corny the melodrama built around *RUR* robots. Mechanization produced satiric comedy. Automation has not, possibly because we haven't yet seen the medical patient of the future—far worse than a woman in hair curlers; bristly, like a quilled porcupine, with electronic outputs from all over his body. And science fiction, watching reality overtake imagination, prefers treating automation with sophisticated resignation. Thus, one of Isaac Asimov's stories about Multivac, the supercomputer that runs everything on earth. Eventually it wearies of nursing wearisome mankind. When police ask it why it has tried to sabotage itself to destruction it prints out a card that says, "I want to die."

That is a fable. In real life, American industry, driven by both competition with rivals and its lessening control over the output of human workers, invests in costly machines, and labor has been re-examining its opposition to less work. Years ago, when coal miners clamored for a six-hour day, their leader, John L. Lewis, told them they could have it any time they wanted to loaf more but eat less. Times have changed, the twenty-hour week is no longer a radical dream. Wage rates can be adjusted to allow more "loafing"; there is also the protective tactic pioneered by the shipping industry—it agreed to pay into a special fund that would care for workers forced into unemployment by new labor-saving devices.

And if, as pessimists say, automation portends a nation composed of a prosperous, brainy elite and a vast population of the idle, thoughtful members of the science establishment are baffled by what course to take, the more so because they sense that science will be blamed. When the then Vice President Lyndon Johnson announced that the space program "is starting a historic new boom on earth, creating new industries, new jobs, and new projects," a retort came from the anti-Space editor of a scientific journal: "What we are witnessing is the expansion of a new sophisticated form of prewar WPA. Science is being used increasingly as a front for leafraking."

And what about the freedom to loaf? In a basement office at Harvard let us visit one of the nation's foremost experimental psychologists, B. F. Skinner. Among other things, he fathered the teaching machine. I found him disillusioned. His concept had degenerated into a tinny box. For this he blamed the "commercial distortion" that turned the machine into another glamour growth stock on Wall Street, plus distortion by the traditionalists who still dominate education. Also: "I lectured on the subject a lot to overcome the lack of interest—the lecturing led to the fad and that's why I'm partly to blame, I guess. Anyway, I just cannot go on giving years of my life to it."

Even before the teaching machine, he had written his challenging novel *Walden Two*. It gave his ideas of how to program a practical utopian colony. Now he wanted to return to the biggest problem he foresaw resulting from automation—how to get people to convert their newly found leisure into something more productive than do-nothingism, faddism, and complaints about the high cost of high living.

Unquestionably, the possibility that machines will eventually leave everybody—plebeian as well as patrician—with time on his hands is unique in history. For workless boredom can be as mischievous as workless hunger. There is room, of course, for the unexpected. At a conference on the mass-transportation problem, Melvin Kranzberg of Case Institute of Technology offered us a tongue-in-cheek hope for a self-solution. He suggested leaving the situation as is: eight-hour working day, traffic jams—and be sure to include portal-to-portal pay. Traffic, the one variable, will continue worsening. Result: the worker will spend three hours getting to work, three hours getting home, and two hours on the job. Thus, Kranzberg said jubilantly, the eight-hour workday will remain entrenched.

More seriously, if labor faces bizarre situations, so does industry. For instance, IBM suggests that big business can now resume the march to uncomplicated bigness. Communication breakdowns made it difficult for management to manage, and the result was a "negative philosophy" that brought decentralization. But now, with speedy electronic networks and clever systems analysts who demand re-searched answers from the machines, top management can take back control from the branch managers. On the other hand, what of the arts? The Authors Guild, for instance, feels that the mushrooming growth of microfilming and other such methods of quick copying endanger the book sales to which writers are entitled.

The various problems await genuine investigation, decisions—and compromises too—by the politician, industrialist, labor leader, social scientist, farm leader, and so on, including the "public." It is too much to expect that all these be people of perfectly good will but certainly they should be imaginative; and this means that they cannot remain illiterate about the technical aspects of labor-saving. An un-complicated example: Banishing the horse to the glue factory because he is no longer needed as a freight-mover would overlook his con-tinuing value as a blood donor for the production of vaccines; nor can we ignore the therapeutic value of associating with him on a social plane, even if we get no closer to him than by way of the TV tape of a Western movie.

The Challenge

Man's personal future unquestionably will be shaped by the increasing interchange between biology and electronics. The possibilities were introduced by mathematician Wiener in 1948, in his seminal book *Cybernetics*. Twelve years later, W. A. van Bergeijk and L. D. Harman of Bell Labs recalled the effect: "Psychologists suddenly discovered that their stimulus patterns could be described in bits, and a rat or human being could be considered a 'black box.' Physiologists were awed by the realization that the all-or-none nervous impulse they had known for a couple of decades was a 'digital' pulse and the nervous system was really a miniaturized digital computer. The engineers could not help being infected with the excitement in the biological camp."

This mutual stimulation was feedback. It was also the interdisciplinary approach increasingly important in modern science. Each camp could learn from the other. In space programs, each has been forced to. In earthier electronics, however, the marriage was voluntary and the two partners have not shown equal ardor. Biologists remain reluctant to adopt the hardware of electronics engineers; but the latter have "gone wet," happy to learn from animals with an actual, live nervous system. Concerning his memistor, Widrow says, "We were inspired by the liquid-state electronic system of the brain."

It was in 1960 that the one-sided marriage was finally legitimized, at a symposium on "Living Prototypes—the Key to New Technology," sponsored by researchers at Wright-Patterson Air Force Base. Here, the existence of the hybrid field was announced, also the new word for it, "bionics." The symposium report proclaimed: "Specialization is OUT: universalization is IN."

Bionics means studying such creatures as blind fish, waltzing mice, and congenitally deaf cats. It means going, for radar and sonar, to the bat and more phenomenal porpoise . . . for analysis of X-ray and aerial photos, to the horseshoe crab's method of intensifying contrast between the background and the object it is reconnoitering . . . for new transducer techniques, to the stretch sensors that control the muscles of a cockroach stomach . . . and certainly, for the pregnant mysteries of luminescence, to that living prototype, the firefly.

It goes even farther, beyond the teaching machine to a taught machine, as did the British neurologist W. Grey Walter when he built the small mechanisms that he called *machina speculatrix* and *machina docilis.* For these turtle-like vehicles, Walter programed actions that quickly remind us of the reactions conditioned into live animals by experimental psychologists. With a photoelectric cell serving as its eye, an electronic sensor for touch, and two electric motors for maneuvering, the "turtle" would back away and detour around obstacles in the dark; crawl toward light but back away when too near for "safety"; overcome this caution and head for a recharger when its battery needed "food."

And bionics goes still farther, to the prize question in the field of programed machine intelligence—how lifelike can a computer be? For the easiest, quickest automation is electronic, and the computer is its symbol.

The idealized Multivac that will rule earth, sun, and stars remains in the remotest reaches of science fiction. Equally fascinating, and a bit less challenging to the engineer's sense of realities, is the concept of ultimate computers that will build everything for us, including themselves. Here, computermen have had to turn to molecular biology to see just what they would face. Biologists in turn have been translating DNA and genes into the number of bits of genetic information that a human cell contains. A guess is that the cell's DNA can theoretically encode so many variations on the human theme that the number of genotypes would run into the figure 10 followed by hundreds, perhaps thousands, of zeros.

Computermen do not waste time dreaming that far. Even von Neumann would have been content with the simplest genesis—to build and encode a computer that would reproduce identical daughters: to supply it with the necessary parts (corresponding to amino acids, of course) and the instructional program (corresponding to DNA); then to push the button that starts it assembling replicas. They would be "barren." Only after that succeeded could come a next step. Each replica would now inherit the template program and pass it on to its own progeny. And finally might come bravura. The computer would be programed to reach among the parts blindly, as humans do when they mate, and reproduce random variations. Or it might even be encouraged to commit errors, as DNA does, that would result in mutated machines.

These exemplify the reaches of imagination in the 1960s. Closer to reality, automation has reached into the manufacture of computers as it has elsewhere. However, when a newspaper headlined "Computer Made by Computer," it meant that a template was given to a computer, which then directed a machine to drill hundreds of corresponding holes in circuit cards for another computer. This was an automated step toward the goal. Enough such steps may eventually justify the headline. Though the prospect is possible, it is not yet feasible. But we scent here how far a programed machine might go if need becomes urgent enough to justify the expensive R & D needed first.

Still closer to reality, computers will talk to each other in machine language. But this is nothing new. In their punched-tape fashion, teletype machines have been doing so for two human generations and it is already common practice among those computers that use the same language. They predigest data for each other; they share memories. The Library of Congress, largest repository of information in the world, looks forward to automating its vastly overgrown card catalogues and eventually to a $70-million project that would link it electronically with research libraries throughout the nation. This, however, is only to dig out of a bibliographic swamp. The art of information retrieval has not yet reached the point where computer-like equipment can capably reach into the stacks, find, and print out what a researcher wants. But the possibility is there, given enough R & D money.

All in all, automation will spread as ingratiatingly as the mechanization that began whipping the housewife's potatoes and threw the human ditch-digger out of work. And if we overlook the background existence of the huge variable called war, advances of all kinds, accompanied by gadgetry of all kinds, are inevitable. How speedily they come in a private-enterprise system will depend on the economics of any situation.

The "looky-talky" telephone is a case in point. By 1964, it had arrived, but not yet for the home. At Bell Labs, I found that the picture-phone would not be popular enough at $200 a month; but at $30, enough people might be eager for it—whether as more chewing gum for the eyes, or for the serious business of seeing one's conferee. Bell's engineers had solved enough technical problems to bring the figure down midway between those two figures.

Such hardware changes will make today's America seem colonial a few decades from now. Some are easily predictable; others require the imagination of a Hugo Gernsback, the modern Jules Verne. However, more important than the hardware will be changes in software, therefore in society as we know it. For instance, education is entering an age of programed instruction and audio-visual aids. This, despite complaints that some teaching machines are silly tin boxes and others educate the students to treat them as slot machines; despite the electronic machine that gave wrong marks to a thousand students tested by the College Entrance Examination Board; despite jibes by Young Turks that Old Guardsmen have changed hardware but still teach ancient knowledge in the ancient way.

Industry, of course, is already deep in automation and not only for process-control and on production lines. The latest versions of the managerial class are either themselves recruits from the automated business office or lean heavily upon its world of human-factors engineers and other successors to the old-fashioned efficiency expert. An auto manufacturer, for example, relies on a computer system to decide the assembly-line schedule. It notes which of the company's new cars are the "fast movers" popular in this and that section of the nation. Besides this, of course, it is receiving orders from salesmen, instructing assembly lines to give a car this engine, that instrument panel, this color, and a host of other specified options.

This is a tide. Computers have not told us how far it will go, so the question is passed to human commissions, committees, and *ad hoc* panels. Some prophets foresee an age when most people will be comfortably unemployed, supported by a special class of humans who tend the machines. Such forecasts are not new. H. G. Wells was a Fabian Socialist whose optimism called for utopia while his pessimism raised doubts of mankind's capability for it. In Wells's fourth-dimensional novel *The Time Machine* the time-traveler finds that labor-saving has led to degeneracy of the race. Herded among ruins are the gentle non-workers who call themselves Eloi. They are fed by the bestial Morlocks; and in turn are beef for these subterranean machinists. This was in A.D. 800,000.

Let us play safer, project only a generation ahead, and borrow the Census Bureau's proviso that there will be no major catastrophes. Obviously, vast changes are coming in the makeup of the nation's work force. We are told that 70 per cent of Americans lived by farming in 1860; by 1960, a complex of conditions resulting from mechanization had reduced that figure to 7 per cent. Such trends will continue; industry's white-collar workers already outnumber its blue-collar workers and many of them already dread losing their jobs to the machine.

Yet it is nonsense to picture automation as an indiscriminate ax. The quickest example is the fact that, like any new industry, the manufacture of automation's devices itself opens new jobs, notably in electronics. There is also feedback. The more automation, the easier it is to turn out paperwork—and a variety of white-collar people are needed to wrestle with the flood of paper. Furthermore, there are ways to cuddle up to the enemy. Salesmen, for instance, are a rugged lot, needed in good times and more so in bad. Good ones know how to switch from legwork to machine methods, to market research, motivation research, and the other statistical appurtenances that hunt new markets and liven old ones.

Most important, whatever the ultimate goal and however it may be reached, automation as we know it now cannot be all automatic. It needs human associates and caretakers. Elinor Langer, a vigilant staff writer for *Science*, noting that the government owned 512 lie-detecting machines that cost $428,000, noted also that the annual salaries of their operators came to $4 million. More than that, the computer desperately needs its programers.

Hence the looming importance of the skilled worker called technician. But this person needs training, one more problem on education's crowded doorstep. For instance, military SAGE, the world's largest data-processing system, had to train its own force of computer programers and others in the "software" category. Atomic power plants also train their own technicians. And the need for capable programers has seriously retarded progress with the teaching machine (as well as with its counterpart, the programed textbook). Similarly, people better trained than auto mechanics are needed to understand a superjet's electronics. Others are needed to provide weather forecasts and radar for the plane's guidance.

Most striking, however, is the fact that steps taken toward "automatic" programing and providing off-the-shelf programs for standard computer procedures have not sufficed. The most glamorous automatic machine remains hobbled by the shortage of capable human attendants. This, despite seductively inaccurate ads offering $16,000 for the person with only a year's experience, and the fact that barriers have been lowered. The girl who is no mathematician but has a liberal-arts degree and intelligence can start at $100 weekly as a trainee. Or she can be like the two stewardesses on my trip back from St. Louis, congratulating each other on having finished their course in computer-programing.

How many technicians will be needed? The estimates given too often depend on who is agitating for what education program. Anyway, a Presidential panel on vocational education predicted in 1962 that technology would wipe out 2 million jobs, mostly the unskilled ones, in the next decade. It also foresaw 2.5 million new jobs, notably in the technical field, and warned that we face an acute shortage of technicians and highly skilled craftsmen. Various estimates boil down to a need for between 75,000 and 100,000 more technicians per year. It is easy to double that estimate by ending an abnormality. At present, we have fewer than 1 technician per scientist or engineer (in the nuclear energy field, for instance, 16,000 technicians support the work of 25,000 "creative" professionals). The argument is that the professionals would be freed to be truly creative if capable technicians were in the majority: a ratio of 2 to 1, even 3 or 4 to 1.

In any case, whatever automation does to other people, the future of the technician—if somebody bothers to train him—looks secure. The rest re-emphasizes the layman's need to know more science, so that he can better cope with this wave of the future—as a citizen, by making his vote count more intelligently; as a parent, by understanding better how to prepare his child for the changing world. For here is something too inevitable for calamity-howling and rabble-rousing. Automation will be evil only if thinking man allows it to be. And unless there is a senseless revolt against science, its people will go on reducing labor, just as employers will welcome the labor-savers.

The only debate can be over whether education, government, and industry are programing intelligent ways of living with mechanization and automation.

Meanwhile, computermen play with their potent machine. Its technical shortcomings are many, but in this it corresponds to a 1913-vintage automobile. The hope is to improve the car, and the driver too. The man at the console stands watch over the computer. And researchers have now designed a Vigilometer that stands watch over the alertness of the man at the console.

X: *Uranium—the Big Experiment*

"These questions are not technical questions;
they are political and social questions."
—Henry D. Smyth,
*Atomic Energy for
Military Purposes*

Speaking of zoning, would you care to see a nuclear power plant move into the neighborhood? Its restless, unstable atoms provide the same chain reaction that explodes a nuclear bomb or missile warhead. The difference is that the weapon deliberately allows the reaction to become a runaway.

But how dependable are brakes that control the peaceful power plant? How significant is the fact that it must carry not only maximum insurance of the ordinary kind against public liability, but another half-billion dollars' worth underwritten by the government? And could even this cover the possible harm? There would be more than the eruption. When a nitrate-laden ship killed over five hundred at Texas City in 1947, the tragedy had a conventional terminal point; similarly when munitions blew up in Halifax harbor in 1917, killing three times as many. But nuclear violence has its unconventional side-effects, notably fallout, and its after-effects, notably genetic damage. Consequently, plans to erect nuclear power plants have agitated American communities from Long Island to San Francisco.

It is not my purpose to cry calamity. Whatever other troubles the Atomic Energy Commission has had in its first two decades, the facts show a remarkably successful technical program, both for national defense and for peaceful uses of what the United States Supreme Court has called "the most deadly, the most dangerous process that man has ever conceived." And there is progress. The more things change, the more they are the same—but not quite. It was a token victory of sorts when the Government-owned *Savannah*,

319

a proud and primping ship, the world's only merchant vessel powered by a nuclear reactor, brought her cargo and passengers to the Port of New York in December 1964, and was allowed to dock facing the city. Six months earlier, on her maiden visit, the skittish welcomers made her tie up with her rump to the city—because her reactor is toward the bow. This was with the delightfully optimistic notion that facing the Hudson would make any worthwhile difference if *Savannah*'s reactor blew its lid.

Credit for the ship, the patient handling of her special problems— and the nation's over-all control of potent uranium—goes to two special supervisory agencies unique in our history: the AEC and its congressional overseer, the Joint Committee on Atomic Energy. Together, not always in step but with the Joint Committee ready to pull and prod its sometimes faltering ward, they made their way through much barbed wire. In the area of peace: public utilities vs. private; fossil fuels vs. nuclear; atom-smashing physicists vs. water-desalting chemists. In the area of war: bombers vs. missiles, Pentagon vs. AEC and Navy vs. Rickover's submarine, "clean" weapons vs. "dirty," the Oppenheimer and test-ban controversies. And throughout they were resisting hungry politics, sometimes clean and sometimes dirty, eager for more power and porkbarrel, usually illiterate about the methods and goals of nuclear science. Accordingly, the AEC and its duenna sometimes stumbled. Yet it is doubtful whether any dictator or strong executive could have matched the performance of this combination— an agency of experts closely watched by the people's representatives.

They were working with something more tricky than man's familiar molecules: with the stupendous power residing deep in the atom itself, its nucleus. (Hence, except where accuracy or historic usage requires, I will call it "nuclear power," "nuclear energy," etc., instead of "atomic power" and "atomic energy.") Here was R & D with too much potency for *laissez faire*. So, for the first time, driven by grim necessity, government sought a suitable new way of living with science.

The result has been pioneering, which is not easy. And the outcome of the experiment will depend less on science than on the citizenry and its political spokesmen. For the atom's nucleus is deeply involved today in war plans, in medical research, in space projects, in many other pregnant programs that will change the nation. The layman may not know, for instance, how easily uranium becomes plutonium but he is deeply concerned with nuclear reactors—who will control their production of electricity, how cheap it will be, how safe its generators will be.

And the nucleus is deeply involved politically too. This matter of control is remindful of the birth of the United States Constitution. Again, there was the reality and the dream, and both were extraordinary. Again, there was postwar emergency, this time stirred by the portents of Hiroshima. For instance, there was the proposal to create an international monopoly run by the United Nations, which would be somewhat of a landlord with contented tenants. It would take over America's reactors and the world's uranium deposits. It would soothe other nations by building nuclear plants for them too. This idea came not from internationally minded radicals but from American industry, which was both tempted and terrified by prospects of the Nuclear Age. The idea was offered by such leaders of industrial research as Charles A. Thomas of Monsanto and Henry A. Winne of General Electric.

No project in history had faced so many big, unprecedented problems as did building the $2.2-billion A-bomb; none now required such decisions as where to go with the bomb. Again, a mandate was needed, this time for civilian control of both the warlike and peaceful nucleus. Again, sincere men of diverse interests hammered out a historic compromise. And again, there has come dissatisfaction and debate over what the founding fathers meant, though the Atomic Energy Act, which became our organic law covering control of nuclear energy, was born no farther back than 1946 and many of its sponsors remain alive and alert.

In sum, what has been done with the nucleus scientifically and politically are equally important after seventy years of researching deep into the atom. And how the AEC fulfills its mandate becomes an indicator of whether American science, industry, education, and government can solve the array of other problems they share.

The Pioneers

For centuries, atoms were the private property of chemists. As their knowledge grew, they added more kinds of atoms to their menagerie of the elements. But the atom itself remained inviolate. As the smallest building blocks of matter, atoms could be assembled to give many kinds of molecules. And the twentieth century saw conventional chemists make prodigious progress. Nitrogen atoms from the air were inserted into synthetic fertilizers and new explosives. Atoms from coal tar reappeared in dyes and drugs. Usually, paraphrasing the Du Pont slogan, this was making a better world through chemistry. Sometimes it did not. But the wartime explosive could also do pick-and-shovel work. And, if a nitroglycerin or picric acid, it could even be a medicine.

This was, and still is, an ingenious way of playing with the building blocks. By means of heat, pressure, and catalysts, atoms are joined and pulled apart. But through it all even the atoms in exploding TNT remain intact, as far as instruments can determine. They merely form stabler molecules; the freed energy does not come from within the nucleus of the atom. If it did, if a pound of uranium atoms, for example, were torn into nuclear fragments, the pound would release as much energy as the explosion of eight thousand tons of TNT. This, manifestly, is not conventional chemistry.

It was inevitable that the twentieth century should bring the discovery of nuclear energy. Long before the Bomb, of course, there was research. And chemistry, physics, and astronomy were learning too much about atoms to remain ignorant of the forces within them. Physics, for example, shunned the smells of chemistry but its curiosity about energy was thrusting it into the atom's internal affairs.

Physics started doing so importantly in the 1890s. Almost simultaneously, England's J. J. Thompson established the existence of the electron, Germany's Wilhelm Roentgen discovered X-rays, and Henri Becquerel of France, seeking another source of X-rays, accidentally found something puzzling. Here was not only a new kind of radiation; it came spontaneously from the scarce element uranium.

It also happened in France that a woman was invading the mannish field. She wanted a project for her Ph.D. research. The so-called "Becquerel rays" seemed to qualify. She would measure the strength of what she was already calling uranium's "radioactivity." So began the heartwarming story of two scientists who happened to be natural bridges: part physicist, part chemist. They were Polish-born Marie

Curie and her French husband Pierre; she the indomitable, he the impractical dreamer; each richly in love with the other and with science; neither specialized enough nor political enough to get help from the scientific establishment of that day. For this insufficiency the Curies paid with penury and neglect, with ill health and lost years.

The climax, of course, was their discovery of polonium and, more important, radium. Chemists had been racing to fill blanks in Mendeleev's prophetic chart for nature's elements—ninety-two in all. The two new species took their places neatly up near thorium and uranium at the heavyweight end of the chart. But the family resemblance didn't end there. All four were not inviolate atoms. They seemed in a state of chronic decay, a kind of slow explosion. Measured by volts or calories—or by the lesions burned into Pierre's skin—the energy released by microscopic bits of material was unprecedented. Equally strange, the explosion was so self-controlled that the radioactivity of a specimen went on and on, seemingly forever.

Anyway, here was energy that radiated like waves of light or X-rays but was neither. Experimental physicists began thronging into the field. In a few years they had identified three kinds of interesting radiation from such material: positively charged "alpha" particles (the equivalent of helium atoms that have lost two electrons); negatively charged "beta" particles (high-speed electrons); and "gamma" rays (a short-wave, high-energy version of X-rays). Furthermore, the radium was giving off a gas later christened radon, which was itself radioactive.

And soon, out of research at McGill University, came a theory by physicist Ernest Rutherford and his chemist associate, Frederick Soddy. It wrapped all this debris into an answer, though it smacked of alchemy. It proposed that one kind of atom could indeed change to another. Why was there always radium in an ore containing uranium? And why was there always lead too? Because the uranium atom is heavy and unstable. Consequently, it goes through a series of disintegrations, throwing off excess baggage, until it becomes a stable atom of lead. Radium, polonium, and radon are some of the intermediate steps of that decay; helium is a byproduct. Each step in this disintegration occurs at nature's fixed pace; the chemist's standard methods of heat, pressure, and catalysis cannot change it. The best he can do is average how fast the atoms are changing. Some of the steps are almost instantaneous, others amazingly slow. Common radium, for instance, is unstable but not sensationally so. Its "half-life" is about 1600 years—the time it takes for half of a supply of radium to go to the next step. In another 1600 years, only one-fourth of the original radium would remain, and so on. Meanwhile, of course, more radium is being formed from its ancestral uranium. Won't all this come to a stop when the uranium supply is gone? Theoretically, yes. But calculations showed that uranium's half-life is long—this element is half depleted only after several billion years.

It was such interplay of experiment and theory that further doomed previous concepts of the atom and led to a better one. By the time of World War I, additional evidence and theory were ready with the picture of a planetary atom.

Our chief interest in previous chapters has been in the outer atom —the electrons that explain conventional chemistry, electricity, and so on. Now we come to the source of radioactivity—the nucleus. Here, it will be recalled from Chapter V, is where the atom's mass is concentrated, thanks to its population of protons and whatever neutrons the nucleus also possesses.

First, about the protons because they are the basic physical reason why one species of atom differs from another chemically. The difference is in the number of protons. In radioactivity, for example, the noticeable changes result from the fact that when the unstable atom decays it loses protons. As long as it has 92, it has that many positive charges and is uranium. Accordingly, it is assigned the "atomic number" of 92. After losing 10 protons, it is lead, whose atomic number is therefore 82. This applies to nature's building up an atom as well as breaking it down. It was presumably from simple hydrogen, with its single proton, that the other atoms were created.

Such is nature's alchemy. And, in 1919, Rutherford became nature's first successful rival. By bombardment with alpha particles he forced ordinary nitrogen to accept an extra proton and convert— "transmute"—itself into oxygen, with hydrogen as a byproduct.

This kind of pioneering was experimental; results were obtained without knowing all the reasons why. But purely theoretical physicists, too, were helping to fashion the new concept of the atom. As early as 1900 came Planck's bold quantum idea that electromagnetic radiation can be considered small particles as well as the traditional waves. Five years later brought Einstein's first statement of his theory of relativity, with its doom for the long-revered law of the conservation of mass. It substituted the interchangeability of mass and energy. With this, science could now explain why the original uranium atom is a bit heavier than the material it becomes. Some of its original mass is annihilated during the transition from uranium to lead, and reappears, according to Einstein's famed equivalence equation, as energy.

Although some scientists went on worrying whether these theories were sin or salvation, others were mulling over the implications. By the early 1920s, freshmen were reading in their college chemistry textbook: "A wonderful new source of power will be put into our hands, namely, *atomic energy*. . . . The disintegration of a pound of uranium salts would furnish enough power to drive an ocean liner across the Atlantic. But 8,000,000,000 years is entirely too long to wait for the completion of the trip. Chemists are looking forward, however, to the possibility of using the enormous stores of energy as soon as a catalyst for the reaction is obtained."

The guess on fuel was good, but chemistry still thought in terms of adding a pinch of platinum or such to hasten the radioactive steps. That was not the way the 14,000-ton *Savannah*, 40 years later, was traveling 10,000 miles at normal speeds on 2 pounds of nuclear fuel.

The practical way had to await the full-scale attack on the atom that physicists began in the 1930s. Now came the first artificial radioactivity. Now, thanks to atom-smashers, theorists began locating and measuring forces within the nucleus. And now the next step, splitting an atom instead of chipping away at it, became realistically predictable.

All this was catalyzed by experiments with a mysterious new radiation that James Chadwick discovered in 1932 to be made up of "neutrons." This was discovery in the sense that the equally invisible electron and proton had been discovered. Chadwick could describe the new atomic particle only by its behavior. When it was fired into a nucleus and stayed there it added about as much mass as a proton would. But it was judged to be electrically neutral because it left no vapor trail in a cloud chamber. Hence "neutron."

From only two "fundamental particles," theory had now gone to three, and eventually there would be too many for comfort. It is conceivable that even the three will some day be traded in for a more basic building block. Meanwhile, the neutron can be judged by its handiwork. In broad terms, it gave man a chance to do what nature had been doing since the universe began. He could seriously go into the business of building a nucleus or breaking it. Specifically:

1. The neutron made nuclear bookkeeping simpler. For one thing, it gave an easy way to explain isotopes. Chemical analysis had already found many instances where the same species of atom—same chemical properties—occurred as variations that didn't weigh quite the same. Common chlorine was an example. Its atomic weight—the chemist's standard way of grading the elements—was 35.46. This unwieldy number didn't make sense until chlorine was found to be a mixture of two isotopes. The atomic weight of one was 35; of the other, 37. But nature produced more of the lighter one. The 35.46 turned out to be the resulting average of the two weights. The neutron concept does not banish the atomic weights of ordinary chemistry. But for nuclear affairs it substitutes the more informative "mass number." This is a whole number—protons added to neutrons. Uranium, for example, has 92 protons—but its mass number can vary. The abundant isotope, 92 protons plus 146 neutrons, consequently has a mass number of 238 and is called uranium-238. The scarcer but more explosive isotope, with three fewer neutrons, is the lighter uranium-235.

2. The short-form version of the idea made it easy to play the isotope game. To make a nucleus heavier, add a neutron; to lighten it, knock out a neutron. Either way, the mass number changes. The result was a rash of new isotopes. America's Harold Urey had already found an isotope of the lightest element, hydrogen. Ordinarily, it is the only element without at least one neutron. It is simply one proton and one electron. But now came the isotope called deuterium, whose mass number was 2 (one proton, one neutron). Obviously, this so-called "heavy hydrogen" makes a molecule of water heavier. Urey found that ordinary water is actually a mixture of two kinds— 1 part of heavy water per 5000 parts of normal "light" water containing ordinary hydrogen. Then two English physicists wondered if the deuterium could be forced to accept one more neutron and be-

come triple-weight hydrogen. Bombarding it with nuclear material, they created previously unknown tritium—a hydrogen, scarce in nature, whose nucleus contains two neutrons plus the proton. The two overweight isotopes, one natural, the other artificial, were eventually used to manufacture the "hydrogen bomb."

3. Neutrons account for isotopes, but these are only variations of an atom. Neutrons can also transmute one species of atom into another; this, as we have seen, involves changing the number of protons in the nucleus. One way is through the neutron's apparent capability of changing into a proton. Though precisely how this happens remains one of theory's many questions about the nucleus, neutrons make the transmutation procedure simple. As a "neutral" unhindered by the atom's electrically charged electrons and protons, the neutron can generally be beamed easily through the atom and even into its nucleus, much more easily than a proton can. This is especially true when the target is a heavyweight atom, whose large nuclear charge would strongly repulse the proton. Best example is the conversion of natural uranium into manmade plutonium. Of uranium's main isotopes, uranium-235 is not only radioactive but fissionable. The fact that its atoms can be split easily make them a handy fuel for both nuclear weapons and peaceful nuclear reactions. But this isotope is relatively scarce. Uranium ore contains 139 times more of the heavier isotope U-238. This one is not ordinarily fissionable. However, the nucleus of its atom can absorb an extra neutron, thereby becoming U-239. This new isotope is very unstable and is transformed first to neptunium-239 and then to longer-lived plutonium-239, which has 94 protons and is fissionable enough to rival the scarce U-235. *Little Boy*, the Hiroshima bomb, used this uranium; *Fat Man*, the Nagasaki bomb a few days later, used plutonium. And today the routine conversion of U-238 into plutonium is a major key to peacetime programs for wasting less of our uranium reserves.

Chain Reaction

Man's ability to split atoms is itself a product of the versatile neutron. Today's hindsight makes the discovery of fission look easy. It was not, and without two alert women it would have been harder. In brief, science first had to swallow something astonishing. It had become dogma that a radioactive atom lightens itself by casting off nuclear particles. But nature had given no hint that a nucleus could crack wide open. When researchers bombarded an atom with nuclear particles their purpose was to tamper with it, not wreck it; theirs was part of no grandiose project to convert matter into energy. Yet by forcing neutrons into uranium's dense nucleus, they were already splitting it occasionally.

This failure to recognize the lucky accident happened even to Enrico Fermi. When he got queer results, he made himself believe that he had created an element heavier than uranium. Other researchers fell in line with Italy's brilliant neutron expert. Only one person in the world of science demurred. When Frau Ida Noddack, a German chemist, read Fermi's report, she at first suspected sloppy chemistry. Then she thought more about it and took a chance in a paper of her own: "It is possible to imagine that when heavy nuclei are bombarded with neutrons, these nuclei fall apart. . . ." Fermi's reaction was that physics allowed no such possibility, and he added that Germany's chemist Otto Hahn, "the best-known radium specialist in the world," agreed with him. That was in 1934.

The Noddack suggestion remained banished to the background while experimenters stumbled another four years. Then Hahn, dissatisfied, ran still another experiment on the effects from directing neutrons at a uranium target. He didn't make the uranium heavier. Instead, he found an isotope of barium, an ordinary middleweight atom. This was astonishing. He had used pure uranium: "We could not understand why we had barium in the stuff. We had not started with any barium." So he sent a letter to Niels Bohr's institute in Copenhagen, asking Lise Meitner what she thought of it. This Austrian physicist had worked with him in better days. She was now a refugee from Hitler; Hahn had helped smuggle her into Denmark.

She replied that the evidence pointed to only one thing: fission. Hahn was tempted to agree but he feared ridicule. So his published report hedged: "We cannot yet take the decision to make this big step, which contradicts all the previous experience of nuclear physics. It still could be that a series of rare accidents misled us."

Whereupon Fräulein Meitner and her nephew, Otto Frisch, ended the nonsense with the letter they wrote in January 1939 to the noted English journal *Nature*. Of course there was barium. And it was barium, they suggested, because the uranium atom had absorbed a neutron, become unstable, and "fissioned." Meitner calculated that it had exploded roughly in two, producing two middleweight atoms, of which barium was one, and she went on to approximate the energy that was released.

Almost overnight, a new creed was born. The reaction by great Bohr was: "How have we been able to overlook that so long?" On a visit to the United States a few days later, he spread the word. Within another few days, American and European laboratories were testing the Meitner theory, proving it, and guessing a future for it. In America, even before the A-bomb project got under way, physicists imposed a self-censorship to keep their research results from reaching Germany's warmakers. Also to thwart Hitler's possible plans, Belgium shipped to the United States its supply of suitable uranium ore from the Congo, the world's biggest source.

Clearly, science was rolling up its sleeves for a practical job. It had no time to theorize over what kind of meiosis was caused by the intruding neutron. Merely splitting the atom was not enough. It could be only a preliminary to the main nuclear event. Without a so-called "chain reaction," practical uses for fission would remain a dream.

In a very real sense, uranium was a new fuel. The energy came from the core of the atom, so was fantastically higher than from merely rearranging the atoms of molecules in coal, oil, or TNT. Yet the idea was the same. Uranium could be "burned" in a nuclear sense. If violently, the kinetic energy of the fission fragments could be the blast of a bomb. If controlled, this energy might do peaceful things. The bomb had to come first; but either way, the problem was the same—how to start the "fire," then keep it going.

To begin with, if fission is an extraordinary fire, then neutrons are extraordinary matches. Inside a nucleus they are stable enough. Outside it, they exist only about ten minutes before changing into protons. Researchers had learned, however, how to get enough fresh neutrons for their experiments. One of the first ways was to mix a bit of radium with some beryllium. The radium emits alpha particles; these extraheavy bullets then knock neutrons out of the beryllium.

But such "matches" couldn't solve the main problem. Without a chain reaction, "burning" a supply of uranium would be like igniting each molecule in a piece of paper. This would be preposterous. Combustion must be self-propagating. In a bonfire, the heat from one burning molecule ignites the next, and so on. Fission cannot do this for uranium. For each nucleus it needs another match, another neutron.

The solution was guessed almost from the start. Theoreticians figured that the violence of fission was tearing some neutrons off the daughter nuclei formed from uranium. And hasty experiments showed this to be true. Soon it was known that the average output from a single fission was somewhere between one and three neutrons (the eventual figure was between two and three). Now, physicists could talk seriously about the goal, a high-energy, self-sustaining reaction.

Simple arithmetic showed that the energy would be rewarding. In physics a minuscule unit of energy is the electron-volt (ev). The movement of 1 electron in a 1-volt flashlight would give 1 ev in the form of light and heat; in a 110-volt lamp it gives 110 ev. For comparison, each uranium fission releases about 200 million ev. And the chain reaction would allow collecting the reward. Assume two usable neutrons are produced per fission of U-235. Supply a neutron to start the chain. The first fission gives 2 neutrons; they cause two fissions that produce 2 neutrons apiece, or 4; and so on until the number of fissions quickly becomes astronomical. Furthermore, the nuclei are closely packed, and neutrons can move up to thousands of miles per second. This explains why it is instantaneous from one generation of neutrons to the next; and why in a little over 50 such generations a fission bomb equivalent to 100,000 tons of TNT is ready to explode. We also see why a peaceful nuclear power plant needs brakes to prevent a runaway reaction.

But this, too, is hindsight. Building a bomb right away was out of the question. No project in history faced so many big, unprecedented problems. Only a few grams of doubtfully pure uranium had ever been produced in this country, and the same deficiency applied to other necessary ingredients. Most important, it was still unknown in 1940 whether neutrons would obey the simple arithmetic. Hence the first major experiments were to see if a chain reaction could really be started, and if yes, whether it would blow up in one's face. The research took three main avenues that led to the A-bomb, and to the fission techniques of today:

1—Fuel

The experimenters already knew several traps that could rob them of the precious neutrons. For instance, impurities in the uranium would capture some without, of course, giving fission. Nor could every uranium nucleus be useful. Here, the evidence was tantalizing. In natural uranium, less than 1 per cent was the fissionable isotope U-235. Almost all was U-238, a nuisance that could capture many neutrons without splitting. So the first job was to get a fuel as purely U-235 as possible. But separation wasn't easy—by definition, the isotopes of an element act alike chemically. Three complicated tactics offered themselves: separating by gaseous diffusion, by centrifugation, by electromagnetic means. The chances of success seemed equal; time was precious. Thus was born the strategy of the "crash program." Money and talent were poured into all three methods—for a chain reaction that might not work and, after that, a bomb that might not. Soon appeared two other methods, also iffy. Both were roundabout ways of allowing the U-238 to remain. They would depend on the fissioning U-235 to supply suitable neutrons to the U-238. The latter would thereby become plutonium, which is easily fissionable. So, though they had no chain reaction yet, the researchers already worked on five possible ways to produce explosive material for the bomb.

2—Moderation

For various reasons, there is no fixed speed for neutrons. And here nature is again uncooperative. The otherwise useful U-235 gives relatively fast neutrons when it splits, but the splitting itself is done more easily by "slow" neutrons moving at the rate of perhaps one mile per second. So a fast neutron had to be slowed down somehow between the time it left an erupting nucleus and struck a nearby nucleus that needed it for fission. Hence the idea of moderators—lightweight, untroublesome materials that could be mixed with the uranium. Inside their atoms the nucleus would act like a bumper rather than neutron-absorber. The neutron would bounce off, losing speed at each such collision. Here again, there was choice among several candidates. The first moderator was the atoms of carbon in purified graphite.

3—Triggers

The neutron freed by fission shoots through matter easily. It takes a straight path and may travel in any direction. But there is space between atoms in matter, and each atom is itself mostly empty space; there is no certainty that the neutron will immediately enter another uranium nucleus. So the probabilities of a chain reaction quickly concern the size of a lump of suitable uranium. If too small, its freed neutrons could escape out of the fuel without meeting and splitting enough nuclei to keep the reaction going. If too large, the runaway speed of fissions would prematurely explode the material.

The answer, then, is to increase the size somehow to the "critical mass"—the smallest amount of fissionable material needed to sustain the reaction. The methods for doing this today are merely improved versions of the one used for history's first self-sustaining reaction. It started on December 2, 1942, in a so-called "pile," a flattened sphere 15 feet high, built secretly on a squash court at the University of Chicago's football stadium.

The fuel was slugs of uranium and uranium oxide. The moderator was long bricks of graphite. The slugs were regularly spaced through a latticework of the bricks. Without interference, neutrons could pass from one slug to another, hence the entire sphere might be considered a large, explosive piece of fuel. But there were slots through the pile. Into these were slipped control strips made of cadmium, a metal that absorbs the neutrons avidly but doesn't fission. When fully inserted, the strips obstructed the traffic of neutrons between slugs of fuel. As the strips were pulled out, the traffic increased. For a safe chain reaction, they were adjusted to the critical point that provided only as many effective neutrons as the pile was consuming. All this, to prevent the reactor from erupting. A bomb, of course, requires the opposite. It must be designed to go past the critical point in a flash—and yet, before the moment of triggering, it must be safe. For instance, stray neutrons could explode a loaded bomb prematurely. One answer is to load fuel in the form of entirely separate pieces. Then, at the desired moment, a small blast of ordinary high explosive slams the pieces together. The bomb goes supercritical; the main blast occurs.

To Hiroshima

The nuclear age was inevitable. But it often didn't seem so to General Groves, actual chief of the project evasively named Manhattan District. His authority was sufficient. He reported only to the President, the Secretary of State, and the Army's Chief of Staff. His technical credentials were also sufficient: he was from the proudly competent Corps of Engineers. But he had to adapt himself to unprecedented R & D. When he asked scientists to guess how much fissionable material would be needed, they warned that the estimates might be 1000 per cent wrong. Also, though they had ambitious plans for plutonium, there had been evidence of it only in a cyclotron; not until 1942 did they have enough to see under a microscope. In peacetime, no technical man in his right mind would dream of building a production plant when his only information was from a scant half-milligram of test material.

And always, worrisome, often paralyzing, sometimes providing the comic relief needed for any drama, was secrecy. Robert Oppenheimer, directing the actual bomb-making at Los Alamos, thought that Coordinator of Rapid Rupture was "a wonderful code name" for his job. But gossipers couldn't be stilled, and sometimes there was open rebellion. Groves recalls sadly that Ernest Lawrence, father of the cyclotron, went up to a blackboard one day, said, "I know General Groves doesn't want me to say this, but . . ." and had his say.

Other times, there was serious trouble with technical plans. For example, after starting well enough, the production of plutonium spluttered to a standstill: an unexpected case of xenon "poisoning" the chain reaction. But Du Pont engineers had doubted scientists who scoffed that there was no need to run their tests twenty-four hours a day. The engineers had insisted on installing reserve fuel elements. These enabled the reaction to go on.

Such were problems that Groves met with some of the nuclear pioneers. They upstaged engineers. They complained that they should not be ruled by such non-nuclear scientists as Vannevar Bush and James Conant. They insisted that, if given a few junior engineers and draftsmen, they could design and build the necessary production plants themselves. They resented the military. Looking back on the fussing between Army and scientists, Henry D. Smyth, the Princeton physicist whose electromagnetic separation method was the first to produce worthwhile amounts of U-235, and who served in key roles elsewhere, told me, "I was often tempted to say a plague on both your houses."

Finally, however, on July 16, 1945, came the historic test explosion in New Mexico. It was a success. The War Department, in its memorabilia of the occasion, recorded: "Dr. Kistiakowsky threw his arms around Dr. Oppenheimer and embraced him with shouts of glee." And there was the blind girl 120 miles away: when the flash lighted the sky before the sound could reach her, she exclaimed, "What was that?"

There was something else—opposition from those nuclear scientists who urged restraint. Some felt that such a weapon would be barbarous and its use against a city even more so. Some protested that they worked on the bomb only for fear that the inhuman Nazis were doing so, but Germany was now out of the war. This is why a leading physicist said years later, "Perhaps I should now respect myself more if I had left the work on V-E Day." And mathematician von Neumann explained, "But of course we were all little children with respect to the situation."

By contrast, James Franck had molded himself into a man. He knew war first-hand; he had won the Iron Cross for heroism in the First World War. Later, this Nobelist in physics had emigrated from Germany in protest against Hitler. Even before the successful test, he was aroused to hear the same talk about the end justifying the means—based, as it turned out, on incorrect intelligence estimates concerning battered Japan's power to resist further. But Franck placed his hope in logical rather than emotional arguments. He thereupon gathered a group of like-minded A-bomb scientists and prepared a report stressing that the world—friends as well as foes— would be shocked by impetuous use of the new weapon; and that

America would be in no position thereafter to urge a ban on its use. It urged a better way: using a desert or a barren island to show Japan and the world what America could but did not want to do with this bomb.

Franck brought this report to Washington, for Secretary of War Henry L. Stimson and, he hoped, for President Truman. There is no evidence that it reached Truman's eyes. If it didn't, this could hardly have been censorship by his personal Chief of Staff, Admiral William D. Leahy. Though his career might label him a "militarist," he bristled, "These new concepts of 'total war' are basically distasteful to the soldier and sailor of my generation."

But perhaps all this didn't matter. As in a script by Sophocles, but not so neatly limited to a few characters, fate seemed inexorable. The next nuclear explosions were for Japan, and the rest is history.

The so-called "Smyth Report" was more successful. Written by the Princeton physicist, it was the government's official history of the Manhattan project; timed for publication immediately after secrecy was ended by actual use of the bomb, in whatever fashion. To make this speed possible, Smyth had finished writing the book shortly before the New Mexico test, so confident was science by then that if the idea didn't work well the first time, it would on the second or third try.

Equally confident was allowing publication of the book at all. Might it not give away precious details of our big secret? But there was a rising demand by scientists that they have free access to knowledge again, and they argued that facts would be better than leaks and rumors. Why not, then, describe the state of the nuclear art without divulging the engineering technique that went with such a bomb? This, Smyth could do, and did: skillfully, lucidly, sincerely. At the end, concerned about the future for a newly harnessed form of energy that could be used for good or ill, he added: "This is a semitechnical report which, it is hoped, men of science can use to help their fellow citizens in reaching wise decisions."

"Wise Decisions"

The advice by Smyth and others who pondered the future was taken. Congress had been in recess. However, immediately after

Truman announced the bombing of Hiroshima, Congress returned to Washington, and its members began immediate work on the awful challenge. Also to Washington came scientists with their fears and cures. Some of these advisers made sense; others didn't. In this, they were about on a par with the few laymen aware that the A-bomb was not just a bigger bang.

The House had no sooner assembled than it received a bill ordering death for anybody who disclosed A-bomb information, presumably to a Russian agent. On its heels another congressman offered a resolution calling on the brand-new United Nations to ban the bomb. Each in its own way revealed America's twitching with terror. So did a poll that showed the nation's high-school students overwhelmingly against "sharing bomb secrets" with other nations. So did the Pentagon's destruction of Japan's five innocuous research cyclotrons (American scientists quickly likened this to Nazi book-burning). But so also did the triple warning by industrial researchers as well as newly created bands of university scientists: that neutrons were no secret; that Russia would soon have A-bombs too; that there was no defense against the bomb and none in sight. Nobelist Langmuir was specific and close to the mark. Aware that Russia had nuclear physicists too, he scoffed at military guesses that America could monopolize the bomb until around 1965. Russia would start making bombs in 1948, he predicted; by 1960 or so there would be urgent international need to outlaw the bomb-making race.

The Senate got down to wise decisions sooner than the House. On its own first day it received a bill from Brien McMahon that would give our government strict controls over the new energy, for war and peace alike. This lawyer-senator was quickly named chairman of a special committee to hold public hearings "on the entire question of the atomic bomb and atomic energy."

Hasty decisions would not do, but speed was needed. Already, scientists were disgusted with the red-tape kind of secrecy, were rebellious against making still more bombs, were deserting government service for more satisfying research. On the other hand, evidence was coming in that Russia's bomb-planners had been helped by her spies. And, ignoring future wars—if one could—what of the "peaceful atom"? Medical research was eager to explore it. Industry wanted to know how free it would be to plow the new field. But who would protect the public—against monstrous explosions, against a frustrating monopoly?

The bomb had worked; here now was another, more complicated venture into the unknown. Over it hung a sense of urgency that soon obliterated political party lines. But there were many sharply conflicting interests. Consequently, the McMahon hearings and the congressional debate that followed them added up to something reminiscent of the Constitutional Convention of 1787, and needed even more time. The protagonists had their say, and Congress forged a compromise—not a new Constitution but likewise a historic document that set up rules for the future: the Atomic Energy Act of 1946. It was amended importantly in 1954, and again ten years later, but its mandate remained the same.

Declaring the nation's nuclear policy to be no longer strictly military, it restored the future of nuclear energy to civilian hands. With this responsibility came all the real estate and equipment that the military project had accumulated. But also the stern proviso— nothing should weaken "the common defense and security." Accordingly, the civilian agency must set up secrecy safeguards, must continue to research and produce nuclear weapons, must work in liaison with the Pentagon.

The rest is procedure for promoting world peace, fostering science, and encouraging industry to exploit the field. This big assignment is based on the choice of end-products from a modern reactor that "burns" fissionable U-235.

1. For fission weapons, the objective is plutonium. So the reactor is fueled with enough U-235 to keep a chain reaction going and thereby change the rest—the more abundant U-238—into plutonium.

2. For basic research, plutonium is less important than two other products—the neutrons themselves, and the various radioactive fragments into which the U-235 splits. These are prized for a wide variety of radiation experiments, for cancer therapy and so on.

3. For electric power, the need is to tap the fission energy. Coming off as heat from the chain reaction, it is mainly a nuisance to the weapons-maker and the researcher. Usually a cooling liquid removes it, as the automobile engine is cooled by a radiator. But water heated this way by a nuclear reactor is as useful as hot water obtained by burning coal or oil. It can be changed to steam, which then spins

the turbine that generates electricity or heats seawater to remove its salt.

Scientifically, all this seems simple. Politically and economically, it is a formidable choice of sword in one hand, plowshare in the other. This could not be handled by pious platitudes. Consequently, throughout our atomic law runs the theme that only one monopoly would be tolerated, that of the United States Government. Until 1964, for example, it was the sole owner of the nation's fissionable supplies, which it leased or gave to those who met licensing requirements. And administering the law is a system of checks and balances reminiscent of that set up by the Constitution.

First, over-all control is vested in civilians—an Atomic Energy Commission of five "qualified" members forbidden outside professional activities while serving their five-year terms. They are appointed by the President with advice and consent of the Senate, but the President alone designates which of the five shall be chairman. The first chairman was David E. Lilienthal, a capable administrator who had headed the TVA and who brought to AEC his belief that "Scientists should be on tap, not on top."

How to keep scientists on tap? The commission has its own force of technical people, of course, with a general manager to carry out its policies. The commission also delegates assignments to several advisory groups, of which two are mandatory: the Committee on Reactor Safeguards, an AEC-appointed group of fifteen experts whose doubts about hazards must be satisfied before the commission will license the construction of a new reactor; and a General Advisory Committee of nine experts whom the President appoints to six-year terms without need to consult the Senate or AEC. The latter group has led the AEC into its most explosive episodes; the Oppenheimer case was one.

Obviously, the law also had to recognize the Pentagon's continuing needs. But what chance is there of the warlike atom's becoming too belligerent? The law makes no attempt to legislate against a nuclear *coup d'état.* Anticipating only the normal hazards of a stable republic, it spreads responsibility and prescribes that the President will not be ignored. The AEC is authorized to work on weapons only with his "consent and direction, which shall be obtained at least once each year." It is he who "from time to time may direct" the AEC to deliver nuclear weaponry to the Defense Department. His is the final decision if disputes arise between AEC and a Military Liaison Committee named by the Pentagon; he names this committee's chairman, with the Senate's approval. In recent years, much of this part of the mandate has been disregarded or bypassed by the White House and Pentagon.

Finally, both to prod and to protect the AEC, the law specifies an unprecedented group. This is the Joint Congressional Committee on Atomic Energy. Senate and House each provides nine members: five from one political party, four from the other. It handles all legislation concerning the AEC and nuclear energy in general. It is also a policy-maker: it put a moribund power program back on its feet; it stepped in with its own experts to rescue both the H-bomb and the nuclear submarine. Furthermore, it is a watchdog. When the AEC commits a misdemeanor, that is because even the best duenna must sometimes be somewhere else. To this committee the AEC not only brings its budgets and other major requests; it must also submit an annual report, and quarterly progress reports as well. There are also the "Section 202" hearings: the law says that sometime during the first ninety days of each session the Joint Committee shall receive "information concerning the development, growth and state of the atomic energy industry." To keep the Joint Committee itself alert, the law threw out the idea of a chairman who succeeds himself. The chairmanship changes with each Congress, alternating between Senate and House.

Here, then, was a new experiment in American government. Although not of cabinet rank, AEC was part of the executive branch; that is, it was tucked in as another "independent agency" along with various others such as the FCC and the Committee on Purchases of Blind-Made Products. In one of his curmudgeon moments, New York's Robert Moses referred to such an agency as "one of those curious floating kidneys that bedevils the metabolism of the body politic." But kidneys like the ICC and FTC have demonstrated they can handle their specialized assignments healthily when the rest of the body politic is healthy. Furthermore, AEC was unlike all these in having so broad a mandate and in being chaperoned so tightly by Congress, therefore being theoretically so responsive to the will of the people.

The law would seem a conscientious job of legislation. Neither kind of specialists, those from science nor those from the Pentagon, would be "on top." Undeniably, in the military sector, it has given America a powerful nuclear shield. But what about the rest of a program that started off 95 per cent military and 5 per cent peaceful?

Seventeen years later, AEC's first chairman, Lilienthal, looked back and wrote a disappointed article for *Harper's* magazine: "Whatever Happened to the Peaceful Atom?" By the standards of science, he was a lawyer-administrator. At about the same time, I was talking to Princeton's notable and very mathematical Eugene Wigner, who had been one of the Manhattan project's top physicists. His disappointment went past Lilienthal's: "We were mistaken enough in expecting a postwar prosperity based on cheap nuclear power; but to expect atomic weaponry to do away with international conflict was our greatest, and least excusable, failure of insight."

Was this disillusionment the price for the error of equating a new weapon with lasting peace? and for expecting peacetime miracles in a postwar period that hasn't been peace? The weapons race not only claimed first priority but forced more secrecy than was healthy for a civilian energy program. Secrecy in turn nurtured loose talk of "breakthroughs." But the mandate was not that exuberant. Just as the love of a maid for a man cannot be decreed, industry and consumers must first admit the need for a radically new product. Years ago, for example, faulty scientific reports and promotional tracts were announcing that we were running out of petroleum, natural gas, coal, water power, and should therefore obey the chemurgists and start driving autos with "power alcohol" from the Corn Belt's corn.

But more. Both men overlooked the obvious fact that the AEC was itself an experiment. It required patient trial-and-error; it could even fail. For example, the "five statutory wise men" idea. Back in 1950, Chairman Lilienthal had resigned with the advice that AEC could be run just as well by one man. However, conditions then were different. The commissioners had been caught in the crossfire of whether America should try to build the H-bomb. Lilienthal had been on the losing side.

Four years later, after Eisenhower succeeded Truman, the Joint Committee had to face again the issue of one-man rule, this time in another form. There had just been two new and bitter controversies.

One, a sequel to the H-bomb decision, was the security investigation called the Oppenheimer case. The other was the public-versus-private utilities fight called the Dixon-Yates case, so complicated that it was comical—but not to the AEC, which was led into the mess by the President's Budget Bureau. Both issues quickly became partisan politics. And now, for the first time, newspapermen were comparing the performance of Republicans and Democrats in the commission.

This was not easy because Lewis L. Strauss, the AEC's new chairman, was too nimble for labeling. Though a devout Republican, he was a world apart from the party progressives symbolized by such public-power senators as George Norris and George Aiken. Yet, though suspected by liberals generally, he had previously been an AEC commissioner named by Truman. Also confusing were his qualifications for the chairmanship. Though a Naval Reservist whose war service was that of an inspection officer, he was primarily an ex-Wall Streeter. Yet he was considerably more than a layman. He had made it his business to know anybody important, and this included physicists. Long before the war, from men like Ernest Lawrence, Irving Langmuir, Leo Szilard, he became aware of the neutrons game and had even helped finance some experiments that might produce something practical from the nucleus.

At any rate, Strauss was definitely ambitious and under constant fire for conferring with Eisenhower too much and his fellow commissioners too little. A result was one of the amendments in 1954 to the Atomic Energy Act. The new wording proclaimed the chairman to be also the AEC's "official spokesman," but no more than that. All five commissioners would share "equal responsibility and authority" and have "full access to all information," and AEC decisions would be only by majority vote. Like the chairman of the Pentagon's Joint Chiefs of Staff, he would be only a "first among equals."

The Pentagon arrangement had not brought utopia. Unable to control his warring Chiefs, Defense Secretary Forrestal committed suicide. The AEC arrangement was happier. The commission seemed all the healthier for having survived the occupational stresses of Washington. The political vendettas subsided. So did panicky reactions to Russian hostility, and their terroristic byproduct called McCarthyism. The AEC could now operate more freely in its civilian sector. Research on fission power plants need no longer remain under the secrecy required for warheads. The most important amendment in 1954 invited civilians to come in and get electricity from the nucleus. Four years later, the doors were opened to explorers of the rival method that would fuse atoms instead of splitting them; the Promethean attempt to steal the simpler, more fruitful secret of the sun.

Here seemed a way to live with massive science, if live with it we must. Here was a bureaucracy that had enthusiasm for its job. It was tightly managed; staffed with people who were unterrified by the high energies and dangerous radiation that confront nuclear workers; dexterous enough to switch easily from one mission to another. And it was not getting into headline-making brawls. For example, the hope for 4.5 trillion kilowatt-hours of nuclear electricity in the year 2000 brought no hosannahs from investors in coal, gas, and oil, but neither was it a TVA-like ogre that threatened private industry. Government-subsidized R & D was nonpartisan; it awaited any competent enterprise, public or private, willing to try the nuclear way of generating power. True, the complex called the AEC also had plants of its own—arsenals that eclipsed Army's; research labs more glamorous than the Agriculture Department's. But AEC's method was different. It ran these facilities only in the sense that its people were planners and inspectors. The actual work was "private enterprise"—plump contracts to educators such as the Universities of Chicago and California, to corporations such as Union Carbide and Du Pont.

Within the government, too, the AEC tried to keep out of trouble. Unlike the National Science Foundation and National Institutes of Health it required no whippings to make it keep its accounts in order: it had capable comptrollers from the start. Unlike NASA, the new space agency, which had to fight Air Force for *Lebensraum* above earth, the AEC could not be accused of being expansionist. Though the atom's nucleus is indescribably small it kept AEC much too busy for empire-building adventures. Here was a jurisdiction that started with the mining and stockpiling of a raw material, mainly uranium. Then it fanned out into munitions, electric power, biology, atom-smashing, education, foreign aid, and so on.

And all this did not require battling for necessary funds. Congress was not niggardly. For a yardstick, let us use the 2.2 billions of World War II dollars risked on the A-bomb. By 1958, the AEC was receiving more than that yearly for the postwar atom. In recent years, the annual figure has run about $2.75 billion. Almost half is R & D money split equally for the warlike and peaceful atom; the manufacture of actual weapons is another major item. All told, by 1965, AEC appropriations had totaled $36 billion. This is an enormous sum. It is also equivalent to what NASA may spend to put Americans on the moon, and less than the Pentagon's $50 billion each year.

If such be the brighter side, there is another. The AEC is not what it was. In the past few years, sounds of a threnody have broken through the triumphal nuclear march; the Joint Committee has had to play its duenna role constantly, and often futilely. Why?

The shortest answer is Washington politics in its various manifestations—empire-building, jealousy of the AEC, hunger to seize its powers and assets. Here was a busy, neatly run, big-budgeted but relatively small agency that whetted the appetite. Its very· existence was a galling anomaly. It stood primly aloof from the usual gross kind of porkbarrel. It watched its dollars: for example, its ratio of purchased computers to leased ones was highest in the government. Unlike NASA, it obeyed its mandate: the patent for a government-financed discovery made by one of its contractors becomes government property for public use, rather than monopoly use by the contractor.

The AEC might have remained immune to interference if not for a phenomenon known to historians. A nation goes through cycles, forgetting when it returns to euphoria the high resolves made during emergency. In the 1960s, a nation that was prosperous, and for the moment less fearful of nuclear attack, could regard the onetime benefactor as a fussy disturber of business as usual. So, few protested when usurpers began initiating, "integrating," and vetoing nuclear programs. The AEC was enjoined by the White House to cease being a "sacred preserve"; and in Congress the Joint Committee could only resort to delaying tactics while its ward was pulled into mainstream—which here meant invasion rather than coordination. The AEC's portion of control over nuclear weaponry passed to the

Pentagon, of atom-testing policy to the State Department. Even the future of peaceful energy was slipping from its hands, and by now it had become too powerless to do little more than lament.

Obeying President Kennedy's request for "a new and hard look at the role of nuclear power in our economy," AEC dutifully consulted other government agencies and prepared a historic blueprint that was seized upon by science and industry. However, the report "got genesis in the AEC but exodus in the Office of Science and Technology," where the President's science adviser, Jerome Wiesner, embarked upon a quick, superseding study. Sixteen months later, his successor admitted to the Joint Committee that Wiesner had again not been at a loss for words: "Nearly 100 technical papers were prepared. . . . These were reviewed by more than 150 qualified technical reviewers and about 225 members of 22 special *ad hoc* committees. By the end of last summer the team . . . had produced a preliminary draft of 1200 pages. A redraft, on the more manageable order of 600 pages is now ready for further review. . . . What is missing is clearcut findings and conclusions."

So a variety of cooks were stirring the mainstream stew and an R & D chief complained to me, "How can I operate in such a climate?" All this, the AEC meekly accepted. A few statistics and an interview help explain why.

For one thing, its composition had changed. In itself, this was more a symptom than a cause, but it has significance. An unwritten agreement was followed throughout the first fourteen years. Of the five commissioners, four were laymen, one was a scientist. And if they were sometimes troublesome—like layman Lilienthal, the Truman-appointed chairman, and layman Strauss, the Eisenhower chairman—it was because of their zeal in championing the AEC's mandate. Then Eisenhower appointed a second non-layman, and in the Kennedy Administration the scientist-to-layman ratio became 3 to 2. Moreover, the new chairman was chemist Seaborg, who likened science policy to a ship with a thousand helms and espoused mainstream. Before long, the commission expressed its astonishing death wish. It voted to abolish itself in favor of a single administrator.

Its reasons were several. It felt that five men with different backgrounds meant different opinions, which meant time wasted. It agreed with the White House that times had changed—there need no longer be fear of placing nuclear authority in a single man. Further-more, it complained, policy-making powers had leaked away anyway; the AEC was now mainly a technical director of programs decided by two Presidential assistants, the Pentagon, and others.

The situation changed when two layman commissioners departed. A duel between the White House and the Joint Committee followed and led to a compromise over their replacements. One appointee was John G. Palfrey, a lawyer who was pro-abolition. The other was lawyer James T. Ramey, who had spent fifteen years under the aegis of the Atomic Energy Act, first with the AEC and then with the Joint Committee. Unsurprisingly, he supported the mandate; the commission was no longer unanimous; the schedule for abolition was quietly postponed.

Shortly afterward, I visited Chairman Seaborg to determine the status of the death wish. "Oh yes," he said, and repeated the argu-ments for abolition. "But how do *you* feel about it?" I pressed. Here, he was not clear. "Yes, I favor the plan to abolish the commission as such." On the other hand: "It has become a tremendously big business, more like a government department with cabinet rank." But also: "It's not that I want more power for myself." At any rate: "Congress doesn't seem ready for abolition yet, so I am not agitating for it. A year or two isn't important. Meanwhile, Congress may change; others may change."

Here, then, was a chairman ready to preside over liquidation of the AEC. Not that it would go out of business. It would simply wither into a technical agency that administered programs decided elsewhere. This seemed a pity. The "hot atom" still needed statutory wise men and having five of them, representing varying viewpoints, would be more reassuring than a marionette organization trying to navigate in theoretically placid but actually turbulent waters of main-stream.

The situation changed again a few months later when Lyndon Johnson moved into the White House and proceeded to seek the Presidency in his own right. Military scientists wondered at his confident statement that general war was now "impossible." Others had doubts about this dynamo who liked breakthroughs and showed little empathy when attempts were made to explain the patient re-search that must precede breakthroughs. Furthermore, he wanted to prove that he could relax international tension. One way was to cut the soaring stockpile of nuclear weapons that his predecessors had built up. And the AEC speculated on its own future. This slowdown could easily affect its research on the peaceful atom too. Johnson's record already showed distaste for the Joint Committee's "No Trespass" signs around the atom's nucleus.

For the time being, however, the nuclear people did not fare badly. Though no expert in science, Johnson definitely was one in politics; his art was compromise, and he certainly saw no point in warring with a Joint Committeee dominated by members of his own party. For instance, he renamed the AEC's energetic layman Ramey, who had been an interim appointee, to a full term of five years: an indicator that abolition of the five-man commission was not yet a certainty. Meanwhile, in the AEC's pending business he had found two choice items for the Great Society. He announced a breakthrough for nuclear electricity. And he ordered a breakthrough for desalting seawater with the same nuclear heat. Whereupon New York's Governor Nelson Rockefeller, not to be outdone, announced that his state was planning the world's first nuclear desalination plant. All this was politics, to be sure, but it was the kind that prodded the AEC rather than paralyzed it.

Johnson also joined in the most important change in nuclear law since 1954. Now, ten years later, the Joint Committee agreed that the government monopoly over nuclear fuels could be safely ended, and a corresponding amendment to the mandate sailed easily through Congress and the White House. Stringent AEC regulations would continue, but industry was enjoined to mine, buy, and sell the fuels freely. The AEC was jubilant to be through with this nursing duty. Industry was ambivalent. It had looked forward to independence. It was also sorry to see what could develop into the end of lavish subsidies.

In sum, there seemed nothing wrong with the nuclear-energy program that human energy could not fix. And the mandate had again shown itself to be more than pious platitudes. Uranium was no longer 95 per cent military and 5 per cent civilian. It was even possible now for advertising folk to aim glisteny new promises at their perennial targets out in the suburbs: "Atomic energized seeds can develop an amazing garden for you."

Yet the big experiment was still young. The dream of lavish nuclear power was still in the blueprint stage. So was the rest of the idealism. So was the hope that AEC would demonstrate a practical way for big government, big science, and the rest of modern society to live together fruitfully. Let us now see the directions that AEC has been taking, and what they could mean for the future.

XI: *The Military Atom*

"Three of the nine reactors at Richland and one
of the five at Savannah River are to shut down.
The Commission is keenly aware of the impact of
these reductions upon the communities involved."
—Cold War communiqué from the AEC,
January 8, 1964

Like other important patrons of science, the AEC has busied itself
with both basic and applied R & D. But it has ranged far. It has
also had to be a manufacturer, spy-fighter, educator. Its most press-
ing responsibility has been preparation for war; yet, obeying the
mandate, it also has pacific programs. Seeking uranium supplies, it
is like a Bureau of Mines. Regulating producers of electricity, it is
like a Federal Power Commission. And, as we shall see later, its
research on nuclear engines—without which journeys to Mars and
beyond could remain fiction—take it into NASA's orbit. These may
seem a strange conglomerate of functions. But they reduce to a
common bond, the nucleus of the atom. The AEC therefore adds up
to a very integrated industry. Or rather, one with two unofficial
divisions—international and domestic. The former concerns us here.

Under its mandate the AEC is enjoined to make peaceful nuclear
benefits "available to cooperating nations." Accordingly, the Atoms
for Peace program has spent millions cooperating with the UN and
with Euratom, the European Atomic Energy Community. In all such
foreign relations, the AEC must, of course, cooperate with the
Pentagon and State Department. This is not always easy. It has been
forced to trim its scientific opinion to suit the way the Cold War
blows.

Even the purely nonmilitary work has complications. Seeking

348

friendship abroad, and glutted with our stockpile of nuclear materials, we began begging foreign customers to take plutonium and enriched U-235 off our hands for research purposes—at a time when domestic industry could only lease such stuff from AEC. We even managed to sell one ounce of uranyl acetate to Russia, because it would be used in a virus laboratory. On the other hand, there is Thailand, for whom at last count we had helped build eighteen research reactors. "Thailand was heart-warming," a returning AEC man told me. "Its technicians and schoolteachers swarmed to see our portable lab. They brought things to be irradiated. They jammed our instructional classes, 100 per class, 7 days a week, 8:30 a.m. to 9 p.m."

But what of large reactors for producing electricity? By its very nature, fissioning uranium cannot help making warlike plutonium. Accordingly, when India announced plans to buy a power reactor from America, fearful Pakistan asserted its right to buy one. When India then decided on two, Pakistan likewise changed to two. And with good reason. Before long, India was debating whether or not to use byproduct plutonium for her first test explosion and thereby force her way into the nuclear club. Such problems obviously have needed vigilance and pressure by AEC and other United States agencies supporting the International Atomic Energy Agency's safeguards system. Meanwhile, embarrassment. Nations still without nuclear arsenals complain that they are lectured and inspected by club members who themselves remain free to go on with the proliferation of such weaponry.

Secrecy and Oppenheimer

After the war, America learned that neither the FBI nor Army Intelligence had prevented agents of our erstwhile Soviet ally from exporting details about our bomb project at Los Alamos. The result was fright over spies, and over saboteurs who might blow us up with Russian uranium. Meanwhile, as early as 1945 and 1946, Canada and England were revealing details of Russia's atomic espionage. This was the period in which our AEC was born, and inherited the security assignment. From the start, it knew enough to distinguish between what was secret and what any physicist should know. Yet as late as 1955 it had to admit "a regrettable snafu." This was after its refusal to allow geneticist Muller to lecture at the Geneva Atoms for Peace Conference on a subject that had won him the Nobel Prize: "How Radiation Changes the Genetic Constitution." Why the ban? Because his paper contained "material referring to nonpeaceful uses of atomic energy, namely the bombing of the Japanese city of Hiroshima." Thereafter AEC learned how to apply alertness where it might do some good. The commission spends $7 million a year for security investigations; a $500,000 reward awaits anybody with information that a nuclear weapon has been smuggled into the United States.

This problem of policing the atom inevitably brings up the AEC's most memorable security case, and certainly the one that aroused the most bitterness. The man concerned was physicist Robert Oppenheimer, whom fate led from hearty participation in the A-bomb project to obstruction of the H-bomb, from official applause in the first role to official condemnation in the second.

The decision that exiled him from government councils was made in 1954, but the case lives on, mainly because Oppenheimer and his partisans have unceasingly labored to erase the condemnation. And there are interesting implications. One is very applicable today. As laymen, the world's highest policy-makers are increasingly helpless without a scientific priesthood. Now suppose that the government's most influential nuclear adviser insists on a course which, it turns out, would imperil the nation. Oppenheimer happened to be such an expert. The field was nuclear warfare and the time was Stalinist Russia. Had America relied on his preference for A-bombs, she would soon have faced a Russia brandishing far deadlier H-bombs.

But what does one do with the erring expert? In a modern democracy, certainly, it isn't decorous to execute him. With Oppenheimer the answer came more easily because the question was broader. There was also "proof of fundamental defects in his character." So the decision, made by seven out of nine men representing a cross-section of backgrounds, named him a security risk. This allowed him to prosper elsewhere but no longer as a government adviser with a "Q" clearance, therefore ineligible to know high military secrets.

That, in essence, was the Oppenheimer case. But more details are needed. For instance, how good is the judgment of a scientist outside his field? Oppenheimer participated creditably in building the A-bomb. But did this justify his influencing the decision to bomb Hiroshima? Later, explaining some of his behavior at Los Alamos, when he was thirty-nine, he argued that he was naïve then. This was echoed by a character witness, von Neumann, who appraised the Los Alamos Oppenheimer in terms of adolescence: "There are certain experiences which are new for an adolescent, and where an adolescent will behave in a silly way."

Unquestionably, Oppenheimer was unprepared for the rigors of realities. The son of a wealthy businessman, he studied physics at the proper universities here and abroad. This led to a dozen teaching offers, and his accepting two. For twelve years, beginning in 1929, he taught theoretical physics at both Caltech and Berkeley. In testimony years later he drew this self-portrait of his life during early years of the Depression and challenging liberalism of the New Deal:

"My friends were mostly faculty people, scientists, classicists and artists. I studied Sanskrit . . . I never read a newspaper or a current magazine like *Time* or *Harper's*; I had no radio, no telephone; I learned of the stock-market crash only long after the event."

He went on to relate that this remoteness ended abruptly in the mid-1930s. Through some Communist friends and relatives he became interested in the fight against Fascism abroad, a supporter of the United Front, and a financial contributor to, though not a member of, the Communist Party.

Then came the big war. In 1942, the research on explosives for an A-bomb was under way; now the Manhattan project needed development of the bomb itself. Though a theoretician, Oppenheimer handled graduate students capably and was widely known in the physics establishment. He was chosen to direct the science part of the project. The circumstances were odd. On the one hand, he had *carte blanche*. He chose the scientists and engineers; he set up the lab at Los Alamos, near his summer ranch. On the other hand, military supervisors were nervous about his "leftist" background and continuing friendship with Communists, but decided he was indispensable, therefore a calculated risk: "We kept him under surveillance . . . we opened his mail."

Intellectual, slangy, a lanky supervisor who was crew-cut almost to baldness, popular despite a self-confidence that was sometimes arrogance, "Oppie" kept the sometimes difficult scientists in line. The first bombs were built and used.

After the war he took two jobs at opposite ends of the R & D spectrum. One, as director of the Institute for Advanced Study at Princeton. The other, as a member of the newly born AEC's General Advisory Committee. At the first meeting of these nine scientists and engineers he was elected chairman. And inasmuch as the AEC's own chairman was Lilienthal, a layman, Oppenheimer emerged as the government's top adviser for nuclear affairs.

Two years later, Russia tested its first A-bomb. Our monopoly had ended. Oppenheimer's GAC was given this double question: (1) was it technically possible to build a hydrogen bomb; and (2) if so, should we start work on this "super" at once? The chairman reported back that he and the other experts agreed: a discouraging answer to the first question, and a nay to the second, on strategic and moral grounds. As we have seen, the Joint Committee mistrusted this advice, a race with Russia started, and we won by nine months.

The AEC elbowed Oppenheimer out of the committee in 1952 but retained him as a consultant. When his contract was due for renewal the next year, there was trouble. Security regulations had been tightened. Complaints had reached the FBI about Oppenheimer's trustworthiness. The result was Eisenhower's ordering a "blank wall," pending a hearing, between the scientist and government secrets.

The law allowed Oppenheimer his hearing before a special Personnel Security Board, to prove he was entitled to restoration of his "Q" clearance. It was April 1954. The witch-hunting smell of McCarthyism was still in the nation's air. But this was no McCarthy-type probe, and Robert E. Sherwood, the famed playwright and a Roosevelt liberal, wrote Eisenhower: "The announcement of the manner in which you are handling the case came like a breath of clear, fresh air on the front pages this morning." The so-called "Gray Board" was a politically nonpartisan panel of three men independent of the AEC and acceptable to Oppenheimer—Gordon Gray, president, University of North Carolina; T. A. Morgan, ex-president, Sperry Gyroscope Company; W. V. Evans, professor of chemistry, Loyola University. Testimony was behind closed doors. Oppenheimer had three attorneys and could confront his accusers. One of the witnesses who hurt Oppenheimer most also went out of his way to damn the country's Red-baiters. The hearing ended with Oppenheimer's counsel praising its fairness.

The transcript was 992 tightly printed pages. It, and the resulting reports and recommendations that went to the AEC, can be summarized quickly. There were three charges:

1. That Oppenheimer had a long record of associating closely with Communists, some of them militants, until 1942, and with some of them after the war. By itself, this charge was insufficient. It was a bizarre fact that security officials knew about most of this, yet Oppenheimer was kept on at Los Alamos. Furthermore, no disloyalty was proven against him, and he produced reputable witnesses to confirm his loyalty. The worst against him here was that he carried too many secrets after the war to justify his being friendly with whomever he chose, wherever he chose.

2. That he had opposed the H-bomb program and, after it started, not only supported it insufficiently but swayed other scientists not to participate. By itself, this charge would also seem insufficient. The board stated: "We must make it clear that we do not question his right to the opinions he held. They were shared by other competent and devoted individuals, both in and out of Government." This was true enough—even in the Defense Department were some opponents to the program. The damage to Oppenheimer here lay in two things: "His influence in the atomic circles with respect to the hydrogen bomb was far greater than he would have led this board to believe"; and frequent references by the board to his "lack of candor."

3. That this "lack of candor" showed frequently in his behavior. For example, he had told the AEC that his committee was unanimously against the H-bomb. It turned out, however, that one GAC member, Glenn Seaborg, was not present but had given his opinion by letter. In it he deplored the need to develop the superbomb but continued, "I must confess that I have been unable to come to the conclusion that we should not."

Another "candor" incident went back to 1943, when Oppenheimer was under surveillance at Los Alamos. Now, in 1954, he told the Gray Board how he quieted suspicions against himself then by giving security officers a complicated story about repulsing a friend from France, Haakon Chevalier, when the latter sought A-bomb secrets for Russia. All that, Oppenheimer testified now, was "fabrication" and "a tissue of lies." This left him in the position of (1) falsely incriminating a friend in 1943 or (2) committing perjury in 1954.

There was, of course, the suggestion by von Neumann that Oppenheimer was still adolescent at thirty-nine. But in 1949, six years older, he was in similar trouble. At a hearing before the House Un-American Activities Committee he referred to "this guy Peters" as "a dangerous man and quite Red." As a result, Bernard Peters almost lost his professorship at the University of Rochester. Oppenheimer was reminded about this at the Gray Board hearing. He explained that he saved Peters by a retraction that was demanded by several scientists, including physicist Edward Condon:

"He said I should not have hurt an innocent man and loyal American in that way . . . that if he lost his job, it would be wholly my doing. That I must try to make restitution, and that he hated to believe that I could have said such a thing, and in an attempt to protect myself. I knew very well if my file were ever made public, it would be a much bigger flap. . . . I don't know what business it was of Dr. Condon's, except that he was outraged at any harm brought to a scientist."

All told, there were three verdicts. The AEC's was the final one. Its four nonscientist commissioners agreed that "fundamental defects" in Oppenheimer's character and excessive association with known Communists made him a security risk; one of the four, T. E. Murray, added doubts about the man's loyalty. The fifth commissioner, physicist Smyth of Princeton, dissented. He expressed distaste for Oppenheimer's conduct but found no proof that the man was a security risk.

To help them decide, the AEC commissioners had the opinion of their general manager, K. D. Nichols. It was a blistering indictment of Oppenheimer. And, of course, both Nichols and the commissioners had the testimony and report from the Gray Board. Its verdict was two-to-one against Oppenheimer. Here again, the minority report was by the scientist member. Evans subscribed to much of the majority report but said Oppenheimer was more adult now, and ended with the warning that the man was supported by many scientists: "I am worried about the effect an improper decision may have on the scientific development in our country."

The majority report showed the same worry and tried to anticipate criticism by stressing that Oppenheimer's trustworthiness could not be judged by any one charge: "We have sought to address ourselves to the whole question . . . not to consider loyalty, character and associations separately."

But one of the tragedies of McCarthyism is that open minds clang shut. Intolerance breeds counter-intolerance; not all the martyrs are genuine. And in the uproar over who is "un-American," reasonable men find it hard to be heard. It so happened that, at the very time of the Oppenheimer hearing, Senator Joseph McCarthy was at bay and would soon see his career crumble. But McCarthyism had become a brand-name. The idea of weighing all the Oppenheimer evidence fell on many deaf ears; certainly, few people with strong opinions, either pro or con, bothered to read the transcript. This helps explain why many sincere scientists—and "humanists" for that matter—saw here another victim of "thought control," "guilt by association," and the like. Anyway, the president of the Federation of American Scientists charged that scientific freedom had been "dragged into the dirt." Others, aware of the antipathy between Oppenheimer and Edward Teller, reduced it all to jealousy between giants—the "father" of the A-bomb versus "father" of the H-bomb. And then there were odd characters who argued that because Oppenheimer "was superior intellectually, there should be special criteria in his case." This, despite the fact that his chief counsel agreed with the Gray Board that "because the loyalty or security-risk status of a scientist or any other intellectual may be brought into question, scientists and intellectuals are ill-advised to assert that a reasonable and sane inquiry constitutes an attack upon scientists and intellectuals generally."

Such was the Oppenheimer case. The physicist emerged neither a traitorous Benedict Arnold nor a persecuted Alfred Dreyfus. Whether he was a tragic figure in the classic Greek sense depends on how one responds to the entire testimony. Also, doubts have arisen whether the case was tragic at all. But these were raised by Oppenheimer. In 1964, he objected to a German play based on the Gray Board hearings. He contended that they should be treated as a farce rather than the tragic ordeal that his supporters had long supposed them to be.

Tragedy or not, it is fruitful to compare the Oppenheimer outcome with what happened to two nonscientists in recent years. They, too, had promising careers and had to face dramatic charges of lying. One was Alger Hiss, the State Department official found guilty of perjury. The other was the young college professor Charles Van Doren, of the TV quiz-show scandals. They were disgraced and, without a strong establishment to support them, had to withdraw into the shadows to rebuild their lives.

To be sure, Oppenheimer lost his governmental credentials. But he was in no way cast off by the scientific establishment. He continued as director of the Princeton institute, and its leading trustee was no other than AEC chairman Strauss, who was being damned by some scientists for having conducted a personal vendetta against Oppenheimer. Scientific societies continued honoring Oppenheimer. The institute's public-relations man told me that Oppenheimer now spent 25 per cent of his time as "a public figure." There were fewer references now to Oppenheimer as "father" of the A-bomb. He published essays that recorded his thoughts on the future of mankind. His public image approached that of a martyr. A visiting scientist came away exclaiming, "He looks so ascetic, almost Christlike." Others paid tribute to "the American scientist who has paid the highest price for his role in increasing the light from the tower."

Eventually, Oppenheimer supporters steered the case back into government politics. First, there was a trial balloon to gauge public reaction. In 1962, although not a Nobelist himself, Oppenheimer was invited to a White House dinner in honor of Nobelists. This was interpreted as the ripening of a quiet campaign to restore his security clearance. The surmise was good but wrong in detail. Four months later, Oppenheimer was chosen by the AEC's General Advisory Committee to receive the annual Fermi Award—the gold medal plus a $50,000 tax-free United States Treasury check.

This time, reactions were quick. First, a revival of charges that the "same old gang" of bomb-makers were giving the award to each other; and, specifically, that of the seven winners so far, Oppenheimer and AEC Chairman Seaborg were among five who were on GAC at one time or other. Critics asked why the Fermi never went to a highly qualified outsider—Vice Admiral H. G. Rickover, for example.

In Congress the Joint Committee followed with demands to know how and why the size of the award had grown from the original $25,000 given Fermi. And Representative Craig Hosmer guessed that the award to Oppenheimer was "a delicate balance of judgment between his qualifications and disqualifications." He was not objecting this time, Hosmer warned, but "any attempt to restore the security clearance on any pretext would be a grievous miscalculation that would not be tolerated by even a small minority of the American people."

It remained debatable whether Congress had won or, as Oppenheimer partisans contended, they had fully "erased the disgraceful stain on the name of J. Robert Oppenheimer." But the displeasure of the Joint Committee had other results. The AEC reduced the award to $25,000, and the next winner was Admiral Rickover.

The Thermonuclear Difference

In 1950 the opposition to the H-bomb had lost. With an end to the seminal complications came the scientific challenge—could AEC laboratories give birth to such a weapon? So let us resume where we left off with the A-bomb, whose explosive energy matches that from kilotons of TNT (the Hiroshima bomb corresponded to something under 20 kilotons) and move to its superior, which can be engineered to give energy measured in megatons, units that are a thousand times greater.

Although the two devices are very different—the first is a fission weapon; the second is primarily a fusion weapon—both confirm Einstein's idea that mass and energy are versions of the same thing. The two weapons also obey the same principle: the so-called "binding energy" of fission or fusion is released when an atomic nucleus changes to a more stable kind; stability depends on the mass of the nucleus; and the most stable elements are toward the center of the atomic chart.

From here, the two methods go in opposite directions. Fission splits a heavyweight atom like uranium into lighter ones. Fusion starts with two nuclei and ends with a heavier one. The fuel is isotopes of the lightweight hydrogen nucleus, and there are these familiar choices—two nuclei of deuterium, or one of deuterium and one of tritium. Either way, the isotopic hydrogen becomes helium, and possibly some ordinary hydrogen, with a bit of the original mass vanishing and reappearing as useful energy. The fusion idea seems simple enough now. It was a massive gamble, however, until a way was found to ignite the reaction. Nor was that all. Before any test, theoreticians had the serious science-fiction assignment of guaranteeing that the thermonuclear reaction could not spread under any circumstances—that it could not end the world by igniting the atmosphere or the oceans. Such men as mathematician Emil Konopinski and physicist George Breit proved this beyond doubt, and the work could proceed to the next problem.

In fission's chain reaction, the nuclei are deep inside their neutral, relatively large atoms and there are not serious electrical problems. Free neutrons serve as bullets that penetrate the atoms and cause their nuclei to split. But fusion is totally different, a thermal reaction requiring enormously high temperatures rather than free neutrons. Here the nuclei are not only smaller but naked—atoms that have been stripped of their satellite electrons. This means all are positively charged and strongly repel each other. The only way that man can crowd them together closely enough to force union is by imitating the sun and other stars: their energy, too, comes from fusion; and they, too, must use part of this energy to maintain the temperature that keeps the reaction going. But for a similar thermonuclear reaction that would be more than a laboratory experiment, man needs even more heat than the 20 million degrees centigrade at the interior of the sun. These are not only fantastic temperatures, but after years of research, as we shall see later, they still trouble the scientists who want fusion for peacetime purposes, because these researchers need both the high temperature and a containment method for the reaction. There is no such limitation on a bomb. By definition, it blows up. So the H-bomb gets its heat in a drastic way. It contains what amounts to a small A-bomb. This means a flash of three explosions. First, an ordinary high explosive. Its blast triggers the fission device, which blows up according to the Los Alamos formula: "Take some fissionable material in several pieces as pure as possible and slap them together as fast as possible." This becomes the hot trigger for the thermonuclear fuel. The result, of course, is nuclear energy from both fission and fusion. And the amount from fusion depends on the choice of hydrogen fuels. Such is the basic idea.

Engineering had to work out many other problems. Of the two

fusion fuels, for example, deuterium is an uncommon commodity, and the other isotope, tritium, must be manmade. Furthermore, both must be used in a special form. For our first test, the fuel was compressed into liquid, but this required refrigeration machinery too massive for a practical bomb to carry.

A deft answer was to use solid fuel, a special compound of a lithium isotope and deuterium. Here, the triggering A-bomb does two things. Neutrons produced by its fission split the lithium portion into helium and tritium. And its heat then forces this tritium to fuse with the deuterium. Thus, the bomb is making part of its fuel while it explodes.

Meanwhile, the fusion process is itself a lavish producer of surplus neutrons. An important use was found for them too. They helped strengthen the bomb with a previously unworthy material. This is the common uranium-238, normally too stable to work in an A-bomb, therefore inferior to U-235. But stability is a relative term. The U-238 does not respond easily to slow neutrons, as U-235 does when it fissions. But, as we have seen, faster neutrons change U-238 into plutonium. And physicists now had considerable data about its response to still faster neutrons of the kind produced by fusion. Their energy causes it to fission at a worthwhile rate. So the rest of the fuel was surrounded with a blanket of ordinary uranium and became truly a superbomb because the thickness of the blanket was not worrisome. The normal stability of this U-238 meant little fear that it would "go critical" spontaneously; the rest would have to be exploded first, to produce enough fast neutrons.

In such ways the engineers enlarged their choice among thermonuclear weapons, super and small.

Rickover's Submarine

In itself, a thermonuclear device is not enough. There must be an effective way of delivering the explosive. And though the Soviet Union was not forgotten, it often seemed so while Washington fought out its own rivalries. The transition from propellor-driven bombers to jets was peaceful enough. But then came the battle between jet bombers and missiles; between kinds of missiles, and kinds of propellants for them, liquid or solid. Eventually, our missile power grew from equality to a superiority that even fearful Americans had to admit. Then returned the basic fight over deterrent strategy. Should we continue holding over Moscow's head mainly the Overkill threat of our retaliatory Strategic Air Command; or change, as we did, to the McNamara concept of flexibility—the hope that many kinds of defense would keep the Soviets guessing, would be less provocative, would worry an enemy's military forces rather than his people in general.

Meanwhile, the AEC had the continuous and dizzying assignment of satisfying the nuclear requirements of Air Force, Army, Navy, who were waging three-way war at the Pentagon. Nor was this all. There was sometimes war right within one of the services. As an "independent agency," AEC could easily be a defenseless agency when the internecine shooting began. But here the Atomic Energy Act had shown wisdom. It backboned AEC with the protection of the Joint Committee, and the protection ranged far.

At about the same time that this duenna was interceding for the fusion-bomb program, it was rescuing mutinous Rickover in the other nuclear field, fission. The troubles he had with his idea for the nuclear-propelled submarine *Nautilus* are one of two notable blemishes on Navy's proud R & D record; the other, of course, was its insistence on building a mammoth radio telescope in West Virginia. Failure to build Admiral Rickover's submarine would have been far worse than the telescope fiasco. But here the Joint Committee could intercede because of AEC's unchallengeable interest in such a vessel.

It would be designed around an underwater steam engine that burned nuclear fuel. Even on land, a fission reactor needs shielding and a host of other safeguards. The engineers would therefore have problems aplenty with this reactor that would have to fit inside the bowels of a vessel—a small undersea one at that.

The basic idea, however, was simple. By its very nature, fission produces much heat. Consequently, the reactor must be cooled in some way. One way is by circulating water, as in the radiator of an automobile. This was already being done in the AEC reactors that were busily turning uranium into plutonium. The submarine required a radically different viewpoint because its reactor would not be intended to produce plutonium. Rather, it was the hot water that was wanted. Of course, it would be intensely radioactive. But it would be pressurized water carried by pipes through a second supply of water at lower pressure. This water would not be radioactive. And, receiving the heat, it would boil into steam. The steam, in turn, would spin turbines connected to the submarine's propeller shafts.

How the technical problems were solved is a technical story. The launching of the project was a political one. To ensure that Rickover would have complete control, the Joint Committee arranged that he wear a second cap. He was already with Navy. Now he became also "Manager of Naval Reactors, Division of Reactor Development" of the AEC. And the power plant was built. First as a land-based prototype at AEC's test station near Idaho Falls, Idaho. This led to the actual reactor that Westinghouse built for *Nautilus*. (The Rickover team was so confident that the keel for the submarine was laid a year before the prototype tests were finished.)

And *Nautilus* became a progenitor. Ten years after the vessel slid down the ways, fifty-two other nuclear submarines had been launched and the Joint Committee reported: "Through Admiral Rickover's boldness we are far ahead of the Russians in atomic undersea forces." Navy also had its first nuclear aircraft carrier, cruiser, and destroyer; and the first nuclear merchant ship, the *Savannah*, was exhibiting herself at world ports.

But nuclear-powered ships were expensive. So Rickover began pushing for a more advanced reactor. In performance two of them would equal the eight installed in our first nuclear aircraft-carrier, *Enterprise*. And President Johnson seized upon this for one of his "breakthrough" announcements.

Not that the admiral was content. He remained a Spartan in pleasure-loving Sybaris. He railed against the faultiness of the naval hardware furnished by industry. He blasted regularly at the establishment in our educational system. And he very much insisted on staying in the Navy. He had to go on the retirement list in 1964, but the Joint Committee arranged that he be recalled to active duty. The fanfare of publicity that Navy was now giving each offspring of *Nautilus* softened him not one whit. He asserted that Navy was distributing the subs "like so much confetti so that everyone could have a nuclear submarine to play with," and demanded that the vessels be used to their full capacity—as escort vessels as well as lone wolves lying in wait. Simultaneously, he warned that Navy was not providing sufficiently trained men: "In the reactor business we cannot wait for accidents to learn our lesson."

Meanwhile he could look back on another accomplishment. What worked undersea ought to be workable on land. *Nautilus* was launched in January 1954. Two months later, the AEC announced that Rickover would now direct construction of the nation's first civilian nuclear power plant—the same method, except for refinements, but now the steam turbines would generate electricity instead of propel a vessel. This plant, too, became a progenitor, as we shall see later.

At sea, of course, the advantage of the *Nautilus* idea was that it produced a true submarine, in the Jules Verne sense. Now, for the first time, a vessel could go almost anywhere, hide almost anywhere, because it needed only a small amount of long-lived fuel and no oxygen with which to burn it. The sub could remain submerged for weeks, even months. But this was only half of the story. Early during the Pentagon skirmishes over missiles, Navy was ordered to work jointly with Army on the liquid-propelled Jupiter. But Navy is a traditional loner. Within a year, it maneuvered permission to go ahead with its own weapon, a solid-fueled one.

Thus was born Polaris, the fusion missile fired from under water by a fission submarine. It became operational in 1960 and was continually improved. Its fourth generation was announced in 1965. With its Air Force counterpart, Minuteman, another example of a missile program carried through neatly, Polaris marked the beginning of a new defense era. We now had missiles that were lighter, cheaper, simpler, and more accurate. Like the new Titan, they benefited from our series of thermonuclear tests in 1958, before the ill-fated moratorium. The tests showed ways to get more explosion per pound of missile. As a result a nuclear submarine carrying sixteen Polaris missiles could boast more firepower than all of the bombs dropped in World War II. Technically speaking, Minuteman was a long-range ICBM and Polaris could reach anywhere important, thanks to its submarine carrier.

Overkill

Test bans and moratoriums affect research for new weapons, not the production of those already developed. In two years while disarmament talks droned on at Geneva, our nuclear arsenal tripled. To be sure, this information came from our chief negotiator, and he could hardly cry poor. But it jibed with other indications that America's munitions industry had been booming, perhaps overenthusiastically.

For example, missile warheads. In the early 1960s apparently nobody at the White House was checking on the Pentagon requests, as the Atomic Energy Act prescribed. When AEC received a shopping list it filled the order patriotically. But not always happily. Its bills, from raw materials to final weapons, ran about $1.8 billion a year, and the Pentagon wasn't dipping into its $50-billion budgets to repay any of it. The entire expense was charged to the AEC and was consuming two-thirds of its total budget. Eventually its complaints brought a Joint Committee rescue mission. But by that time we had more than enough Overkill, a situation sharpened by evidence that, while we were overproducing, Russia's weaponry program was lagging. Defense Secretary McNamara figured that we outweaponed the Soviet by 3 or 4 to 1 in quantity and by more than that in quality. Another estimate had it that megadeath from our megatonnage could Overkill the Soviet population 1250 times, even if half our weapons failed, and theoreticians began calculating our DOE ("Death of Earth") capability with a Doomsday Machine.

Some of this is merely an exercise for statisticians. Also, the well-being of our nuclear stockpile varies with the political climate. There is election time, when Outs criticize our posture and Ins retort with glowing data. At any rate, the situation had to change and began doing so in 1964 when our glutted stockpiles of plutonium and enriched uranium became all the more embarrassing after the test ban. The AEC was allowed to seek foreign buyers. It also began shutting down some of the nuclear reactors producing the stuff. But this brought criticism, so the nation was assured that the cutback in weapon-making meant only "a reduced rate of increase of the stockpile."

Meanwhile, the issue had helped enliven the 1964 Presidential campaign. But even here, the main excitement was over which family man was more likely to be trigger-happy, Lyndon Johnson or Barry Goldwater. However, the issue did lead to further reassurance for those who have faith in hardware. President Johnson revealed that there were not only the "hot line" to Moscow and other personal ways of interfering with a rash decision. He explained that several of our nuclear weapons "have electromechanical locks that must be opened by a secret combination before action is possible."

More significant was the fact that Red China had just detonated a nuclear explosion, entitling her to membership in the nuclear club. And intelligence reports indicated that she had come relatively far. She could produce plutonium. She also had mastered the more difficult technique of separating U-235, which is quickly useful for enriching less efficient fuel. And with it, there was no reason why in a few years she could not also produce a thermonuclear explosion. The rest would depend upon her capability of delivering bombs or warheads.

Against such prospects of mutual annihilation could be set a growing hope for the human race. Total kill and Overkill are not a certainty. Aside from what protective shelters may or may not be able to do, much depends on density of population. Cities can be murdered. Lone humans, even small pockets of population, might survive.

This possibility is based on the currently revealed state of the art. But future nuclear weapons need not necessarily be the present types. Some may even be more lethal, yet less murderous.

Future Weaponry

Specifically, what about the prospects for either "dirtier" or "cleaner" nuclear weapons? We already have A-bomb and H-bomb; why not a C-bomb or N-bomb? Like the first two, they would give blast, shock, and heat from the fireball. The difference is that they would be designed to increase the other hazard—radiation. Each offers its own uniqueness. Neither has been announced, and nothing mentioned here is from classified information; but it would be extremely naïve to suppose that research stands still in explosives or, for that matter, in chemical, bacteriological, or psychological warfare. Possibility of the C-bomb has been discussed off and on since the mid-1950s. Here could be the super of all superbombs. The C stands for cobalt, normally a peaceful metal used mainly in alloy steels—a handsome metal, silvery with a suggestion of pink.

When bombarded with neutrons, it changes to the isotope cobalt-60 and is now radioactive. Like radium, it emits gamma rays, but stronger ones, and it is incomparably cheaper. For instance, an Army laboratory irradiates foods with radiocobalt equivalent to $26 billion worth of radium—if the world tried to assemble that much radium. The idea here is to cold-pasteurize meats and such so that they will not need refrigeration, and the problem has been to find out why the product sometimes has off-flavors reminiscent of burnt chicken feathers or wet dog hair. Meanwhile, the isotope has found many other peacetime jobs. Its rays sterilize bandages and destroy deep-seated tumors; in Australia they also kill the deadly anthrax bacteria in wool. At Brookhaven Lab's "gamma garden," they produce experimental mutations. Also, they serve widely as tracers, and not only in medical research. Entomologists insert some radiocobalt into a wireworm larva and the insect's movements through the soil can then be "watched"; similarly, repairmen locate buried telephone conduits. The chemical industry has begun catalyzing difficult reactions with the same gamma rays.

Most of this radiocobalt is made by bombarding ordinary cobalt with neutrons from the AEC's plutonium-producing reactors at Savannah River. For war, the neutrons produced by an exploding H-bomb could do likewise. Ordinarily, the bomb is held together by a steel casing. On explosion, this shell vaporizes and contributes a little to the radioactive fallout. Cobalt in the casing would produce an isotope intensely more deadly. Technically, building such a bomb is feasible.

From here the C-bomb or C-warhead becomes conjecture, or science fiction, whichever one prefers. Actually, cobalt-60 was seriously considered as a weapon as far back as the Korean War. The idea then, supported by some military physicists as well as by General Douglas MacArthur, was to "sanitize" a zone along the

Chinese-Korean border with the stuff, but not from a bomb. Presumably, the ground would have been coated with a sand made of cobalt oxide, which is normally used for coloring ceramics and the like. Here, however, its cobalt would have been the radioactive version, therefore hazardous but only for troops passing over it.

The bomb, obviously, wouldn't be that discriminate. Nor need the weapon be carried by air. Its casing could weigh many tons and it could be exploded off a ship placed in an ocean where the prevailing winds should carry the radioactive cloud to the enemy. Or, in terms of bombs dropped from the air, an estimate of the possible result was made by physicist Leo Szilard, one of the busiest pioneers of the A-bomb. He considered relatively small hydrogen bombs, with cobalt encasing a ton of explosive deuterium, and warned that four hundred of them would be enough to exterminate life on earth, plant as well as animal. Either way, here would be a doomsday weapon.

There are drawbacks, of course. Shielding, such as from fallout shelters of the right kind, can stop gamma rays. Prevailing winds, as the poison-gas people learned long ago, cannot always be relied upon. Testing such a bomb secretly would be more than a little difficult. Anyway, the madman willing to risk all-out nuclear war would probably find it simpler with standard thermonuclear weapons delivered by bomber or missile—or, for something novel, dropped. from a space-platform satellite.

So the neutron bomb, the so-called "clean" bomb, is held in more esteem. This weapon has adherents in Congress; its economical advantages have been cited by the United States Arms Control and Disarmament Agency; and the highly respected, unwarlike-minded physicist Freeman J. Dyson of Princeton's Institute for Advanced Study argues that, because it could be a small, effective tactical weapon, it offers a way to prevent all-out nuclear war.

How close are we to this N-bomb; and what are its pros and cons?

When asked at the Senate's test-ban hearings, Edward Teller dodged. "Sir, at one time I was told very clearly that I must never confirm, deny, or say anything about the neutron bomb. I have some knowledge. I believe that it is unclassified but I am not sure. If I tried to keep up a detailed knowledge of what is classified and what is not, I would have no time to do anything else." A few minutes later, however, he said yes, it is possible to develop weapons so clean that atmospheric testing would not produce hazardous fallout.

But how clean is clean? What did AEC Chairman Seaborg mean when he hedged: "We can make as much progress as it is possible to make toward the development of the all-fusion weapon"?

By all-fusion weapon he meant the neutron bomb—a species of H-bomb that wouldn't need the A-bomb for a trigger. This would have obvious technical advantages. But more—pure fusion promises the ultimate "clean weapon" because, by definition, a clean weapon is one in which "measures have been taken to reduce the amount of residual radioactivity." Yet the neutron bomb has also been called the ultimate doomsday weapon.

This conflict in labeling is understandable:

1. An A-bomb is inherently "dirty." Most of its fissioning uranium or plutonium turns into the isotopes that give fallout its bad reputation. The AEC counts about forty ways in which the exploding nucleus may split. This means about eighty possible kinds of fission fragments, most of them radioactive—and does not include still others that "salting" the A-bomb can give if it is deliberately intended for radiological warfare. The burst of an all-fusion weapon, by contrast, would carry little radioactivity. There would be some, of course. A bomb must have a mechanism of some kind and a casing, and any nuclear blast turns these into radioactive debris. It also creates isotopes out of atoms in the surrounding atmosphere and in the soil. Nevertheless, the neutron bomb itself would be inherently clean. Its main products would be helium, which is not a fallout menace, and a spray of neutrons, which are not atoms and do not undergo conventional radioactive decay. In other words, there would be practically no fallout.

2. In another sense, however, because of those same neutrons, the all-fusion bomb could be dirty indeed. Again, a comparison with the A-bomb. Only about 1 per cent of the weight of its fuel becomes free neutrons. They are important, of course; they build up the chain reaction. But quantitatively they are a byproduct. In pure fusion, however, freed neutrons account for much more of the fuel. Putting it another way: in plutonium fission most of the reaction energy is carried off by the isotope products; in deuterium-tritium fusion most goes with the neutrons. And the neutrons are as sinister as fission's

gamma rays or any other rays that maim or kill by penetrating various cells of the body and disrupting the electrical makeup of their molecules. Cells are destroyed outright, or no longer can reproduce, or, if they do, give mutations. Such radiation, then, is the next hazard if one survives the explosion itself.

The neutron difference is in timing. With the fission weapon, most of the follow-up effect is slower; the worst of its isotopes are long-lived and give a radioactive fallout that continues many months. In contrast, a free neutron lasts only a few minutes. And this becomes the neutron bomb's big advantage. With its instantaneous burst of neutrons it would fulfill the dream for a kind of "death ray" weapon.

And now some of the realities, pro and con.

It is calculated that an ounce of pure fusion material would give more than enough neutrons to kill everybody on earth. But this is fanciful. Even from a gigantic blast, neutrons could travel only a mile or so before losing their power. And, as with gamma rays, shielding is possible, though more would be needed.

Also, as we have seen, fusion weapons require an A-bomb-like fission device to trigger the thermonuclear reaction. The all-fusion weapon would need a "clean" trigger. If one has been developed, it has not been made public for security reasons. However, I visited several leading laboratories that want a nonexplosive and clean version of fusion for peaceful purposes. All, as we shall see, are trying elaborate versions of an electromagnetic trigger. Some physicists had enough token results to show that this approach isn't wrong. Likewise, none was entirely confident and all foresaw the need for more years of experimenting. Not that a "breakthrough" is impossible —we never know when a bright young fellow, in America or elsewhere, will toss away the book and produce a radically different answer.

Furthermore, the neutron bomb already has a precursor of a sort. This was revealed during a security fuss in 1963 when our Arms Control and Disarmament Agency let it be known that we had developed a weapon with "enhanced radiation." The revelation was intended to gain votes in the Senate for that year's test-ban treaty.

"Enhanced radiation" did not satisfy knowledgeable Senator Thomas J. Dodd. He continued insisting that an all-fusion weapon is possible; that it should be developed and tested. Like others, including ex-AEC Commissioner Murray, he is confident that the Soviet Union is working on it and warns that we must have it first, test bans or no. He points to Soviet research aimed at producing fusion with a high-explosive assembly rather than the fission trigger, and adds wryly, "The Soviet people, strangely enough, have been told far more about the neutron bomb from official sources than have the American people."

Should there be such a race? Emotions aside, the prospect also alarms practical people who feel that nuclear weapons are sinister enough already; that a modest test ban may not be entirely dependable but does provide a sort of raft in dreadfully troubled waters. But the argument for a neutron bomb, persuasive or not, cannot be overlooked. It wraps up various aspects of the military atom.

Its logic is this. Because of their indiscriminate nature, H-bombs have brought deadlock. Neither side has dared start nuclear war. The radiation effect of even a large neutron bomb, however, would be limited by the short range of its neutrons. It would therefore be a tactical weapon, not a killer of cities. It would bring warfare back to the battlefield. Hence, it would be "clean" not only technically but in a civilized sense. In fact, when dropped from sufficient altitude, this weapon would not give blast and shock enough to destroy buildings. And the radiation would vanish quickly after performing its mission against troops. This would allow the victor to move in quickly. In short, if there must be war, it would be fought "conventionally." But if Russia gets the N-bomb first, we become the victim of nuclear blackmail. The weapon would free her from nuclear deadlock. She could use it tactically, where she chose, confronting us and our allies with what Dodd calls "the terrible choice between surrender and all-out thermonuclear war."

This, of course, is only a new version of the concept of limiting nuclear war. How to do it has been debated ever since Hiroshima— in Congress, the AEC, the Defense Department, the White House. The debate has been constantly influenced by harsh realities. In the Korean War, we refrained from using even small A-bombs for fear that they weren't discriminate enough and would ignite the third and possibly final world war. Simultaneously, however, we were developing H-bombs, which would be even less suitable for limited war and the strife euphemistically called "brush war." Eventually, Russia was building bigger H-bombs than ours.

This has brought many reviews of our own strategy. Should we outweigh the Russians? Each time, our policy-makers decided to disdain Moscow's 100-megaton claims and produce smaller hydrogen weapons but more of them. The largest we had tested before the 1963 test ban was 15 megatons. But even this is stupendous enough— the equal of 750 Hiroshima models. And in the other direction—for the battlefield—the AEC was developing nuclear shells for howitzers and rockets for bazookas. These are relatively small, but even the smallest is estimated to be six or seven times more powerful than the biggest conventional blockbusters of World War II. And there has been no claim that they are "clean."

But Plowshare Too

Combine the assignment to develop and produce weapons with the hope to detect clandestine tests performed by others and to develop missiles that will intercept hostile missiles. Add the fear that missiles will be directed from satellites parked out in space, and the possibility that an enemy's nuclear attack, or even our own nuclear response, will electromagnetically paralyze our electronic launchers and communication system. Then add the testing restrictions, and we have another reason for the AEC's frustration. A project manager at one of its big labs exploded to me, "There are so many things you can't know until you try! Extrapolation from limited underground tests can go only so far. How the hell can we tell if we don't really test?"

He was discussing the weapons rivalry that continues, test bans or no. He was also referring to Plowshare.

In terms of expenditures, Plowshare is a pygmy. It gets about $14 million of the $600 million that AEC budgets for nonmilitary R & D. But for showing the world that we do believe in "atoms for peace," its fervent advocates say it could outdramatize the smashing of atoms, research on mutations, building of power plants. Plowshare is a mighty mover of earth—the use of nuclear explosives for constructive programs. In Project Sedan, for instance, a test displaced

12 million tons of earth and left a 320-foot crater. Plowshare's hope is to dig harbors and canals, change the course of rivers, carve passes through mountains, blast down into the earth for mineral riches, and much else. The AEC has even announced what it would charge: $350,000 for a blast half as strong as Hiroshima; $600,000 for one a hundred times greater, plus extras for such things as safety studies.

But that is for the future. For instance, Washington's quarrels with Panama brought the suggestion in 1964 for a quick solution. Let Panama have the outdated canal; we would blast another, twice as wide and needing no locks, in nearby Colombia. With nuclear explosives it could be built for one-third the money needed to modernize the old canal. But AEC then reminded Congress that five years of tests would be needed before actually blasting the canal could start.

In general, testing is needed because built into the Plowshare dream is a nightmare. How to blast without nuclear contamination? By their very nature, peaceful Plowshare and the cleaner bomb are twin programs to scrub the "dirtiness" out of nuclear blasts. AEC Chairman Seaborg told me, "There is certainly no secret about the fact that we are working toward cleaner weapons—if for no other reason than Plowshare."

A few months later, both programs were in trouble because of the new test ban. True, it was not a total ban. It forbade tests in the atmosphere, in outer space, and in water, but it did allow them down in the earth. This, however, had an understandable proviso. The blasts must not send radioactivity to another nation. This limitation embarrassed the AEC as much as the rest. It was relying heavily on the underground tests.

There are two kinds. The "crater" explosion tears a hole down into the earth. A row of these, for example, would speed the digging of a canal. The other is the "self-contained" kind that would be used for deep mining or for creating subterranean reservoirs. The crater blast obviously can send radioactive debris into the atmosphere. The other type does likewise if its radioactive gases "vent" upward and out through the earth's surface. A classic case, involving a group of tests, happened in 1962 at the isolated Nevada Test Site, an auxiliary of AEC's Los Alamos Laboratory.

The main culprit was iodine-131. Fallout dropped this isotope over

Utah and other states. Then, from highly contaminated grass, it went into cows, from cows into milk, from milk into children, settling mainly in the thyroid gland, where it is a cancer-producer, and, perhaps worse, entering the bloodstream to produce leukemia. It also went into controversy. How many thyroid cases would there be per thousand children? Had the AEC been monitoring the tests carefully, so that a fallout area could be warned against food danger? At first, AEC blamed the radioiodine upon Russia's atmospheric tests and ours at faraway Christmas Island; then it conceded some had vented in Nevada. Later, it agreed that some infants had received twenty-eight times the safety level of radioiodine, but said this wasn't harmful. Then it turned out that neither the AEC, Public Health Service, nor anybody else in Washington or elsewhere in the science establishment had ever determined a useful safety level for such isotopes, whether they come in food or another fashion. The best was gross guesses. This ignorance has continued and becomes an exact echo of the ignorance that Rachel Carson condemned—research has been too busy elsewhere to determine the harmful effect of pesticides.

And, not knowing, radiation science resorts to obfuscation that challenges its own experts. To estimate the possible harm, they must hack through a tangle of measurement units—the rad, the rem, the roentgen, the rep, the picocurie, and so on. Each is assigned a different meaning: "exposure dose," "absorbed dose," etc.; layman and scientist alike have no over-all word useful for intelligent discussion. This despite the fact that, upon examination, the rad is usually interchangeable with rem, roentgen, rep. Even the picocurie is manageable—a rad in the Utah milk corresponded to 58,000 picocuries.

Usually scientists are delighted to coin a new word, but not here. The obfuscation serves to shield ignorance. And it breeds ignorance. There has been needless twittering about radiation's dangers. Fluorescent lights throw ultraviolet at us, but so does the sun, and we tolerate it. Statisticians add that people in mile-high Denver receive half again as much natural radiation as do people in sea-level San Francisco, yet the Californians have half again as much leukemia and bone cancer as the Coloradans. But the figures are not enough—the explanation seems worthy of research. Again, through the years, the doctor and dentist have made X-rays a part of the nation's diet.

These are useful. They also account for many times the amount of radiation we get from fallout or any other source. Just how much X-radiation can we take before its harm outweighs the help? Nobody knows, yet billions are spent for medical research elsewhere. The Public Health Service concedes that their effects remain "one of our greatest gaps in scientific knowledge." And into the gap come intriguing reports: the doubled rate of thyroid cancer coincides with the onset of X-ray therapy for other thyroid trouble; half of New York City's seventeen thousand X-ray machines are found harmful because they either are defective or are being used incorrectly; statisticians add that radiologists die earlier than other physicians.

Meanwhile, the lack of worthwhile protection guides does not pass on the benefits from worthwhile research that *is* done. At Oak Ridge National Laboratory, William Russell has irradiated hundreds of thousands of mice. Examining their offspring, he found this eye-opening fact. Neutrons were as genetically harmful as expected, and it seemed to make no difference whether the dose came in one day or over a long period. The effect of gamma rays was likewise cumulative, but with this difference—the harm was much greater at higher dose rates.

Now move back specifically to fission's strontium-90. Unlike its twin menace, iodine-131, it lodges mainly in the bones. But after billions of words expended in debate about fallout, some scientific, some emotional, some ideological, we still do not know enough quantitatively about the effects. For this there is an explanation. Young children absorb more of it, so are the preferred subjects for study. But they have not provided enough bone samples, which must be obtained at autopsy. Only recently did bright researchers decide that a child's discarded baby teeth are equally useful.

The paucity of cures for radiation sickness is understandable—it is insidious. The absence of knowledge about hereditary effects is understandable—many do not reveal themselves soon enough. But the absence through all these years of reliable advice for the presently living is a dereliction flagrant enough to be scandalous. The explanation for this ignorance goes beyond the laboratory. It is found in Washington, where responsibility for assessing fallout's effects and preparing safety guides theoretically rests with the Federal Radiation Council. Its heads are the AEC's chairman and the Secretaries of

Agriculture, Commerce, Defense, Labor, and Health-Education-Welfare. At a Joint Committee hearing, the council's director, Paul Tompkins, was asked repeatedly whether he had such guides for harmful radioactivity, in foods for example. "No sir, there are none," he replied, and again. "None exist." But he hoped there would be eventually.

Why were there none? Because reliable facts were lacking. Challenged to give a more complete answer, Chairman Seaborg brought the matter down to relativity: "I don't know that any permissible amounts have ever been set or had any official sanction. It would depend on the rate, which isotope, what amount might get into people, and it would certainly have to be related to the reason for the fallout; that is, the testing that led to the fallout might be of paramount importance to the country, therefore a factor that couldn't be ignored."

Science advisers to AEC put it this way: "The public has been confused. There is a real need for clear, simple exposition of the facts of fallout." What to eat? how to dress? the safety limits? The experts offered no help. Instead, they suggested: "It should be clearly explained that weapons tests are an essential part of our effort to prevent nuclear war." Common sense says that this is wiser than "Better Red than Dead." But the point is: here is propaganda policy, not science. Scientists of the AEC and Defense Department were influenced by military needs. Scientists of the Public Health Service were more interested in danger from radiation. And they had been overruled. In short, more proof that when policy changes with situations, scientific method changes with policy. And the AEC loses reliability as a technical expert. In 1962, after the USA–USSR moratorium on testing was wrecked by Moscow, our National Security Council reacted accordingly. Now testing was ordered, with President Kennedy's assurance to the public that it need not fear fallout. As a layman, how could he know? And what had changed the opinion he had as a Senator: "There is no radiation so small that it has no ill effects"? A year later in his Presidency, the situation changed; Washington policy now required national support for a test ban. Whereupon he cited Nevada's irradiation of milk as proof of the need to stop testing. And Seaborg, the scientific expert, stayed with the mainstream now flowing in the reverse direction, regardless of how this would affect hope for a clean bomb and Plowshare.

In sum, the AEC's laboratory men are often distraught: castigated for poisoning milk supplies; then blamed for not having tested enough to blast through a quick answer to Panama; then ordered to switch to make-believe testing. Faced with this, they do what they can. It was illuminating to talk to Director John Foster of Livermore, the lab that the University of California runs for AEC. It turned out that not all biologists are bemused by DNA; not all physicists by baryons and leptons. There is also the health physicist, and he doesn't care for the hush-hush about radiation's effects. He is greeted joyfully at Livermore, despite its opposition to nuclear test bans. Foster explained at lunch that he could understand the public's fears. "After all, we still know next to nothing about the effects on humans, or the dose levels. I want such research because I want the Plowshare test program to succeed. I want interdisciplinary scientists to find the facts. Heading our new bionuclear group is John Gofman, who holds doctorates both in medicine and nuclear chemistry. And you should have seen the wonderful response he got when he wrote fifteen prominent scientists, asking if they'd sign on with us for such research. He got fifteen answers. Each said yes."

But this is at the grass roots of science. Higher up, the AEC has had to do what it is told rather than what its scientific attitude calls for. And it is troubled by cacophony. What its experts officially recommend depends on their connections.

Consider the testimony from Livermore. Because it is the main research center for nuclear weapons, and Plowshare too, it should be the ideal expert witness. Furthermore, its scientists had called themselves the Young Turks because of their dislike for red tape and their bouncy self-confidence. But as with massive R & D elsewhere, its top people move freely into and out of government, and their scientific viewpoint can change with the climate, with whether they are still at Livermore. At the time of the test-ban hearings in Washington, the witnesses included Livermore's director and his three predecessors.

. . . First in this sequence was Herbert F. York: "We always asked for more money. We asked for more buildings. We asked for more test explosions." Then York went to Washington as the Defense

Department's first R & D chief. Later, as a university chancellor, he continued Washington service as a member of the President's Science Advisory Committee. And now, at Senate hearings, he testified for the test ban.

. . . Livermore's next director for a while was the older Young Turk, Edward Teller. After that, he continued with the lab. He, not surprisingly, was against the test ban. And when confronted with York's opposite advice, he replied: "I don't know about his connections."

. . . Next director was Harold O. Brown, who had become York's successor at the Pentagon. When he approved the ban, one of his former Livermore associates told me charitably, "I'd guess that he feels as I do, but he's with the government now. When the decision higher up is against him he's got to live with it."

. . . Livermore's director at the time of the test-ban fight was dynamic Foster, brimming with infectious enthusiasm for the laboratory's mission. He took some mauling at the Senate hearings but wouldn't budge from his disagreement with York and Brown, and threw in the warning that Livermore was operating under "severe nontechnical restrictions."

Can there be a nonpartisan expert? Willard F. Libby was a witness with splendid credentials. This Nobelist had a laboratory background but not at Livermore. He had been an AEC commissioner. He was now professor of chemistry at UCLA. He said he would probably favor the test-ban treaty but first needed assurance that it would not interfere with research both on Plowshare and on sufficiently large weapons.

SENATOR KUCHEL: Now, let me put my tattered senatorial toga over your shoulders for a moment. How would you make a decision when some scientists urge that we approve this treaty, when others with equal and no greater patriotism urge we disapprove it?

LIBBY: Well, Senator, it seems to me you have no choice but to make up your own mind by careful investigation.

KUCHEL: Give me back my toga.

XII: *Peaceful Power*

"You can't conduct a society without electrical energy."
—Vice Admiral H. G. Rickover

The traditional highway from Albany to Boston is Route 2, the Mohawk Trail. Part of the way, it corkscrews through a loneliness known best to loggers, fishermen, and deer hunters. This is along state borderland where the Berkshires of Massachusetts become the Green Mountains of Vermont.

Now drive a few winding miles up a side road to the hamlet of Rowe, Massachusetts, then a mile farther up the valley. Here, alongside a reservoir formed by damming the busy little Deerfield River, gleams a $50-million testimonial to the restrained atom. The location and the humming sound announce that electricity is being generated in the first building. And the great white sphere silently looming behind it on sixteen slim legs proclaims that the power comes not from coal or oil but from uranium.

The difference in fuel explains things you don't see, like the staggering amount of public liability insurance required for this power plant. It also explains the requirement for the exotic sphere. Its diameter is 125 feet and its wrapper is thick steel. It, too, is insurance—if anything serious happens, it is the final defense against hazardous radiation's escaping into the atmosphere. This so-called "containment shell" encloses the heavily shielded power reactor as well as the pressurized-water system that removes heat from the chain reaction and turns it into steam. Obviously, this dome is no environment for humans. Safe from radiation, they monitor three consoles in the other building, where also is the turbogenerator that converts the steam's energy into electricity for New England. The method is now so matter-of-fact that the operators belong to the International Brotherhood of Electrical Workers.

377

This was the nation's first privately owned power plant built under an AEC program that paid part of the bill, one-fifth in this case; the idea being to entice industry into nuclear energy. In August 1954, President Eisenhower signed the liberalized Atomic Energy Act, permitting private companies to own reactors. The next day, ten New England utilities organized Yankee Atomic Electric Company. It built the Rowe power plant. The AEC aided with R & D money plus a five-year waiver of charges for the nuclear fuel.

The plant didn't go up immediately. This was pioneering. Checking out design proposals and blueprints with the AEC took two years. Then another sixteen months for safety tests before a construction permit was granted. Now the plant was built, operators were trained, and Yankee Atomic eventually got permission to load fuel and test. On August 19, 1960, the plant "went critical": it had a chain reaction. Then came the usual debugging changes and the plant finally started production under its hard-won operating license. Unlike several later reactors, it had few troubles. It was ready two months ahead of schedule. The cost was $14 million less than expected. And it worked so well that the AEC allowed the output to move up in stages from 110,000 electrical kilowatts to 185,000, with $1 million worth of plutonium annually as a byproduct. The town of Rowe was content too. No explosions, and 93 per cent of its taxes were being paid by the company.

Yet, though other plants were built, the "red tape" continued. For example, Rowe was so successful that Yankee Atomic decided to build a second plant, on the same principle but three times larger. It, too, would be away from people, at Haddam Neck, on the Connecticut River. But the site is within twenty-five miles of Hartford and New Haven, so AEC required extra safeguards.

In addition to engineering considerations it was painfully aware of public-relations realities. In the AEC's first eighteen years the nation had not had one reactor accident known to have hurt anybody outside a nuclear plant. Elsewhere, Americans had endured exploding factories, raging fires, bursting dams. But the public's dread of nuclear bombs continued reaching to nuclear power plants. This was one reason why AEC had allowed Yankee Atomic to build at Rowe —the lonely region had a "favorable public attitude." It also explains the $500-million insurance policy, ten times the plant's value, underwritten by the government (similar public protection has been urged against havoc from exploding missiles and spaceships). But just what are the risks from the "hot atom" in peacetime?

To Stop a Runaway

No honest scientist can guarantee that a nuclear reactor will not blow up after staging what the euphemistic jargon of the craft calls an "excursion"—in other words, a runaway reaction.

Even the dread of this happening can be effective. The first serious battle erupted in 1963. New York's giant Consolidated Edison tempted AEC with a proposal to build the nation's biggest nuclear plant—a million kilowatts. It would be a triumph for nuclear power. But AEC replied that, despite Con Edison's assurance of safeguards, this was a radical concept. The plant would be in heavily populated Queens. AEC asked for more details. Meanwhile, the public was forming such protesting groups as CANPOP. The argument was spilling over into Congress. New York's City Council was planning ordinances to outlaw reactors. This alarmed AEC. After reminding New York that it never granted a permit without first holding a public hearing, it warned that such ordinances would usurp the federal government's exclusive rights over nuclear power. Then Con Edison withdrew its proposal, explaining that it had found a way to get hydroelectric power from Canada. New York, Congress, and members of CANPOP returned to their other problems. The AEC could not.

True, its licensing powers had been upheld by the United States Supreme Court. True, a non-nuclear power project farther up the Hudson faced public opposition for the simpler reason that it threatened the scenic beauty. And it is certainly true that serious boiler explosions of the non-nuclear kind happen frequently. But such blasts are quickly forgotten. A nuclear excursion would not be; public panic could endanger the entire program for the peaceful atom. (Physicist Smyth: "Reactions to atomic power are not rational reactions.") And after an excursion AEC could not defend itself easily. Under the mandate it is enjoined not to endanger "the health and safety of the public." The best it could do would be to explain that its three groups of experts had triple-checked against everything but "the unlikely event of a major credible accident." This is careful language but what is "unlikely" and what is "credible"?

This much is certain. The nuclear reactor is not a nuclear bomb because it is not built to explode. Even in a runaway chain reaction it would not erupt with so much pent-up energy. What it could do— if its safety devices failed—is overheat. If this happened, the result could be something like a boiler explosion, but much worse. The reactor equipment would scatter its dangerous fuel and a cloud of other radioactive debris.

The safeguards are many. The reactor itself has brakes that should be enough. This system of heat regulators, called safety rods and control rods, is a refined and automated version of the method used by Fermi for the first chain reaction. At Rowe, for example, the fuel is again assembled in elements far enough apart so that their interchange of neutrons needed for fission can be increased, decreased, or stopped. Again, this allows open channels through the fuel supply. In these slots the control rods move up or down. Like drawn windowshades that stop light, these rods absorb neutrons. They are moved by motors run from the control room. As the rods are raised, neutron traffic increases, the reaction goes faster. Drop them all the way and the chain reaction stops. The rest is an electromagnetic system that holds each rod in the desired position, but only while electricity flows normally through the magnet. If the console shows trouble signals, the operator immediately "scrams" the reactor by shutting off current to its equipment. This kills the magnetic grip, and the rods, like released springs, ram home. Meanwhile, the protection is also automatic, sometimes too much so. Even a flicker in the current, caused by distant lightning, may scram the reactor. Scrams are a common and reassuring occurrence.

But are brakes always safe? And why does AEC refer to the "unlikely, credible" accident? Is it remembering the Biblical warning: "He that cleaveth wood is endangered thereby"? The chain reactor cleaves atoms, not wood. Canada had its bad excursion at Chalk River and England had one at Windscale. America's first fatal accident, in 1961, was at AEC's testing station in Idaho. The SL-1 was a small experimental reactor for the Army. It had just gone through overhaul, and three technicians were working on it, preparing it to operate again. It overheated, built up water pressure, and exploded like a boiler, scattering lethal fuel and neutrons: only a 200-kilowatt reactor, which, unlike a commercial plant, required no special containment, yet decontaminating the building and its surroundings cost over a million dollars. The entire sequence of events that caused the accident will never be known; the three men died too soon. However, investigators concluded that fail-safe had not prevented "human error." One of the technicians had pulled out a section of one control rod. Why? Investigators offered this choice of guesses, none of them comforting: (1) he was inadequately trained; (2) his mind was on other things; (3) he grabbed the rod in response to "an unusual or unexpected stimulus"; (4) he did so deliberately because of "emotional stress or instability."

From that extreme, let us go to the other. A few miles down the Potomac River from Washington is Naval Research Lab's reactor. It was not required to have a containment dome for a second line of defense, nor are there other outward signs of living with disaster. This reactor, inside an ordinary building, is the "swimming pool" type. A small boy had a chance to see it. He stood on a movable bridge at one end of the 40-foot pool and looked across. The electric lights were off. Down in 21 feet of water at the other end, glowing eerily with its own violet light and topped by its control rods, was the reactor core. "Gee," said the boy, "suppose I fall in the water—what will happen to me?" A scientist grinned. "You'd get wet."

This was no tall story. One reason for the water is its dependability as a shield against radiation. Another is its ability to absorb fission heat, which warms the 150,000 gallons only a few degrees. But here, hot water is not wanted. It would be a nuisance because this is a reactor for research, not power—in electrical kilowatts, Rowe's capacity is 185 times larger, and Rowe is relatively small now. So the pool's water goes to a cooling tower that dumps heat into the atmosphere. The researchers want something else. They work in a pit below the reactor end of the pool. Here are port openings to the reactor core. These give access to neutrons for a variety of metallurgical, chemical, and biological experiments.

Also, this reactor is away from urban Washington. The AEC demands safety mechanisms but it always likes wide open spaces. This brings complications where big power reactors are concerned. Utility companies protest that they are forced to banish their plants to lonely sites many miles from their customers. The result: higher costs for many reasons. Hence this paradox: their customers want cheaper electricity; they also don't want to desegregate to the extent of allowing the "hot atom" to live next door.

Even this restriction does not always solve problems of public relations. Northern California's biggest utility, Pacific Gas & Electric, was already generating over 6 million kilowatts from conventional sources, also from a small reactor of General Electric's boiling-water type. It got permission from the state and the AEC to build a giant version that would supply much of San Francisco's needs. This was no invasion of a big city. The reactor would be at Bodega Bay, on a secluded peninsula that reaches into the Pacific. Yet, although this is sixty miles north of San Francisco, there were protests aplenty. The plant would be windward of an important dairying area. Nature-lovers were embattled. So were biologists who were planning a research lab at Bodega Bay. On the other hand, AEC wanted the plant built. For one thing it would be a shining demonstration that nuclear energy can stand on its own feet: PG&E would receive no subsidy, the direct kind anyway; yet this electricity might cost a little less than the conventional kind.

But there was a unique worry. The site is almost atop the notorious San Andreas fault that gave San Francisco its historic earthquake. What would happen at Bodega if the bedrock gave way again? We have only guesses that San Andreas's elastic strain builds up slowly for the next quake. How fast, nobody knows—another example of constructive research that science could be doing. There was another complication. Some of Bodega's electricity would travel along PG&E's lines to feed another of AEC's prides, Stanford's great linear accelerator south of San Francisco. And the public was protesting here too, though, as we have seen (p. 130), for other reasons—the transmission lines would infringe upon their rights to a tranquil landscape.

The worst complication, however, was a split in the AEC's opinion. Its Advisory Committee on Reactor Safeguards, after consulting experts in the AEC, the United States Geological Survey, and the United States Coast and Geodetic Survey, conceded this was an unprecedented problem, also that a major earthquake could be expected. However, it pointed to the safety record of General Electric's reactors, to safeguards, including a special containment method, and decided that the plant would come safely through both a quake and the tidal wave that could accompany it. But AEC's own Division of Reactor Licensing, while praising the design engineers, concluded that "at the present stage of our knowledge" the location for the power plant was unsuitable. So the final decision was put off for more public hearings and the opinion of another group of experts, one of AEC's three-man Atomic Safety and Licensing Boards.

But faults like San Andreas are not a normal part of our subterranean inheritance. The problem is bigger. "I would live next door to the atom," says Chairman Seaborg—then his proviso: ". . . built and operated under our regulations and controls."

On the need for such regulatory power, those for and against the AEC way of doing things agree. But suppose conditions change. In its first quarter-century, for instance, the nuclear age has not had an excursion sufficiently serious to show whether or not containment by a dome, or by one of the various newer versions being tried, will hold a big blast as well as a small one or ordinary leaks of radiation. Yet an increasing number of engineers assert that containment was never needed and is now just "a price paid for our ignorance." And, in truth, Russia scorns the precaution. But AEC rightly continues worrying about the improbable probability; its experts continue debating the difference between "maximum credible accident" and the "incredible." So, like any sensible person, AEC does not expect perfect safety for every moment of one's life; but it would rather be safe than sorry.

It is not enough, therefore, to exhibit the safety record so far, to argue that people living near a power reactor are safer than those next door to a jetport or spaceport, or chemicals factory for that matter. The safety record only demonstrates that the nucleus, a hazardous animal, has been under the whip of an expert trainer. Therein lies the warning against relaxing controls.

Fuel Forever?

But why bother with nuclear power? Even isolated mountaineers are now brought electricity produced by falling water and by burning the fossil fuels—coal, oil, gas. The answer, of course, is mistrust of the status quo. Statistics or not, it is plain enough that the needs for electricity are soaring, and not only because of a soaring population. Even modern war adds its share. The warning radars at Thule in Greenland alone need more electricity than the vast Pentagon building does. And ironically, though the AEC fosters the generation of electricity, its isotope-separation plants for wartime and peacetime uranium have consumed annually as much as 10 per cent of the nation's total electrical output.

Beyond are the generations to come. We now need something like 5500 kilowatt-hours per capita. The president of Edison Electric Institute extrapolates to a figure twenty times larger by the year 2200. Experts differ on details but agree that water power as we know it now cannot be sufficient, that fossil fuels cannot last, and that nuclear electricity will be an important part of the energy picture by 1980 or so. Some transportation engineers already muse about a nuclear-fueled trucking industry.

Now it is true enough that there are other possible methods of tapping energy from the nucleus. "Fissio-chemistry" has made an experimental start on putting the energy from a nuclear reactor's radiation products, such as neutrons and gamma rays, directly into an industrial chemical reaction, without need for conventional heating, pressure, and cantankerous catalysts. And heat from the reactor could generate electricity in other ways than with a turbogenerator. One direct way would be a refinement of the long-known thermocouple method. Make a "loop" by joining together two wires of different metals at both their ends. Apply nuclear heat to one of the two junctions, and electrons would flow around the circuit. Less advanced is the rival thermionic method: the reactor's heat here "boils" electrons from a hot cathode to a cold anode. Either way, here would be a method that needs no rotating parts. And AEC has already made a notable start with the thermocouple method elsewhere. The heat from canned isotopes is generating electricity that illuminates lonely Coast Guard buoys and sends reports from unmanned weather stations in the arctic and antarctic.

But for large-scale needs in the foreseeable future, the AEC relies on the turbogenerator method. It first produced commercial electricity in 1957, at Shippingport, Pennsylvania. The plant was a land-based modification of the one that powered the *Nautilus* submarine. The government-owned reactor was able to generate 60,000 kilowatts. It betokened the beginning of a dream come true.

A-bomb scientists sought comfort in the hope of a grateful world, a wonderful world brimming with limitless amounts of cheap, clean electricity for advanced nations, and civilizing electricity for those that still rely on manpower instead of horsepower and kilowatts. The dream was shared by those laymen who understood that the electrical energy can be transformed into calories of food, man-hours of freedom from drudgery, and much else. In short, the United States had led in nuclear war; it would now lead in nuclear peace.

Thereafter followed neither a crash program nor a neglected one. By 1963, its cost approximated that of the A-bomb. To put it on its feet, AEC had subsidized it with $1.3 billion of "seed money"; industry had added half as much from its own funds. And AEC's help, direct and indirect, continued at the rate of $200 million a year. But if government support was steady, the response was not. By 1964, AEC could count twenty-two sizable power plants operating or seriously planned. This was picayune, however; the more so because half of them were built partly or entirely with government money and the rest leaned heavily on government R & D. Nuclear power was not yet abundant or cheap, and Chairman Seaborg told the competitive coal industry not to worry too soon. Any explanation for the slow progress must recognize realities. These include the frustrating perils of Washington bureaucracy and the need to go slowly with the hazardous atom. But there are also the harsh economics of competition with lively other sources of electricity. So the decision between kilowatts from the two big rivals, fission fuels and fossil fuels, depends on a pair of comparisons. How much of each can the earth provide? How expensive is the process?

1—The Supply

Any estimates of power needs become meaningless, of course, if the population really explodes. There are also here-and-now reasons why an estimate can be chancy. For instance, it may come from somebody whose political or financial ox is being gored, or fattened. But the biggest trouble is simply ignorance. Back in days when science cried poor it could be excused for not knowing what was underfoot. Since then, spending billions, its backwardness in literally unearthing underground knowledge about earthquakes, ground water, gravity, magnetic patterns, and the like has been quaintly ludicrous.

Petroleum is a classic example. Theorists still argue how the stuff was formed. Drillers still don't know how much to count on. Yet here is an industry as alert in R & D as the steel industry is laggard. And unlike nuclear power and aerospace it doesn't sit back waiting for government research aid. Of its annual $300 million for R & D on fuels and chemicals, 90 per cent is its own money. It contrasts this with the one-fifteenth as much spent by its rival, coal, of which half is federal money. But the estimates about petroleum reserves go on being vague guesses, notoriously so. According to them, we should have run out of oil years ago. To be sure, the drain cannot go on indefinitely. But Jersey Standard isn't panicky. It would then get oil a harder way, by extracting it from shale and tar sands. And after that: "We'll even explore seaweed if necessary."

Natural gas is another reason why some parts of the world—those lucky enough to have it—are not desperate yet for nuclear power. More fanciful, what could be neater than the geothermal method? Nothing to burn—just drill down and release ready-made steam from deep in the earth. Such geysers are already generating electricity in California and elsewhere in the world. How much more could be put to work is another challenge to practical science, and awaits something less inept than the NSF's Mohole project.

But all this can be only scraping deeper in the barrel, while the world's need for energy soars. The challenge from nuclear power has given Washington many exercises in estimating how fast the barrel is running dry, therefore how fast the AEC should push its rescue program. The estimates vary. They depend on whether the figures are for rich ores, or for lean ores as well. They depend on the semantics of what are "known recoverable resources" and what are "undiscovered marginal resources." They depend on who is making the estimates. For example, one set of figures for the United States is from the Geological Survey. When AEC borrowed them for its own survey, the Energy Study Staff of the Department of Interior decided they were much too pessimistic about fossil fuels, in which Interior has a loyal interest. So, to the embarrassment of Geological Survey, which is a branch of Interior, the estimates were increased fivefold.

In a delightful understatement, AEC Commissioner Ramey remembers: "These conflicting estimates naturally made our analysis more difficult."

What has been lacking is the kind of grilling that determines what the experts do mean. The Joint Committee, though composed of laymen, or maybe because of that, has been effective in doing this kind of thing. But it has been too busy with strictly nuclear matters to branch out into the world's over-all energy situation. However, a rough idea can be had by comparing those estimates that make some sense and show a family resemblance. They indicate the following for major sources of energy that the world could provide:

. . . Water power—not enough available to change the picture seriously (such exotic variations as using the tides at Passamaquoddy Bay would be only another drop in the bucket).

. . . Oil and natural gas—worthwhile reserves will be 80 per cent depleted by the year 2000 (shale oils might prolong the supply another century or two).

. . . Coal—the same scarcity in 350 years.

. . . Nuclear-fission fuel—theoretically limitless, depending on engineering techniques such as breeder reactors (p. 390).

. . . Nuclear-fusion fuel—apparently limitless, but how to make this method work?

In short, more fission power will be needed, the sooner the better, to conserve fossil fuels for other purposes.

2—The Price

A nontechnical term that utility companies and their customers understand readily is mills per kilowatt-hour. The key word is that mill, a tenth of a cent. Nuclear people glow when they can cut costs by another tenth of a mill. This is because of competition: kilowatts are kilowatts whether from drab coal or glamorous uranium.

The trouble has been that comparisons become a jungle of statistics, not always unbiased ones. But through them it is easy enough to see realities that the nuclear dream has had to face. Some have already been mentioned. Three others stand out:

1. Geography gives the word "competition" different meanings. Oil and gas are plentiful in Texas; coal is plentiful in Pennsylvania.

Nuclear power has had to make its first important challenges elsewhere; for example, in Northeastern states, where the fossil fuels must be imported.

2. Most experts I talked with wished somebody would decide what nuclear costs really are. This is because nuclear power has benefited from so much subsidy, in so many forms, ranging from outright R & D, through free fuel for the reactors, to an assured market for the byproduct plutonium that the defense program no longer needs but the government is required to buy. Nor is the picture simplified by subsidies given the fossil fuels, such as petroleum's depletion allowances.

3. And these competitors have not stood still, partly because of rivalry with each other, partly because of the nuclear threat—and the AEC feels that it deserves some thanks every time the average cost of other electricity goes down one-tenth of a mill. Only a tenth of a tenth of a cent, but AEC claims that each cut will save consumers $15 billion by the year 2000 and therefore repay, many times over, the cost of nursing nuclear power.

Coal, for instance, is the nation's biggest producer of electricity. It has been supplying twice the amount from oil and gas combined, and three times the amount from water power. To defend that position the coal industry has begun heeding the advice, "Stop wringing your hands, Steve," from one of its customers. Coal is now transported more efficiently. It is pulverized to powder that burns with almost explosive violence, supplying turbines with high-pressure, superhot steam. A result of new techniques is Eddystone, which Philadelphia Electric Company proclaimed to the engineering fraternity as "the world's most efficient power plant."

The virtue of competition is that it works both ways. An AEC commissioner noted the coal industry's "violent end of complacency." Another admits that the nuclear people have had to "sharpen their pencils and cut costs." One pencil-sharpener is to use the same power plant for desalinating seawater, of which more later. Another is to design bigger plants, which are more economical for several reasons. Coal-burning Eddystone, for instance, is rated at 726,000 kilowatts. Nuclear plants are growing up too. In the early, nervous days as many as 60 companies were needed to risk enough money for a 60,000-kilowatter. Some of today's plants cost $100 million, are owned by a single company, are in the 500,000-kilowatt class. This size places them among two-thirds of the fossil power plants.

But most important is the rivalry among companies that design and sell the reactors. The two leaders have been General Electric and Westinghouse, each with its claims of superiority. And AEC treats each, because each has done much to make nuclear power practical, with the exactly equal courtesy shown Guildenstern and Rosencrantz in *Hamlet*. The rival reactors both use water as the coolant, also as the moderator to slow neutrons for the chain reaction. The outstanding technical difference is this: in the Westinghouse "pressurized-water" method, as in the *Nautilus* and at Rowe, steam is not formed in the reactor itself; in the GE "boiling water" reactor, it is. Each has its own advantages, both reactors cost about the same. Together, they answer the question: When is nuclear power coming? In a Model-T form, and subsidized, it is here. It arrived in the 1950s.

And in 1964 the picture changed radically when GE stole a march on its rival. Thanks to pencil-sharpening engineers, nuclear power could now claim it was truly becoming competitive with fossil fuels. The change had come so undramatically, however, that it caught the AEC unaware. In 1962, for instance, I was talking with a GE executive. "We're past doubts," he said casually. "Our reactors are now standard merchandise. We sell them here and abroad. We give a guarantee on them, the way we would to a housewife buying a toaster."

True, these were still wasteful Model-Ts that depended on the cream of fuel supplies. But engineers had been cutting costs of electricity these plants would produce. The goal after the war was nuclear electricity for 7 mills per kilowatt-hour. The first commercial reactor started at 50 mills. In a few years, reactors were dropping below 10 mills. Then came 1964 and GE's contract to supply a New Jersey power company with a 600,000-kilowatt, $68-million plant that would be ready by 1967. Costs for a plant had been dropping. From $300 per kilowatt they were now perhaps $130. And the electricity produced would cost under 4 mills—a half-mill less in this "coal area" than the coal estimate even at lower prices for coal. All this, without asking AEC for subsidy.

Repercussions were immediate. Sweden, though rich with hydropower, said she would start building her first nuclear plant. A spokesman for American utilities threw away his flat statement, dated 1962, that nuclear power would need another fifteen years to become competitive. The United Nations chimed in that competition had arrived. The AEC recomputed nuclear estimates for the year 1980—and raised them from 40 million kilowatts to 70 million.

But nothing was more indicative than what started all this rush to honor the atom. It was a Commencement Day speech by a layman at Holy Cross College. He was Lyndon Johnson. The new President had been rummaging in the Washington bureaus for R & D goodies that presaged a Great Society. He had found this choice one and now rushed out the announcement about a breakthrough, though he did heed the AEC's advice and qualify it as an "economic breakthrough." And scientists felt uncomfortable with this President who delighted in the immediately practical, the more so when he called upon nuclear power to produce the breakthrough in desalting seawater during his "upcoming administration."

Again, AEC was facing complex problems that were not technical. As in other fields, the President spoke for a practical public. It is an old story: counting one's blessings now; seizing the quick rather than reaching farther for the good. For this New Jersey breakthrough would still not be the power plant of the future. It would not be that because of many reasons: because the AEC had too frequently assumed a posture of creative inaction when in trouble, had been too willing to go on subsidizing Model-Ts and their builders rather than move boldly toward its dream reactors, had been slowed by oppposition from industries and government agencies that favored fossil fuels. And there would now be battles ahead if AEC tried seriously to fulfill its mandate.

Yet better reactors had to come or nuclear power would be in serious trouble. The dream that "limitless" supplies of fission fuel will give ridiculously cheap electricity for all is based on reactors able to burn those supplies.

The Breeders

An obviously technical word is sometimes difficult but not necessarily treacherous. It flies a warning flag. Even when the jargon of nuclear engineering assigns a peculiar meaning to simple words like shim, scram, and barn, the problem is not serious. The new meaning can be learned. But when the simple word is explained recklessly there is trouble. "Breeders" are an example when they become "reactors that produce more fuel than they consume." This is deceptive to the unwary. It implies that we get something for nothing. The breeder is a worthwhile conservationist without that. It is a converter. While consuming five atoms of fuel, it turns perhaps six atoms of useless fuel into usefulness. Only in this sense does it create anything. But this can be enough to fulfill the dream of extravagant supplies of cheap power for all. It promises six atoms or more of useful fuel for every five consumed, and that is an appreciable rate of interest. But in terms of natural resources, the importance of breeding is the *source* of that useful fuel.

In the A-bomb project, we remember, scarce U-235 was the chain-reaction isotope in natural uranium and U-238 was the tantalizing nuisance, tantalizing because there were 139 atoms of U-238 for each of U-235, and a nuisance because it appropriated neutrons without splitting. The breeder concept looks at U-238 differently. This isotope is now called a "fertile" fuel because, after absorbing a neutron of the right speed, it becomes plutonium-239, which is "fissile." Like U-235, it splits; it carries on a chain reaction; and while producing heat it provides neutrons for more fission. The result is a theoretical 140-fold increase in our reserves of useful uranium. The same concept covers uranium's sister element, the isotope thorium-232. It is no longer useless. It is fertile. It absorbs a neutron, goes through nuclear rearrangement, and becomes the manmade isotope uranium-233, which is fissile. And since thorium is three times more abundant that uranium, here is still another increase in our nuclear reserves.

The sum answers fears over where the world will find energy. It can "burn" the uranium and thorium from rock, and after that from the sea. Director Weinberg of Oak Ridge Lab puts it this way: "It is most remarkable that nuclear breeding gives a way to forestall the catastrophe which our predilection for human breeding has always seemed to make inevitable." These estimates tell the story. Possibly the world's energy needs will level off at twenty times what they are now. The amount of uranium and thorium in the earth's crust is sixteen parts per million. These fuels from rock would then suffice for twenty billion years. With such a supply we need not fret over how much of the ore is rich or lean, or how to reach rock under the sea or five miles beneath our feet. And if our solar system has only a billion years more to live, the rest doesn't matter anyway.

These sober estimates are admittedly guessy. Nuclear breeding itself is not. It is feasible; some has already been done. Progress has been in stages.

First, the conventional reactor. We remember that the method started with a preference for easily fissionable U-235. It needed slow, "thermal" neutrons. So moderators were provided to slow those going perhaps ten thousand miles per second down to an average one mile per second. The first reactor used a graphite moderator. Today's reactors have a choice of many, including ordinary water— the most common because it also serves as the coolant. But so many others have been tried or suggested that an AEC commissioner wondered when he would be asked to approve a beer-cooled, sawdust-moderated reactor.

However, the fuel isn't pure U-235, which is too expensive. So today's power plants use natural uranium enriched with enough extra U-235 for an efficient reaction. The rest of the fuel is U-238. Some of this, it is now known, is split by extremely fast neutrons, and contributes to the reactor's power. More significant, medium-speed neutrons convert U-238 into plutonium. Some of this burns in the reactor that makes it. The rest goes to AEC's stockpile when the reactor needs reloading with freshly enriched fuel.

From this came the next development, "seeding," simply a way to convert more U-238 into plutonium. The seed is a core of highly enriched fuel. Surrounding it is a massive blanket of natural uranium, reminiscent of the one that contributes fission energy to the thermo-nuclear bomb. In the civilian reactor, surplus neutrons from the fissioning core reach the blanket and form plutonium, which then "burns" *in situ*—it joins the nuclear reaction. The seed-and-blanket idea was successful as early as 1957, in the *Nautilus*-type reactor at Shippingport, with plutonium producing half of the energy output.

All this leads to the ultimate, the breeder. Seeding is a patient way to get useful energy from fertile fuel. But why not supply new fissionable atoms as fast as the old ones are destroyed, or even faster? The reactor would not only refuel itself but simultaneously convert fuel for standard reactors, and do all this efficiently—almost all of the fertile fuel would become fissionable.

The developmental work has been mostly with the "fast reactor," called that simply because it favors the faster neutrons. But breeding offers many permutations and combinations, depending on whether the fissile fuel is U-235 or plutonium, whether the fertile fuel is thorium or U-238, in turn determining whether to use fast or slow neutrons, and so on. AEC calls the fast reactor the most advanced true breeder, and England predicts that all nuclear power plants built after 1980 will be fast breeders.

Among them, the experimental favorite has been the breeder cooled by liquid sodium. Conventional water cooling would not do, of course, because water is a busy moderator that reduces too drastically the supply of fast neutrons. In fact, this reactor deliberately avoids a moderator as such. Its sodium and impurities slow enough of the neutrons for the basic fuel. But sodium has its own peculiar problem. The same reactor would also be producing power. This calls for steam to spin the turbogenerator, so the sodium circuit must transfer its heat to a water circuit. And, as a chemistry freshman soon should learn, sodium and water do not mix peacefully. But engineering will be depended upon to keep the two liquids physically apart. At the Atomics International test reactor that I saw in the Santa Susana Mountains, nobody seemed worrying about their special version of the hot atom.

In itself, breeding is simply slow multiplication. Consider a fast breeder with a core of enriched uranium and blanket of natural uranium. Theoretically, the U-235 emits an average of between 2 and 3 neutrons per fission. Of these, 1 is needed to keep the chain reaction going in the core. This leaves an average of between 1 and 2 for the U-238. If 1, each U-235 atom destroyed will be replaced by an equally useful plutonium atom. If more than 1, the reactor does better than stay even. Theoretically, there might be a "gain" of 1.5 neutrons. Actually, there are various losses. Breeder people conservatively count on getting 120 atoms of fresh fissionable fuel for every 100 consumed.

The gain isn't sensational. The breeder may need fifteen years to produce enough for a second reactor. This makes it hard to predict when conventional reactors would become entirely obsolete. But again, the main point is that the breeder is running itself with previously useless fuel.

However, there is something missing in this picture. Although everybody in nuclear power agrees that breeding is necessary and inevitable, AEC's program has moved at snail's pace. It was already under way experimentally in the 1940s, and has steadily progressed at AEC's test station in Idaho. But not until 1964 was there noticeable stirring, and even this was hardly dynamic. A commercial prototype, the smallish Enrico Fermi plant in Michigan, began operating eight years after AEC authorized building it. The rest was still very much R & D; for instance, a small, purely experimental breeder in Arkansas. The $25-million project was cosponsored by AEC; an association of seventeen private utilities; a group of European interests; and General Electric, a reactor-builder protecting its future. More important, the same year saw four reactor-builders start rival design studies for AEC's proudest project—a pioneering million-kilowatt fast breeder. But this was only the beginning of a beginning. If such a plant is designed and built, it may not be operating before 1983. Even the smaller prototypes that must precede it are not expected until 1972. Furthermore, the big one would itself be a prototype, not followed by a commercially competitive version until 1989.

The schedule doesn't promise fast victory in the battle of "breeders versus burners." Nor can it contribute much to AEC's hope that nuclear plants will generate half of the nation's electricity in the year 2000. Apparently, today's reactors and advanced, semibreeder versions will have much work to do. But it is a safe prediction that political wars in Washington will not crush the breeder program. They can only make slower, harder, and costlier what could come more easily.

Tantalus

Breeders seem a reasonable way to guarantee plentiful energy. But technology does not and cannot stand still. Potential rivals to nuclear breeding already exist. They are not yet as near being feasible; neither can they be ignored. One imitates the sun. The other harvests the sunshine we are wasting, and does it by direct methods.

Indirect solar power is an old story, of course. The fossil fuels are our inheritance of solar energy stored in past ages. What we call weather is simply a natural machine driven by solar energy; it gives us wind power and water power. And the conversion of solar radiation into food gives oxpower, horsepower, manpower. All these are man's indirect ways of living off solar energy. Earth receives a paltry one part in two billion that the sun radiates, but that keeps the earth busily alive.

The new part of the story is the revived hope to dispense with intermediaries. The temptation is great. One estimate is that to match the free energy that the sun offers us in three days we would have to burn all our fossil fuels and all our forests. And the tempted include big names. Vice President Humphrey has urged an intensive R & D program to find practical ways of utilizing sun power. In the background looms the figure of Charles Greeley Abbot, former head of the Smithsonian Institution. This redoubtable scientist fell in love with the sun early in his career and became a leading champion of sun power. He was sun-mad in somewhat the sense that his contemporary, Robert H. Goddard, the father of rocketry, was moonmad. The difference is that the moon is now within rocket reach; solar power has not come that far. Too many engineering problems of cost and efficiency remain.

For instance, the transistor-like wafers called solar cells arrived just in time for the Space Age. A few thousand of them speckling the skin of a satellite convert solar energy directly into electricity, which is then stored in batteries for low-wattage use when needed. But Paul Egli, Naval Research Laboratory, points out that with present technology the array of cells needed to supply a homeowner would need 100 square yards of sunlit lawn and the setup would cost $2 million.

There is also the idea of a solar collector, a large somewhat concave mirror that gathers the energy and focuses it upon a converter. This could supply tens of kilowatts. The Air Force has already demonstrated that such a collector can be orbited. And at an earth laboratory I saw a 7-foot collector, made of special plastic, whose "hot spot" was over 2000 degrees Fahrenheit. On the inhospitable moon, a more elaborate version may supply our astronaut explorers with both warmth and electricity. And beyond this looms the promise, or the specter, of the spatial mirror envisioned by Hermann Oberth, who invented Germany's V-2 rocket for the last war and worked out the physics for today's space navigation. His orbiting mirrors, perhaps a hundred miles in diameter, would supply earth with perpetual warmth and sunlight; they could also be burning glasses that would fry armies and cities.

But this takes us too far from nuclear power. Its advocates cannot yet see economic rivalry from solar methods. And if it is iffy whether breeder fuel will last 20 billion years, remember that it is also iffy whether the sun will still be operating then.

However, need we try to capture solar power? Why not imitate the sun? This is the glamorous challenge that has nuclear physicists at many laboratories trying to harness the power of the thermo-nuclear bomb. When they feel frustrated, it is hard to blame them; fusion is already here, yet it is not. Accordingly, they sometimes resemble Greek mythology's thirsty king who went on reaching hope-lessly for water just beyond him. But the lure is irresistible. Also, we have here a nuclear rivalry between two immensities of peacetime energy, between getting it from fission or fusion, that illustrates the problems of the decision-maker in R & D.

At first glance, it seems nonsense for AEC to go on spending $200 million yearly on ways to burn rock, and only an eighth as much on ways to burn seawater; to favor uranium and thorium from earth's crust over deuterium from earth's oceans. From what we know now, the ultimate reserves are comparable, give or take a few billion years. But other comparisons give fusion an overwhelming superiority:

. . . A controlled reaction promises safety. This would not be the fusion of the H-bomb, which is a contrived explosion. Nor would controlled fusion require a fission reactor's unique safeguards. It would need conventional radiation shielding. An industrial accident might occur. But there could not be a runaway reaction as in fission.

. . . It would be much cheaper. Nature's water is a mixture of ordinary and heavy water—"heavy" when the H_2O molecule contains deuterium, the doubleweight isotope of hydrogen. The ordinary, lighter hydrogen is thought suitable for fusion in the stars. For earth conditions, science counts on deuterium because it fuses much faster. True, nature supplies only one part of heavy to five thousand parts of ordinary water. But the oceans are vast; they contain an enormous amount of deuterium; and the cost of extracting this now-familiar chemical is no longer forbidding. The result in terms of "burn-up" usefulness could eventually be a fuel costing 1 per cent that of present-day coal. Another estimate: the 10 cents' worth of deuterium in a gallon of seawater would be enough fuel to supply a year's electricity for a family of five.

. . . Fusion is inherently clean—no need, as with fission reactors, to find safe burial methods and places for radioactive "ashes." The material end-products of fusion would be only nonradioactive nuclei of helium and hydrogen.

. . . It offers possibilities of generating electricity without going through the wasteful steam-and-turbogenerator sequence. This is because fusion occurs with its ultrahot fuel in the so-called "fourth state of matter"—a plasma composed of charged particles which can theoretically transfer fusion energy directly into useful electricity.

Then why not abandon all fission-power programs, including plans for breeders, and concentrate on the controlled thermonuclear reaction (CTR)? After all, such fusion is not imaginary. The answer is simple. Fission power is here. CTR, even without trying to convert its energy to electricity, is still an experiment hagridden by the most important word known in R & D—feasibility.

With their very first test reactor, in 1942, physicists had a chain reaction that proved fission was feasible, for either war or peace. The rest was a matter of working out the techniques. Compare that with fusion. Shown in 1951 to be possible, it was proven feasible a year later—but that was for explosives only. In 1965 America's fusion physicists had not yet reached the fission stage of 1942. And from their free interchange of information with researchers in England, Russia, France, Germany, they were certain that nobody else could yet sketch how to build a self-sustaining fusion reactor that would release energy in steady, commercially usable amounts.

But isn't it risky to invest so much on fission when it may be outmoded eventually, perhaps even suddenly? The answer is that nobody cares to gamble on how long that may be. Experiments indicate that controlled fusion must surely come, in one fashion or other. Laboratories have clocked fusion reactions lasting several millionths of a second. How long that is depends on the outlook. Ordinarily, it would invite optimistic extrapolation. But the trouble with fusion is psychological as well as technical. Along with manmade weather it was one of the "breakthrough" visions—and disappointments—of the mid-1950s. And it turned out to be the most frustrating; truly a Tantalus.

Consequently, it has become as interesting an exercise in cautious English as in daring science. AEC's official position is that CTR "is not yet predictable." This is not surprising. The United States Weather Bureau has grown similarly cautious about claiming that it can make rain. The difference is that a leading Weather Bureau researcher, Joseph Smagorinsky, told me, "Though it would be intellectually dishonest to base our program and budget on any certainty of controlled weather, I think secretly it will come." I found nobody saying that about CTR. The only boast by Arthur Ruark, chief of AEC's program, officially called Sherwood, was: "I've never been caught boasting about its prospects."

Out in laboratories, of course, the men actually working on CTR play with words that don't slam the door that hard. At Princeton, one of AEC's four major contractors for the research, a physicist said: "Who is to say it won't succeed? We still hope for the lucky trick that will change the picture suddenly." To which James Tuck, Sherwood's director at Los Alamos, adds: "We started with wild dreams and a fool's paradise but one can now see traces of getting a break." Perhaps the best comment on record came, in those "fool's paradise" days, from an informed layman, AEC Chairman Strauss: "Anyone who thinks fusion cannot be controlled is a fool; anyone who thinks it will be easy is an idiot."

Precisely what is tantalizing about fusion? Certainly not fusion in itself. The fuel can be deuterium; or the heavier isotope tritium, which could be made from vast reserves of lithium; or a mixture of the two. Depending on fuel, there can be several different nuclear reactions. In any case, the chemical equation could hardly be simpler. Fusion in the sun is a more complicated series of steps. And on earth, much more legerdemain is needed, say, to build a synthetic hormone from amino acids. Here is what happens when a deuterium nucleus (D) fuses with a tritium nucleus (T), as in the hydrogen bomb:

$$\text{D (proton, neutron)} + \text{T (proton, 2 neutrons)} \rightarrow$$
$$\text{helium nucleus (2 protons, 2 neutrons)} + \text{free neutron} +$$
$$\text{17.6 million electron-volts}$$

A fission reaction releases more energy, but fusion fuel is much lighter. So, weight for weight, fusion gives more energy. To be sure, fusion fuel must be in the hot, gaseous, ionized form of plasma—orbital electrons stripped away from the nuclei. Then, because such bared nuclei are positively charged, therefore tend to repel each other, they must be crowded enough, and forced to collide and keep on colliding at high enough velocities, until they coalesce. All this can be done—experimentally. Laboratories can produce plasma by various electrical-discharge methods, and supply its ions with kinetic energy corresponding to temperatures much hotter than the 20 million degrees centigrade in the sun. But a sputter of a few millionths of a second can be only bravura. There must be self-ignition that will keep the reaction going. This introduces the frustration called "confinement time." How to keep the nuclei close enough, hot enough, long enough? In other words, what kind of container? Even if the plasma is not dense enough to melt the walls, even if vaporized material from the walls doesn't contaminate the plasma, there is much worry about that plasma. It must not lose precious heat to the walls. This means its heat-agitated particles must not touch the walls.

The sun and other stars handle this problem easily. They need no container. Their enormous forces of gravitation not only accelerate atoms toward the center and ionize them, but hold them in that hot melee for fusion. Earth physicists have had to settle for a container within a container. The outer one is the reaction chamber. It has real walls. The inner one hasn't, but it is not imaginary. It is being used throughout CTR research. It is one version or another of the "magnetic bottle," a strong, uniform magnetic field created around the plasma. Its lines of force act as diverters. Instead of continuing outward toward the forbidden wall, a plasma particle starts orbiting helix-fashion around one of these incorporeal wires. Such electromagnetic interactions have become a basic concept of plasma physics. In Space, for example, they explain the Van Allen radiation belts of electrons and of protons trapped in the field curving between earth's magnetic poles.

The method has many technical difficulties. For instance, the need for brute-strength magnets. Here, cryogenics offers hope. The CTR people and computer people are equally interested in superconductivity and for much the same reason. With less electricity wasted in the form of heat, the same tremendous magnetic fields for today's CTR could be created without need for immense cooling equipment. And those looking ahead to commercial fusion would no longer puzzle how to produce economical power with magnets that might themselves consume 5000 megawatts and weigh 500,000 tons.

But the heart of the problem is the plasma. Theory can predict the behavior of a single charged particle pretty well. A wild-hot plasma in which a cubic centimeter has a trillion or more particles influencing each other is something else, and AEC says wryly, "Rigorous theoretical treatment of plasma behavior is ·a mathematical nightmare. Existing computer facilities are inadequate." The main frustration is "instability." Ideally, plasma should be a neat core of gas wrapped securely by the magnetic field. Actually, it twitches, twists, writhes, leaks at the ends, bulges in the middle, suddenly breaks through the invisible wall. Richard Post of Livermore says this is like trying to hold warm, quivering Jello in a cage whose bars are rubber bands.

Such are the problems, and the mind of man fights back with a growing menagerie of methods to heat plasma of the right density and keep it squeezed toward the center: with such inventions as Perhapsatron, Toy Top, Stellerator, Scylla, Alice, Picket Fence, and plain DX-2; with sausage-shape confinement, doughnut shapes, pretzel shapes, and the cusp shapes that require a deft three-dimensional imagination.

The first CTR project I saw was a rarity in that it was privately financed—part of General Electric's policy of warily keeping all doors open to the nuclear-power future. It started in 1956, the same year that GE began research on fission breeders. This project is the one described on page 9. It uses "theta pinch," the same method I saw later at Naval Research Laboratory. In essence, this is self-constriction: the plasma of deuterium squeezes itself. First comes the massive electrical discharge that builds up a current of over three million amperes through a single coil around the reactor tube. This induces a strong reply current to flow through the plasma. The induced current, in turn, creates an encircling magnetic field that squeezes the plasma with a force of over a half-ton per square inch. And because the plasma is being compressed rapidly, its temperature rises. Thus the plasma provides its own magnetic bottle and heat for fusion. This method uses relatively modest equipment, yet is as promising as any can be in a field still called "more perspiration than inspiration."

At the other extreme are giant CTR devices, like the $35-million newest in AEC's family of Stellerators at Princeton. But more ambitious is the machine that even plasma physicists regard with perplexity. It is Astron, an AEC project at the Livermore branch of Berkeley's Lawrence Radiation Laboratory.

For two reasons I would not have missed visiting Astron. It is the most imaginative of the hopes for controlled fusion. It is a product of the almost legendary Nicholas Christofilos, the self-taught nuclear physicist with an acquired Greek accent and an imagination as soaring as Olympus.

Born in Boston during the First World War, he was taken back to Athens at the age of seven. There he earned a modest engineering degree and began installing elevators in the 1940s. But his mind was in the wonderland of electromagnetic theory. He read everything available on it and began to effervesce with his own ideas about charged particles made to spiral around those incorporeal lines of magnetic force. One dream was a better atom-smasher of the kind that whirls charged particles in circular orbit while they are being accelerated. To guide them he would use a ring of fairly small magnets that strongly focused the particles in alternating directions, vertically and horizontally. This would allow superpower accelerators without need for impossibly large magnets.

Writing from Athens in 1950, he offered this concept to the famed Californians of Berkeley. It brought the reply that he should study more mathematics. So he reworked the idea. The official story is that the second letter from "that crazy Greek" went into the files without being read. In the background was Berkeley's unfortunate experience with foreign competition. Back in 1945 its Edwin McMillan "invented" the synchrotron; then it turned out that a Russian was a year ahead of him.

At any rate, one day in 1953, the crank from Athens showed up, not in California but at AEC's Brookhaven Laboratory in Long Island. Its people had started designing a supersynchrotron made possible by the "alternating gradient" principle. Splendid, said the stocky visitor with the thick Greek accent. He then proved with patent applications and his California correspondence that he had dreamed up the principle first. "If you can't lick em . . .": AEC bought his idea for $10,000 and hired him to help design the $30-million machine. A few years later it was whipping a beam of protons around the half-mile magnetic track. But he had no sooner started at Brookhaven than he began selling AEC a proposal that had nothing to do with Brookhaven's program. This one concerned CTR. The amateur was given a respectful enough hearing this time. But the idea was radical, his self-taught math was crude. He was urged to ponder some more. This he did, not always silently. By 1956 he had worn down AEC sufficiently. It took the $8-million chance that this cheerful eccentric who qualified as a genius might be wonderful again, and commissioned him to start designing his Astron next door to the stable of rival CTR machines at Livermore. Christofilos had come far. He was now a colleague of the once skeptical Californians.

But his imagination bubbled still farther. In 1958 came the by-product call Argus, a grandiose project that turned the entire earth into a sort of Astron. It happened that he as well as J. Fred Singer, the brilliant Weather Bureau physicist who had predicted the Van Allen belts before they were discovered, wanted to study them in finer detail. Their idea was similar, to send up a satellite-borne accelerator that would inject charged particles into the magnetic belts. Christofilos was a more aggressive salesman. He gave the Pentagon two proposals—do it with a satellite, or simply burst nuclear bombs several hundred miles above earth. The latter was more appealing, and three bombs were exploded secretly in 1958. They not only illuminated earth with an aurora display as bright as a full moon but enveloped it with a sixty-mile-thick sheet of trapped electrons that defined the exact position of the belts, much as iron filings reveal a bar magnet's simpler lines of force. Naturally enough, astronomers complained bitterly about this clutter in their preserve. Christofilos imperturbably returned to Astron.

He brushed aside suggestions to take smaller test steps first, explaining that only a real Astron would mean anything. Five years later, I found the equipment ready for the debugging that precedes actual tests. First, in his cubbyhole office, this burly, disheveled combination of scientist and administrator, tieless, with one collar tip up and the other down, explained motives and money:

"It's controlled plasma I want. The next step, controlled fusion, doesn't worry me. We already know we can make the neutrons [here he meant neutron emission indicating that some fusion was occurring] . . . Anyway, important right now is prestige. We must be the first nation to crack nature's biggest secret. . . . Yes, I've received the funds I need. But CTR in general is being cheated. It's ridiculous to spend only $25 million a year. Russia spends what we do, but from only one-third as much national income."

And Astron itself? With his rolling gait, like that of a trained bear, he led me into the factory-size building erected for the experiment, and we were soon prowling below overhanging sheets of copper that brought in the electric power. What Christofilos had done was wed an electron accelerator to a fusion machine. They were together but separate—each with its own power supply, its own control room.

Success depends on what happens to that accelerator's output of tight, high-ampere, 4-million-electron-volt pulses of electrons. Injected into the fusion chamber, they will ionize the fuel by knocking electrons off its atoms. Then, by further collisions, the incoming electrons will transfer energy to the plasma, raising its temperature.

Though unique, these duties are byproducts of the electron beam. The heart of Astron is a Christofilos interplay between two magnetic fields. One is the customary inner container—lines of force produced by powerful coils outside the plasma chamber. The lines run parallel to the chamber axis. Then, when the accelerator's high-speed electrons burst into the chamber, the magnetic field forces them to travel in large circular orbits and they form a sheath-like layer of electrons rotating around the axis. This "E-layer" in turn generates its own strong magnetic field but in a direction opposite to the first one. Christofilos expects the result to be lines of force so warped that they close completely on themselves. Theoretically, these should make a tight cage for the plasma particles.

I found some rivals who called Astron a Rube Goldberg. Others shuddered at "the most complicated idea yet." But if Astron does not show the right and best way, it cannot be all waste. It built for AEC's collection an accelerator claimed to give the most powerful electron beam in the world, because of its heavy current of high-energy electrons. More important, like other CTR projects it promises new knowledge about plasmas, increasingly important in technology: They are already being ejected experimentally through the tails of rockets to provide thrust; in magnetohydrodynamics they offer a new though non-nuclear way of generating electricity. And whether or not Astron obeys Christofilos, he will rate in scientific history as the amateur from Athens who bestrode two specialized fields within highly specialized physics—controlled fusion and atom-smashing.

XIII: *The New Physicists*

"An analogy cannot be a complete description.
. . . Those who ask what an electron is are
guilty of a sort of rank anthropomorphism."
—D. H. Wilkinson,
Turning Points in Physics

We have already seen physicists at work in many fields. This chapter will concentrate on three major areas that are representative in showing what modern physics seeks. One concerns atom-smashing, a probing of the atom's deepmost mysteries. Another takes us into quantum mechanics, which started with the atom, entered the argument over whether man has a will of his own, and eventually led to the television set. The third deals with a newer piece of hardware, the glamorous laser, that evolved from quantum concepts.

Smashing Atoms

The specialists of controlled fusion are in basic research. So are specialists in the field called high-energy physics. One difference is that the latter does not seek a specific, practical result; it hunts seed knowledge in the new way—with task forces and massive machines. Another difference: it is not so calm and neighborly. It is involved in the hottest jealousies of science. The reason is its craving for mightier multimillion-dollar accelerators, already the costliest instruments in science.

The jealousy is an unplanned byproduct that has given many woes to the AEC, the patron of America's atom-smashing. What this agency really wants is a closer acquaintance with physical reality. And since the atom is the heart of matter, and the nucleus is the heart

405

of the atom, the nucleus is the target of an atom-smasher's "bullets."
The result of this probing, so far, has been a subatomic world of strange particles. It is so truly strange that the layman can tour it as quizzically as the physicist, who, in frank moments, complains that he himself mistrusts Alice-in-Wonderland inhabitants y-clept "anti-lepton," "quark," and the like. So he shields himself within quotation marks. In earlier days of quantum theory he struggled to imagine an elementary something that could be both "wave" and "particle." To-day, he mistrusts even the word "elementary." When the population explosion of "elementary" particles and their associated "resonances" reaches a hundred, how can any be "elementary"? So, back to quotation marks. He literally calls many of them "strange particles," and assigns varying degrees of "strangeness" to them.

In fact, the high-energy physicist has become as interesting as the particles he creates, annihilates, and identifies by their so-called "quantum numbers." His goal is laudable enough, a triumphant unified theory that will close the gap left by Einstein. The esoteric nature of his work makes him a Brahmin in the castes of science. But today's realities are such that, seeking what he calls a "scoop," he must be a joiner. If an experimenter, he needs a team; if a theoretician, he needs experimenters. And the team must be strong enough to win research time with the strongest machines.

All this because the newer physics has gone far out, far beyond the comfortable atom of electrons, protons, neutrons. Like classical zoology, it kept on poking at queer things and classifying them. The meson, believed to be a glue that holds the nucleus together, grew past a half-dozen different kinds of meson. The concept of matter underwent a doubling; "truly elementary particles" were confronted with equally "fundamental" antiparticles of antimatter. This hardly answered the prayer that maybe everything in the confusingly small nucleus might boil down to two simple building blocks: baryon and lepton. Seeking simplification, physics practiced antisimplicity. To make it all fit somehow—the scores of particles, the four kinds of basic "interactions" (a replacement for the traditional "forces"), the opposing worlds of matter and antimatter, came the Eightfold Way, formalistic as Chinese art but more mathematical, less exquisite. And in the same early 1960s that witnessed world statesmen staring eye-ball to eyeball, the particle physicists were living through crises of their own. For example, this sequence of problems fed to the monster smasher that Christofilos helped design for Brookhaven:

. . . To hunt down a worrisome second kind of neutrino, a Columbia team built up a 45-foot-thick barrier of armorplate from a junked battleship. With this they stopped one atom-smashing product, muons, allowing another, neutrinos, to go on into a 10-ton spark chamber to interact suitably with its supply of protons and neutrons. Nine months and 100 trillion neutrinos later came the exciting "two neutrinos" announcement—a new breed of neutrinos had been found.

. . . But then another worry. Every known elementary particle can have a corresponding antiparticle. But one was still missing. A Yale-Brookhaven team moved in and, a year later, discovered the anti-Xi-zero. If the experiment had failed, a physicist explained to the Associated Press, "all hell would have broken loose."

. . . But new tension was already rising at Brookhaven and at CERN's rival lab in Switzerland. The Eightfold Way, born in Japan, nourished in England, had been developed independently by Yuval Ne'eman of Israel and Murray Gell-Mann of Caltech to the point of their predicting that there must be another heavy "strange particle," the omega minus, and describing how it would behave. A 33-member team went to work, and the particle, which decays in a ten-billionth of a second, was "observed." This rightness of the Eightfold Way converted doubters. Apparently it would work like the chemist's periodic table, which had predicted new elements. "Order has at last been made out of nuclear chaos," said one journal. "High-energy physicists are walking around with a slightly hysterical look." Another described them "walking around with glazed and ecstatic eyes."

. . . But four months later Scientific American reported sadly that the Eightfold Way was faltering. Gell-Mann had proposed that the most elementary of elementary particles would be a trio of related quarks. Brookhaven went hunting the quark and couldn't find it.

. . . So the SU-3 Theory, another name for the Eightfold Way, evolved into an exercise in "supermultiplets" called, logically enough, the SU-6 Theory.

Such dithers might be dismissed as child's play in Disneyland, except for several implications. For one thing, many of these people try not to be the culture-philistines scolded by Charles P. Snow. To name his hypothetical particle, for instance, Gell-Mann drew on

Finnegans Wake: "Three quarks for Muster Mark." I found another of Caltech's renowned theoretical physicists, the bouncy Richard Feynman, proud of the buxom nude drawn on the blackboard in his office. He explained that she was his answer to Lord Snow: "I was always arguing with this artist friend and finally made a pact. One week he'd teach me art; next week, I'd teach him science."

The same adventuring beyond physics explains the rebelliousness of such younger men within it. Unable to make the theory of either relativity or quantum physics work, unable to produce better theory, they brush past such details as what causes an interaction and insist on only what is happening now. If this means a deluge of unexplained new "particles," then after them the deluge. Since a particle cannot be located in space-time, says Geoffrey Chew, then abolish the fourth dimension and the rest of the space-time concept. Gell-Mann agrees that chaos of this kind is not bad. And Feynman goes farther. "Chaos is wonderful," he boomed. This is nothing new. It started with quantum mechanics in 1925, at the time of the flapper revolt by American women, and when flagpole-sitters were sitting. It is a renewal of the old fight between Apollo and Dionysus, between form and feeling. It is rebellion that emphasizes the transitory. And, oddly, it leads to a new formalism, like rebels wearing the same costumes and dogmas; like Schoenberg's twelve-tone technique in music; and, of course, like the Eightfold Way. But this isn't surprising. With the emphasis on mere detail goes man's inner longing for the satisfying meaning of it all.

Meanwhile, other physicists are less nihilistic. England's Nobelist Paul Dirac, the predicter of antiparticles, tranquilly calls the pandemonium a transitional phase. He writes: "It is more important to have beauty in one's equations than to have them fit experiment," and suggests that even the universal ether abolished by Einstein's special theory of relativity may have to be restored. Edward Purcell, the brilliant Harvard Nobelist equally at home in astronomy and physics, told a Brookhaven audience, "Personally, I believe in special relativity. If it were not reliable, some expensive machines around here would be in very deep trouble."

On this all can agree: megabuck machines dominate the scene; theory waits while atom-smashing has its fling creating new particles.

"I'm theoretical and that's why I'm happy," said Feynman. "It's experimental physics that has the tough problems." At the Princeton Institute for Advanced Study, mathematical physicist Dyson summed it up: "We have never been farther from answers to the deep questions. It is the same in particle physics as in cosmology. How can one try to unify the theory of today when it will be outdated next year by new data? All we can do is try to read the outpour from accelerators and their computers."

The accelerators themselves are easier to understand, even when their energy is measured in mev or bev (million or billion electron-volts). Though requiring deft design and skilled technicians, they are essentially brute-strength machines that bombard target atoms, mainly with electrons or protons boosted to a speed practically that of light. And there are two basic styles of machine, straight or round. The outstanding straight one is the new linear accelerator in Stanford's $250-million smasher program for this decade. Its method is to send electrons down a 2-mile-long tube before they strike the target. Brookhaven's $30-million AGS (alternating gradient synchrotron) is outstanding among the round ones; in a second, its protons travel 260,000 times around a half-mile circle. Of course, there are variations. Brookhaven also has its cyclotron and cosmotron. But these are round machines too, as is Berkeley's bevatron. And every important machine is asserted to be biggest or best for this purpose or that.

Whatever its name or claim, the energy of its bullets or intensity of their beam, it is a tool for probing atomic nuclei: measuring their inner forces and distances from the way they scatter particles that strike them; from the kind of particles and waves torn out of them; and—most glamorously—from creating new particles when the right target is hit hard enough. Because this requires seeing what happens, the machine is not only a gun but the most powerful of microscopes; and because the seeing must be very indirect, an appropriate eyepiece is needed.

For example, there are the ionization chambers in which the invisible particle, in its fleeting moment, records on film a significant vapor trail or, more fruitfully, a track of bubbles. But one modern experiment may net several hundred thousand pictures. So researchers resorted to automation and now sing praises to the bubble or spark chamber, which sees for them, and the computer system, which can process 20,000 tracks per second. Eventually it is hoped that the computer will decide which tracks denote "interesting events," leaving the reseacher little else to do but plan the experiment and announce its results. Human technicians and automated ones will do the "donkey work."

The researchers themselves do not intend to be automated. They thrive as a coterie but detest the cote. They seek scoops. Therein looms the problem. Though relatively few, the researchers are too many for the giant accelerators. To be sure, there is a multitude of less crowded, less temperamental, more modest machines for nuclear work: smaller accelerators, Van de Graaffs, ordinary fission reactors. But these rate mainly as tools for R & D by industry and for the production of new physicists at the universities. The AEC tries to lessen the tensions. As paymaster, it has been spending on atom-smashing six times what it does on controlled fusion. In hardware alone, it offers an assortment of eight major accelerators. But this invites warfare—the haves against the have-nots. AEC has allocated five of these machines to universities: in California there are Berkeley, Stanford, and Caltech with one apiece; Princeton and Pennsylvania share one, as do Harvard and MIT. But how available are these to "qualified scientists" from the Midwest and South? AEC's other three giants are at national laboratories. Two are at Brookhaven, Long Island, operated by a nine-university consortium that includes the same Harvard, MIT, Princeton, Pennsylvania. The rest of the nation has only Argonne Lab's machine in Illinois, operated by the University of Chicago.

Hence dissension, and the solution—build more of them. And why limit them to mere duplicates? Why not smashers ten, even thirty times, bigger? But this brings megabuck quarrels. Can the nation afford them? What will they accomplish? Will the haves simply have more? And what about other sciences—must they starve so that atom-smashing can prosper? Moreover, budget estimates are shaky. I found Brookhaven delighted with a rule-of-thumb supplied by its big new 33-bev AGS: "A million [dollars] gets you a billion [electron-volts]." Soon came such upsets as Argonne's 12.7-bev plant costing $70 million, and Stanford's giant, new 20-bev plant costing $150 million. Might there be a better way? For instance, the forward-looking plan by the MIT group calling itself AIUR—American Institute for Useless Research. In 1953 it had suggested Circumtron, which would "just nicely go around the world once" and pointed out that the three trillion dollars needed would require only the national income for ten years.

Ten years later, a serious document stated that AEC's schedule for building and operating smashers during the 1960s wouldn't do. It formally offered this substitute instalment plan: 18 years instead of 10, and $8 billion instead of $1.7 billion. Among the new smashers proposed was a $1-billion one 30 times bigger than Brookhaven's 33-bev, the biggest in existence. The program was offered unanimously by a special panel convened by AEC's General Advisory Committee and the President's Science Advisory Committee, and headed by physicist Norman Ramsey of Princeton.

At first, all seemed harmonious, as it should be. The rollcall of prime movers was a Who's Who and mathematically weighted to silence jealousies within the establishment. When they join forces, for example, rival East and West dominate the field. Each therefore had three members on the nine-man panel; just as in AEC, Chairman Seaborg was from California and Commissioner Leland Haworth from Brookhaven. The resulting program was balanced too. For instance, both Berkeley and Brookhaven would plan for supergiants but "it should be noted that [both are] recommended with equal urgency." And so on, including a $170-million pacifier for the Midwest.

All this, of course, without embarrassment over the fact that the program, though administered by the major universities, would have only a nodding acquaintance with education. The money would go mainly to buy atom-smashing equipment and pay researchers who taught little or not at all. This had become characteristic of federal R & D, however. When hostilities began, spokesmen for education remained benevolently neutral.

. . . The first cut was the unkindest because it came from Robert Hofstadter, a big name in the West Coast coterie. He was from Stanford, the wealthy private university whose supersmasher program was already scheduled to spend a quarter-billion of the AEC's taxpayer money during the 1960s. And now, during an international conference at Stanford, up rose this Nobelist presumably to tell more about his elegant measurements inside the atom. Instead, he stunned the gathering ("You could hear a pin drop") with repudiation of the Ramsey panel's month-old report. "My proposal wasn't even considered by the panel," he told me later. "If it had been voted down, of course I'd have accepted with good grace." What did he want? Many machines, smaller ones: "The careers of many physicists are being affected adversely. They must wait a year and a half to get on the big accelerators; their important experiments are submerged by nonsense that fills the zoo with more particles."

. . . Then came outcries on behalf of other sciences. Obviously, $8 billion could explore mysteries down in earth, out in Space, inside man. Director Weinberg of Oak Ridge Lab, though a noted physicist himself, supplied ammunition to the critics. He urged that research be planned in terms of national welfare—by a program's technological merit, scientific merit, and social merit too. Applying these criteria, he compared the projects of today's biologists and high-energy physicists. The latter came off a poor second. Another seditionist was UCLA's Gordon MacDonald, a geophysicist admitted to the National Academy when he was but twenty-nine. He smelled oppressive "medieval air." He hoped that space research might rescue science from "its obsession with the very small, which resembles nothing so much as a charge by heavily armored and highly titled gentlemen crashing through a forest of strange particles in search of the Holy Grail." Even Russia was heard from. There, astronomers claimed they were being starved so that atom-smashing could flourish.

. . . Next came stern questions from the Joint Committee. Precisely what would this $8 billion buy? The committee knew, and had long approved, the argument for "pure science." But now, Chairman Holifield demanded, wasn't physics running wild and "squeezing to death" the practical? One defense was Seaborg's warning that national prestige was at stake; by 1966, Russia might have a smasher twice as energetic as our best. Others pointed to byproducts of such research. In the past, nuclear curiosity had brought the nuclear age. Now, the Ramsey defenders argued, the need for better accelerators might advance superconductivity and the like.

. . . Finally, atom-smashing was advised to fall in step with America's march to the future. But with the establishments of science, of university, of government treading on each other's feet, marching isn't easy. For instance, there was MURA, the Midwestern Universities Research Association. The very reason for its ten years' existence was the dream by its fifteen members for a big smasher that would make the nation's "science desert" bloom. At last, in the Ramsey Report, it was given a 12.5-bev machine, to be located in Wisconsin. But now that item of perhaps $170 million was thrown out. Hell hath no fury like a MURA scorned, especially when it feels it is a victim of something that still lacks a suitable name because it can be called neither political science nor scientific politics. MURA began sending lobbyists to Washington. It enlisted the porkbarrel support of Midwestern congressmen. But President Kennedy was a layman. He could thrill to a space race, not to the need for pions and hyperons. And his successor's affection was frankly for R & D that could be announced as a practical breakthrough.

Still, President Johnson was acutely political, and MURA hoped that the voice of a coterie might somehow sound like that of an important electorate. So, shepherded by the Midwestern congressmen and Hubert Humphrey, still a senator then, MURA spokesmen took their grievance to the White House. Johnson greeted them with a few words about budgetary problems; produced an anti-MURA memo from Jerome Wiesner, his science adviser; went away to take a phone call and didn't return. MURA didn't know whether to blame Johnson or his advisers, principally Wiesner from MIT, or Seaborg from California. Humphrey figured it this way, according to *Science* magazine: "It had to be Wiesner who doublecrossed us. The President didn't know a damn thing about MURA. So Wiesner played the old game of seeing to it that East and West get theirs while the Midwest goes begging." Eventually, to continue receiving AEC financial aid, MURA joined in a "reorientation" compromise. It would have more voice in the operation of Argonne's existing smasher. It would help Brookhaven's people design *their* 1000-bev supersupergiant.

Whether or not the $8-billion Ramsey program would survive its baptism of fire remained for the President, the Joint Committee, and financial rivalries within the science establishment to decide. Meanwhile, the atom-smashers had emerged with a reputation for being monopolists and spoiled children playing with what should be the essence of pure science but had become an expensive new art form.

But they still hoped. The Ramsey Report had looked ahead and suggested a publicity campaign to help high-energy physics capture the "imagination of the public."

Into Reality

From the inner atom, from this kernel crowded with nuclear riddles, we move out into the world of the outer atom. This domain of the electrons has mysteries too, including such seminal ones as what is life—and what is an electron? But scientist and engineer can choose to focus on what the mind impatiently calls reality, the empirical environment of flesh and bone, electricity and light, that everybody knows. The warbling bird and ugly ape alike react consciously to this feelable, seeable, smellable, audible, tastable world.

Busily at work here is the atomic force, the so-called "electromagnetic force" that causes electrically charged particles to attract or repel each other. Consequently, negative electrons somehow surround the positively charged nucleus, forming the complete atom, and atoms combine to form molecules. Though its effect is felt at much greater distances, it is a hundred times weaker than the so-called "strong force," the hypothetical glue that keeps nuclear particles together until perhaps an atom-smasher breaks their bonds. Yet the weaker force is strong enough to account for the stolid strength of steel, of concrete; for the dramatic power of thunder and lightning. But strength isn't all. This force also accounts for the odor of the rose, and our awareness of it. Moreover, it is easily transformed into a social and political force. Its labor-saving machinery turns workmen into supervisors, its surpluses of foods and weapons alike become embarrassing.

To operate in this vast world of reality, science seeks some way to arrange what seem to be the many pieces in the pile. Thereupon it becomes mired in a surplus of its own—specialties. Already in 1959, diligent research counted 1150 different "sciences." But nobody can count them; they subdivide and hybridize too fast into little in-groups. The other extreme is simply to divide the pile of outer-atom activities between usual chemistry and physics. Either then becomes a basket large enough to include dozens of specialties. Chemistry here becomes more than molecules of TNT and DDT; through the life sciences it tries to understand and manipulate the metabolic way of man with food and chromosomic way of man with maid. Likewise, the physics of the outer atom goes beyond the traffic of energy in vacuum tubes and transistors. It deals also with the long-distance radiation with which Venus reveals that she possesses such life-cycle material as carbon dioxide and water vapor.

Even the fence between chemistry and physics, of course, is one that nature doesn't recognize. When both work with the electron the difference between them is only a divergence of interest. Roughly, the difference is this. Physics concentrates on the energy of the electrons and their interactions with other particles. They may be free electrons moving through a simple wire, a computer circuit, a television tube; or they may be still within the atom, dropping from one orbit to another, thereby releasing the energy that our eyes or instruments can detect. Chemistry has a proprietary interest throughout all this—in its spectroscopy, for example—but its main occupation is manipulating the outermost electrons as electrical hooks that join atom to atom and one group of atoms to another. This gives us the reality of familiar matter—of molecules and such variations as crystals.

But always the interplay between chemistry and physics goes on. And the researcher from one is constantly stepping into the other if he is alert enough to escape the self-imprisonment of overspecialization. In the mushrooming field of solid-state physics, for example, the chemist's crystal may also be the physicist's transistor, superior to the radio tube because it does away with space-wasting vacuum gaps and energy-wasting hot filaments. And directing the wealth of major electronic projects at Bell Labs, which developed the transistor, is William Baker, who began there as a chemist assigned to find a wartime substitute material for the protective coating of electric cables. Or take the legendary Irving Langmuir, whose science was "pure" enough to win him the Nobel Prize for chemistry, also practical enough to make him a leading light at General Electric Research Laboratory. He probed wherever electrons led his curiosity: in physics, from better lamps and power tubes, to superhot gases that he christened "plasma" because their free electrons could be made to oscillate in a group pattern that reminded him of a quivering protoplasmic jelly; in chemistry, from the shell picture of electrons surrounding a nucleus, to incredibly thin layers of molecules that have made possible the ultramicroscopic techniques of today's biology and such triumphs of solid-state physics as the miniaturization of computer circuitry. And, of course, this physical chemist began the cloud-seeding attempts to make rain and destroy hurricanes.

But there is more than freedom from the restrictions of specialization. There is also the very essence of liberty. And it is a bit fantastic that materialistic science, blamed for producing the computerized man, modular man, and mechanistic man, and therefore increasingly neurotic man, allows the concert baritone once again to sing the "I am the master of my fate, I am the captain of my soul" of Henley's "Invictus."

The idea originated in a quiet and in no way philosophical confession by Max Planck back in 1900 while he was at the University of Berlin. Unable to make a radiation equation work any other way, he took the liberty of supposing that radiated energy need not obey dogma, need not be a continuous train of waves, but can also be envisioned as coming in packets. Chemists call their fundamental unit of matter the atom; physicist Planck gave the name quantum to his smallest bit of energy transmittable at a given wavelength. Einstein was soon using quanta to explain the behavior of light, then Bohr used them to explain his planetary atom. But there was trouble with Bohr's picture, and this led in the mid-1920s to the theory of quantum mechanics. Highly mathematical, it shuns analogies and other pictorial aids. It doesn't worry whether radiation is waves or corpuscular particles: it will use whichever best fits the all-important data and calculations.

But this preoccupation with "cold fact" brought Werner Heisenberg's shattering Principle of Uncertainty. Science had long acknowledged that its measurements were faulty. It had faith in progress, however. It supposed that, with ever better instruments, there was theoretically no limit to accuracy, no matter how small the thing being studied. And from better, it evolved the idea of bigger and more expensive. This seemed reasonable. As we have seen, the smaller the object, the shorter must be the wavelength for measuring it; and the shorter wavelength, in turn, calls for higher energy. So the electron microscope surpasses the optical microscope. And for still higher energy, physics has gone to giant atom-smashers. Thus, the smaller the object, the bigger the instrument.

This might be only a paradox if not for Heisenberg. He insisted that there must be a limit. For proof, he offered the electron. How can one determine both its exact position and velocity at the same instant? There comes a limit where the greater accuracy of one measurement can be obtained only at the expense of the other. The position, for instance, keeps changing too fast. Well then, get the exact position by somehow stopping the particle for an instant. But stopping it destroys its velocity.

This was in the world of the very, very small, to be sure, but devastating nonetheless when science realized the significance. Without absolute data there could no longer be absolute certainty. Uncertainy meant that the relation between cause and effect no longer could be depended on. Without this causality one could count only on the probability that something would happen. And probability turns self-assured science into a gambler. Causality or not, this reasoning had several after-effects. Probability is made tolerable by averaging how the coin flips. This further deflates the role of the theorist and inflates that of the statistician. Another response was bleak discouragement. Intellect had now reached a final barrier, an unknowable that blocked understanding of reality. Worse, suppose there were no natural laws to understand—suppose nature itself is unpredictable? And soon enough, philosopher-scientists like Sir Arthur Eddington took the logical next step. They announced that Free Will was in again, and Determinism was out.

It was a message that crossed the membrane between the "two cultures" and reached a lay world hungry for affirmation that man can do more than bewail his fate. The young at heart had always gambled on this anyway. But now it was "Science says . . ." and in time to encourage those whose self-confidence or religion was insufficient armor against the Depression of the 1930s, the Fascism, and the mechanistic ordeals of modern times. Free Will could, of course, take many directions. It could justify either the aloneness and drift recommended by some existentialists or the "Happy the man and happy he alone; he who can call today his own" of the hedonistic ode by Horace. It could go on to become an argument for anarchy.

But it could also speak loudly for self-reliance rather than self-pity. With Dostoevski, man could again insist that twice two are not four when the units in the equation are human beings. William Faulkner could proclaim "the duty of every individual to be responsible for the consequences of his own acts, to pay his own score, owing nothing to any man." Even the weakling could help shape his "destiny." To carry her newborn kitten to safety, the mother must grasp the helpless bundle by the nape of its neck. But man might choose to imitate the newborn monkey. It joins in the rescue by clinging to its mother with all the strength of its baby arms.

The Free Will argument will go on, probably as long as man ponders fate. By definition, the Uncertainty Principle and evidence for it are themselves uncertain. And our observation shows cause and effect operating busily. On the other hand, the excursion of physics into the spiritual revealed nothing that the self-reliant didn't already know. Even the newborn monkey knows it somehow, without having heard of Heisenberg.

In science the attack on certainty was more shocking. To the unreliability of the human instrument was now added the ultimate hopelessness of laboratory instruments: a final blow to objectivity. Some physicists went so far as to mourn that their tidy laws were all shattered, data was dust, further research was futile. From biology came the "I told you so" of the vitalists, who insist there is more to life than the mechanists can ever find. Only the atom-smashing people, no longer required to explain causes and guarantee effects, reveled in the dialectic surrealism now allowed them.

But in science, as in philosophy, the furor has quieted. Einstein, though he contributed much to quantum mechanics, declined to join the uncertainty revolution, explaining that he couldn't believe the universe was a game of dice. Another contributor, Dirac, has gone on to counsel patience. He hails the death of determinism; he concedes that the new outlook substitutes new theoretical difficulties for the old ones; he predicts something better will evolve. Meanwhile, there is leeway enough for most science and technology. Archimedes' laws of simple levers still form the theoretical basis of all load-raising machines and, Heisenberg agrees, "no doubt they will do so for all time." Too, the probability is virtually certain that the "sun also ariseth" of Ecclesiastes will be repeated tomorrow and tomorrow. On a smaller scale, there is no need to predict exactly the behavior of each molecule in a gas; with a bit of patching, the so-called "gas laws" respond well enough to changing temperature and pressure—and the household refrigerator works remarkably well.

True, the carelessly produced hardware described by Admiral Rickover is shocking and the need for precision is mounting. A gyro wheel for space travel must be accurately in place to within millionths of an inch. Whatever causes the unreliability of such devices—the tools that make them or humans who inspect and install them—the results are similar. A century ago, Jules Verne's space travelers orbited in frustration around the moon instead of landing. Today, Rand Corporation calculates that a velocity error of only 1 foot per second when the boosting rocket cuts off its thrust would mean missing the moon by 100 miles, and missing Mars by 20,000 miles. Hence the need for flight corrections along the way. But the point is that tolerances of millionths of an inch are now possible. So are speeds, measured in billionths of a second, at which computers and electronic cameras can operate. Theory, too, has not been totally paralyzed by the limits on certainty, or the possibility that the concept of electrons may itself have to be abandoned eventually. Working in hand with experiment, theory gave Einstein's famed relationship, which has proven itself the best way. It works. What we call mass and energy are indeed interchangeable.

The same is true of the equally terse fundamental law of Planck's theory. It works, although why, nobody knows, any more than we know *why* the area of a circle is the square of its radius, multiplied by a ratio number called pi. Quantum theory gave a number as basic as pi.

Physics had long known that light travels approximately 186,000 miles a second. It knew also that such radiation can come in a broad spectrum of wavelengths; that a wave of the light called red, for instance, is about twice as long as a wave of violet. The rest was obvious. Since all such radiation travels at the same velocity, there must be more of the shorter waves per second: twice as many violet waves as red ones. In other words the shorter the wavelength, the higher the frequency. Obvious, but only a relationship. What does it mean in terms of how much energy is transmitted? Without units of measurement, science is shaky. Planck filled this need with his daring trick. He retained the idea of wavelength and frequency but these weren't undulating waves. He chopped them into the quantum pieces. And from this came the fundamental equation of quantum theory:

$$q = h\nu$$

Here, q is the quantum energy, h is Planck's constant, ν is the frequency. The equation looks as simple as Einstein's familiar $e = mc^2$ but has certain oddities. Its q, although a measurement unit, is as variable as the quaint Chinese "li" (one third of a mile), which allowed me to trudge the same 120 li or so every day. In the mountains, where travel was slower, the li shortened; out on the plains, it lengthened. This was control by Chinese common sense. In quantum events the control is the infinitesimally small number h. Among other things, this constant dictates that the higher the frequency, the more energy per quantum.

Whether we regard it as the mathematical artifice with which Planck made his equation work or, as some physicists now suspect, a fundamental something they hope to understand some day, h makes the quantum idea work in the very real world of the outer atom. It brought order into the chemist's understanding of atoms and the atom's electrons. It not only helped explain what happens but gave a quantum currency with which to measure and manipulate changes in the atom. In physics it revolutionized theory and became the foundation for practical electronics. The exciting laser is a recent example.

But first, let us see how the quantum idea works in something very familiar. It made broadcast television practical by the end of the Second World War; by 1950, the United States was producing seven million sets annually. More important for our purpose here, with no ordinary product does engineering play so many skillful variations on the theme of energy.

The first step is conversion of light into electricity. This is the photoelectric effect. Einstein explained it by borrowing Planck's quantum, which, in this application, is usually called a photon. The explanation is that shining light upon a metal is like bombarding its surface with photon particles. The result depends on the kind of metal, on how strongly its electrons are bound by positive electrical charges. If the photons are of the right frequency they can transfer enough "escape energy" to break the bonds. Suitable metal is used in the TV camera, which translates what it sees into a movement of freed electrons. Of course, the more intense the light received, the more freed electrons; hence an electronic replica of light and shade. The final result, an electric current of varying magnitude, is then processed and goes to the transmitter. There, like audio, the video signals of TV are sent out in radiation form. And at the receiver, they are turned back into a current mimicking that at the transmitter. Next, in the picture tube, the signals are decoded back to visibility. Here the method reverses that of the TV camera. Now a stream of free electrons are the bullets, and it is photons of light that are generated when the electrons strike a viewing screen coated with fluorescent material. This step, too, retains the original pattern. Boiled off an electron gun, the number of electrons in the beam that scans the viewing screen faithfully echoes the varying intensity of the incoming signals. And the screen in turn glows in proportion to the varying intensity of the beam.

Fluorescence is simply another quantum way of translating energy. In the TV tube this energy is delivered by the beam of electrons. Precisely how they deliver the energy remains among mysteries of the outer atom, but what they do is palpable enough. In quantum language they "excite" atoms of the receiving material. This language, remember, tries to dispense with planetary pictures. Whether the atom's own electrons are waves or particles is mystical; whether they circle the nucleus like planets or curve around it like clouds is theoretical. It is sufficient that their distance from the nucleus indicates their energy content. And quantum theory allows only specific distances, which correspond to "energy levels" characteristic of the kind of atom. Where atoms strongly affect each other, as in a crystal, the energy levels are less sharp, so are called energy bands.

In terms of a single atom, excitement means that some of its electrons absorb enough energy to overcome part of the pull from the nucleus. They move to a higher orbit. Quantum theory does not allow this to be gradual. It must be in quantum jumps, from energy level to energy level. But now that it is excited, an atom is no longer in a normal "ground" state. It is unstable because of the excess energy. As in a coiled spring, this stored energy awaits release. In fluorescence, the release is immediate. Excited electrons drop back to lower levels and, doing so, radiate their surplus energy. This, too, must be in quantum terms, in specific wavelengths.

Black-and-white television prefers light favoring the blue end of the spectrum. Color TV depends on the fact that different materials fluoresce with different colors. So, at the camera, the picture is broken into its three primary colors: red, green, blue. Then, at the receiver, the resulting electrical images excite corresponding dots of fluorescent material on the screen, and the rest is up to the optical system and brain of the viewer.

The Laser Beam

Atoms go on being excited in television tubes but excitement in the designing of TV sets has waned. Color TV, for instance, is now commonplace after finally rewarding RCA for the march that it stole on rivals. To be sure, there will be new models, new sales appeal. Transistors will continue to miniaturize television. At the other extreme, we may have living rooms whose TV walls glow with Shakespeare, or Big Brother. Such advances, however, are only embellishments of the TV theme. The same is true for the special, clever television with which unmanned spaceships transmit what they see. For a really new principle in electronics, for excitement among researchers as well as atoms, there is the glamorous laser.

Among other things, it offers the brightest light on earth. And when a narrow laser beam illuminated a selected spot on the moon sufficiently to be detected electronically back on earth, physicists were quick to recognize a way of signaling directly from spaceship to spaceship and planet to planet—a sophisticated heliography that can be performed without sunlight and mirrors. Meanwhile, surgeons already use a miniature beam to heal the eye itself when the retina separates from the rest of the eyeball. The detached retina is by no means rare and may lead to total blindness. A laser beam, painless and relatively safe because it can be pinpointed to strike nowhere else and the intense burst of energy lasts only a millisecond, makes a small lesion at the back of the retina. This results in a "weld" that fastens the retina where it belongs. It is not surprising, therefore, that surgeons hope to see laser instruments also become safe destroyers of malignant tumors. Such uses, however, are only on the periphery of the laser's potential. Man outdoes nature in the arts of death, and here could be a killer beam, a "death ray" of science fiction. But here also could be a way of sending long-distance commercial power by beam instead of wire. Here, too, could be the answer to communication woes of the future. Though lasers thrive in only a small slice of the electromagnetic spectrum, there is so much useful space in this high-frequency band that it could theoretically, for example, accommodate millions of television channels. All this, of course, is heady stuff, and has created such skeptics as the laser specialist who remarked dryly, "The flashing rays of the brilliant laser have ignited the imagination of men—and inflamed their pens."

So I visited various laser laboratories and talked to the men who were "pumping" atom-exciting energy, sometimes electrical, sometimes from intense flash lamps, into tiny crystals and glasslike rods, or into gas-filled tubes a few feet long, to make them "lase." Yes, like any self-respecting new specialty, "lasing" quickly developed its own brisk lingo. The difference is that lasing enthusiasm moved so fast. The first laser was announced in 1960. Three years later, about five hundred R & D groups were busy with them and some were already being marketed for as low as $1,000 apiece. Even the sensational transistor didn't stir so much fuss in its early youth.

For example, there was the big step forward—and the squabble— when it was found that ordinary direct current would make a simple transistor-like wafer of gallium arsenide lase satisfactorily. First to offer this semiconductor approach was MIT's Lincoln Laboratory, whose laser research is sponsored by Army, Navy, and Air Force. Lincoln's suggestion followed another serendipity example of chance favoring the prepared mind. Uncertain whether his semiconductor circuit was working, a researcher substituted an emergency crystal of the gallium arsenide. Out came an unexpected red light, not a laser beam but enough to indicate possibilities. Lincoln announced this at a research conference and the race began. A few months later, GE and IBM almost simultaneously did get laser action, followed a week later by Lincoln, which then stepped aside to let the industrial titans stake out claims for glory, and possibly patent rights to the "injection laser." When the jousting was over, neutral physicists figured it this way: GE had discovered this new kind of laser first; but IBM had beaten GE in calling a press conference.

As elsewhere in science, lasers are a sequel to previous research. Britain's magnetron helped win the Hitler war by providing microwave radar. It also whetted the interest of many young American physicists in the very short radio waves and they dug deeper into this marriage of quantum physics to electrical engineering. One was Charles Townes. In 1954, after he had moved from Bell Labs to Columbia University, he and his graduate students confirmed one of fertile Einstein's predictions by inventing a device, called "maser," that used specially prepared ammonia gas to generate and amplify microwaves. A year later, quietly competent Nicolaas Bloembergen of Harvard invented a "three-level" maser, a more efficient type that brought a proliferation of successors, not only gas masers but those using crystalline materials, not only oscillators producing waves of an exact frequency but amplifiers changing a weak wave to a strong one.

Whatever the type, the idea is to keep a majority of the atoms excited. One thing Bloembergen did was introduce the idea of maintaining this so-called "population inversion" by pumping enough external energy into the system. What happens next depends on method and purpose. A few photons emitted spontaneously can then trigger the maser action. Or the needed photons can be supplied, for instance, by a suitable incoming microwave that needs strengthening. This wave does not lose energy to the already excited atoms; it merely "stimulates" them to release their excess energy via electrons that fall back to lower levels. In the fall, the electrons radiate their surplus energy in the form of photons. These stimulate other atoms, and the wave grows.

As the hunt for new and still newer masers underwent an amplification of its own, some irreverent physicists found new origins for the acronym MASER: such blithe phrases as "More Applied Scientists Eat Regularly" and "Money Acquisition Scheme for Expensive Research." But not all masers waste R & D money. The ammonia type, for instance, developed into an ideal "atomic clock." The energy isn't much but the precise frequency of its waves allows a timekeeping accuracy of 1 second in 10,000 years. More important is the amplification possible for wireless communication. Masers strengthen a signal without distorting or adding noise to it as a vacuum tube does. In the microwave region this means a hundred times more sensitivity—valuable for detecting radar signals, and the radiation with which astronomers measure temperatures at our companion planets and at distant galaxies. Also, maser amplifiers have contributed to the success of America's first communication satellites.

The maser's farthest-reaching contribution, however, is its glamorous offspring, the laser. In 1958, Townes and his brother-in-law, Arthur Schawlow, then at Bell Labs, applied for a patent on the idea. In 1960, T. H. Maiman of Hughes Aircraft Company built the first working model. It was a crystal of pink ruby around which coiled a flash tube that pumped energizing light into it. Soon came the build-up: the scores of other types . . . the flood of technical papers, some trying to explain this strange new device, others reaching into Cloud 99 for potential uses . . . the enthusiastic four-color treatment by magazines grateful for a gadget that is literally colorful besides reawakening prospects for a death ray.

The easiest explanation of the standard laser (strictly chemical ones may come next) is to call it a maser that works in a different part of the electromagnetic spectrum. The ordinary maser's microwaves are much shorter than waves of the shortest shortwave radio, but waves in the neighborhood of ordinary light are much shorter still. This is the laser's neighborhood. Townes, faithful to his acronym, insisted that the new device was just an optical maser. But other physicists like to coin words too. They threw out "microwave," declined to let the "m" in "maser" stand for "molecular," substituted the "l" for "light," and ended with "Light Amplification by Stimulated Emission of Radiation"—the laser. And, looking ahead to amplifiers of X-rays, they prepared the acronym "Xraser." This stirred memories. Power of the earliest lasers was measured in "gillettes," the number of razor blades their intense little beam could penetrate.

Such frolicking does not obscure the fact that the laser deserves its own name. It is both potent and unique.

. . . As in the maser, its first few photons trigger the release of more photons. This is an outer-atom version of a nuclear chain reaction and fulfills the old dream of a way to amplify light.

. . . Depending on such variables as the source of energy and choice of gas or crystal, the laser can do many other things. It converts electricity or radio waves into light. It also changes incoming light of one color to another. Experimentally, it can also mix two kinds of light waves to synthesize a third color, or give a different color at a different voltage, or even generate optical harmonics.

. . . But whatever the kind of light emitted, it is highly monochromatic. This is not ordinary light, the disorderly radiation from incandescent lamps or the sun, which a simple prism shows to be "all colors of the rainbow." Laser rays are practically a pure color of only one frequency. This purity frees them from the background frequencies called static by laymen and "noise" by scientists.

. . . Likewise, sunlight and lamplight are like bonfires radiating wastefully in useless directions. By contrast, the beam ready to burst from a laser can be focused later but is already intense, a tight bundle of rays concentrated along a straight line. This is because, to stimulate more of the excited atoms, the light has been bounced back and forth through them by a reflecting mirror of some kind at each end of the laser. In a crystal laser the reflectors are made simply by polishing two opposite faces of the crystal. What about rays that aren't parallel to the laser axis? They remove themselves simply. Nothing prevents their escaping through the side of the gas tube or crystal.

. . . Unique, and as important as amplification, this light gains strength from its "coherence." Unlike ordinary light, whose waves of different length are not in step, a laser's monochromatic waves move exactly in phase, crest matching crest and trough matching trough. Instead of partly canceling the effective power of each other, they reinforce each other.

The sum total is manmade light that is truly remarkable. The rays are not only pure and coherent but they remain a tight bundle. Unlike a radar beam, which loses its effectiveness by spreading quickly, the laser beam can be much narrower at the start and will keep its sharp pencil shape almost intact over thousands of miles. And the shortness of its waves will give higher resolution when it examines, for example, a distant aircraft.

But harsh reality cannot be ignored. Because it is optical, the laser beam is balked by rain, fog, and snow, so it cannot replace microwave radar for all-weather conditions. Similarly, consider the laser as a source of power. When its already intense beam is focused to a fine enough point, its radiant energy is 100 million times greater than that at the sun's surface. It can drill, weld, or vaporize materials in a flash. But this is pinpointing so momentary that it will not boil even a gram of water. Similarly, brute-power experiments have given millions of megawatts—but with a burst lasting only a few billionths of a second. Such are the realities spurring researchers to produce the better lasers that are undoubtedly coming.

Meanwhile, for a sensational prophet, why not hear one whose technical knowledge ranges far? He is editor-publisher Hugo Gernsback, father of modern science-fiction. The busy profession awards its "Hugos" in his name despite his complaints that S-F has strayed into "fairy-tale" directions. Though often impish, even flamboyant, he preferred source material from such friends pioneering in electronics and space science as Nikola Tesla, Lee De Forest, and Donald Menzel, director of Harvard Observatory. As a forecaster, Gernsback built a redoubtable average through the years: his admirers figure it at 90 percent for predictions already come true. When I asked him about some of the others, he chuckled. "I never expect science to catch up with me all at once." Electronics was his forte. He was not only predicting radar in 1909 but explaining the technique to his readers. Admittedly, lasers caught him by surprise fifty years later but he swiftly seized upon its potential. His Mars-bound spaceship would scorn chemical fuels, nuclear fuels, ionic fuels. It would even rival his uplift method of an antigravity shield. It would ride a beam from a "colossal super-laser-power plant." To do this it would be doughnut-shape, so the beam could go through the center like a wireless trolley wire and supply power via an "electronic clutch."

Gernsback would himself agree this is an extremely long-range forecast. For a reliable look at the next few years let us visit Stanford physicist Schawlow, co-father of lasers. No American scientist keeps closer track of laser progress, or is more frank about them. After seeing his own research with the laser as a separator of isotopes and as a catalyst for chemical reactions, I asked him for perspective:

"Debunking of grandiose claims has started, of course, and rightly so," he replied. "Also, though, it's too easy to be influenced by what we see today. There is a new idea every few days—new colors of light, new materials, higher power, different methods—so much excitement that there hasn't been time for concentrated R & D on practical uses. The new ideas add up to an embarrassment of riches. We are already talking, for example, about shooting in a beam to start a backfire that will stop a forest fire. And, of course, we want to combine the laser with fiber optics so as to squirt intense light around corners. Meanwhile, we've learned much, and lasers are already simpler than, say, a television tube."

As a source of power, he conceded, the laser has made only a beginning. It has become a surgical instrument and is being tried as a sharp industrial tool where other methods give trouble—in electronics, for example, where the beam welds a small joint sealed inside glass. But limitations remain: "The tremendous power we get is only a pulse; and the steady power we get is too low. That's why the hunt for the efficient laser that will give steady power and enough of it. When it comes, and no reason why it should not, we can do large-scale metalworking with it, cut lumber with it, and so on."

Like others, Schawlow could not give a timetable for the two areas where laser possibilities become massive:

1. Communications was quick to attract the bulk of R & D spending by industrial giants and the government. The lure is that vast number of messages the laser wavelengths can carry. Ancient men signaled with light in crude fashion. The nineteenth century brought the military heliograph, with its flashes of sunlight reflected by mirror. The laser substitutes electronics. Signals would ride the laser's carrier wave, as in radio. When weakened by long-distance travel, the beam could be amplified by putting it through another laser, a method already used to strengthen the output of experimental beams. But main problems await solution. Because light rays are absorbed and scattered by bad weather, the beam might have to run through a protective pipe of some sort. For spacemen beyond our atmosphere, of course, that earthbound problem would not exist.

2. Related to communication is the hope to transmit power by laser beam rather than over wires. At the receiving end the light would be converted to electricity. This would be the answer to transmission losses. But, again, this awaits powerful lasers as well as paraphernalia that is still conceptually hazy unless, of course, the Defense Department has progressed farther than it cares to announce. Obviously,

the military uses that await lasers are many, and the Pentagon could hardly afford to overlook them.

What, then, about the death ray? Rand Corporation has studied the subject for the government, and General Curtis LeMay, while Air Force Chief of Staff, took notice of a Soviet claim to having a "fantastic" new weapon. Referring to "beam-directed energy weapons," he went on, "Our security in the future may depend on armament far different from any we know today. Perhaps they will be weapons that strike with the speed of light. That would make the 1500-mile-an-hour ICBM a relatively slow-moving target."

So, I asked Schawlow his opinion of the death ray. He grinned. "I'm not in secret work but, of course, that's the one they want. At the moment, I strongly doubt that we are anywhere near to the usual idea of a death ray or to the beam that melts a missile—that intercepts it and vaporizes it. But the possibility is there. In spectrum analysis, for instance, we can use the laser as a microprobe to vaporize a small amount of any known substance. In everything concerning lasers, the safest prediction is that there will be surprises."

XIV: *The Practical Chemists*

"I seem to have been like a boy playing on the
seashore, now and then finding a smoother pebble
or a prettier shell than ordinary, while the great
ocean of truth lay all undiscovered before me."
—Isaac Newton

But Newton, quoted above, lived three centuries ago. Now turn to
The Search, the first science novel by Charles P. Snow, the onetime
physicist. It was published in 1934 and he had his protagonist react
to the revolution brought a few years earlier by quantum mechanics:
"The nucleus and life: those were the harder problems. In everything
else, in the whole of chemistry and physics, we were in sight of the
end. How long before the nucleus was in the same state? A few years,
fifty at most. And life? Not so much longer. *We were in sight of the
end.*"

This augury runs counter to our experience in the pursuit of
knowledge. But if the sciences are indeed to be like the cooling stars,
then it is understandable that chemistry, the most mature, has already
begun losing some of its sparkle, has been dulled by a lack of excitement. The glamour has gone elsewhere—to physics, to biology, to
astronomy.

But not the importance, not quite yet. There are still many of the
details to be filled in, much still to be done under the banner that
proclaims "better things for better living." This is materialism, to be
sure. But materialism can be many things. It produced aspirin that
gave Everyman the quick relief denied kings of old, and nylon that
blurred distinctions between social classes; it is now making the
ocean's salt water fit for consumption.

We have already met chemistry continually in these pages as it

430

joins in research with the other two big sciences, biology and physics. It is not only the most practical of the sciences but the most pervasive. And there are many working in it—chemistry can still claim to be the most populous science. In the schools, biology remains the "easy" course preferred by students, but after graduation narrows the picture the figures change radically for those who choose science as a profession. The 1960 Census counted three times as many chemists as biologists and physicists combined. Such data need qualifying. For example, "electrical engineers" now outnumber "chemical engineers" by about the same ratio. Nevertheless, if we overlook several overlaps it is significant that industry, home for half of the nation's scientists, employs six times more chemists than physicists and three times more chemists than "life scientists."

First, then, what can we say in general about this cookery with its special pots and pans, its ancient as well as daringly modern recipes, its chaste odors and also those that only the organic chemist can love?

For one thing, here is a bonding science. From its laboratory stool it can survey all others that deal with palpable things. It has the least trouble understanding these sciences and crossing over to produce such hybrids as biochemistry, physical chemistry, geochemistry. It can do all this because its method, at the outset anyway, is that of the universal analyzer who wants to know what stars and little girls are made of, and in what proportions. Then, for example, after discovering the chemical formula for insulin, the chemist wants to prove it by reassembling its basic atoms in molecular working order. Next comes the very practical. The chemist may improve nature's compound; he may even invent one that he prefers. This explains chemistry's reputation for synthetics. Chile sees its saltpeter industry wrecked by "fixed nitrogen" from the air; lumber and paper waken to competition from plastics.

Chemistry's other outstanding trait is therefore its materialism. Since alchemy days it has stressed practicality. For instance, great Pasteur's first research, on the polarization of light by crystals, was quite "pure"; but he was using crystals of tartaric acid, a byproduct of wine fermentation. This unobtrusively shaped his sequential career of practical chemistry: on into fermentation and yeast and bacteria; on farther into pasteurization and vaccines.

In nearby Germany, the birthplace of organic chemistry, basic research likewise evolved into far-flung usefulness. Modern industrial chemistry started there in the treasure house of derivatives from black, gummy coal tar—dyes, perfumes, explosives, drugs, paints. Eventually, to free herself for wars—and survive the defeats they brought her—Germany was inventing nitrogen compounds useful for either fertilizers or explosives, plus poison gases and such ersatz necessities as synthetic gasoline, synthetic rubber, and the mixed blessing called detergents.

America's chemicals industry, too, was a war baby of sorts. Forced to shift for itself when German chemicals could not be imported, then helped by laboratory secrets that go to the victor, it has become our nation's most self-reliant technology. It invests nearly a billion dollars of its own money annually in R & D, more than any other industry. Another $200 million of its R & D is government-sponsored. In proportion, the electronics industry receives thirteen times as much federal money; and the aerospace industry, heavily engaged in military and space programs, receives thirty-nine times as much.

Industrial chemistry proclaims such independence proudly. Perhaps it could not get more government largesse even if it wished. Its labs are competent as ever, so are its press agents, but it matured a bit too soon. In the lineup of candidates for a race with Russia, it would look out of place jostling the needy youngsters of aerospace and electronics. And most of its R & D projects lack the breathlessness and porkbarrel rating that would excite Congress and the White House. They can attract only what are essentially subcontracts—improved fuels for rocketry, newer drugs for biological research, technical services for nuclear energy.

This could be galling. But industrial chemistry prefers to regard itself as squire of its own estate, vulnerable only to a national depression. Unlike the physicist of electronics and aerospace engineer of missiles, the chemist of sulfuric acid need not dread the economic perils of disarmament, or simply the possibility that a new President and Congress might kill his glamour project and make him a job-hunter. Millions of tons of sulfuric acid are needed to refine petroleum and to pickle steel; the AEC alone uses a half-million tons yearly, notably to process nuclear fuels.

And if a major war comes? The chemist's products would be in the thick of it, supporting everything the mobilizer can dream of, but not quite in the mainstream. His best chance to take the limelight would be in the field of chemical, biological, and radiological warfare (CBR). However, his poison gases have no lobby; they are loathed by civilians and the military alike, except for the relatively few Defense Department people who are concerned with them.

True, the R & D for gases has continued at Edgewood Arsenal and elsewhere; Rocky Mountain Arsenal and others could go into production speedily. But it is useless for General J. H. Rothschild, formerly head of CBR research, to argue that poison gas is more humane than nuclear weapons with their blast, shock, and radiation; more humane than the rending and tearing by conventional bombs, artillery, and firearms. As an example, he asserts that the person caught by today's nerve gas either dies or recovers completely. And we are promised "benevolent incapacitators" that simply put him to sleep.

Why, then, is gas rated as immoral, inhumane? Would this be a case of shying from more horrors? Or, perhaps, is it a claustrophobia-like revulsion from pervasive danger, and the gambler's preference to take the chance that a discrete object, bullet or bomb, won't catch *him*? Another explanation was ventured by England's J. B. S. Haldane, who was gassed twice in World War I. In Shavian style he railed against "sentimentalists generally willing (after a decent interval) to accept any application of science which is hallowed by use and wont but distinguished by a ferocious opposition to, and contempt for, any attempt at the solution of human problems by honest and simple intellectual effort. Mustard gas kills 1 man for every 40 it puts out of action; shells kill 1 for every 3; but their god who compromised with high explosives has not yet found time to adapt himself to chemical warfare."

Haldane, however, was a biologist. The chemist bold enough to go that far would be regarded askance by his fellows; certainly by the university members of the establishment. In a report, they contrasted chemistry's plastics, drugs, and soaps "that bring cleanliness to the poorest man" with "the blinding excitement aroused by the appalling success of applied physics in developing new techniques of destruction."

These people are unashamed of the materialism for which chemistry is known and for which parts of the world are apparently clamoring. Neither their noneducated rich nor illiterate poor were ready for it in the first two-thirds of the twentieth century. Perhaps it will have another chance to provide what Harry Truman, neither scientist nor intellectual layman, could see: ". . . a bold new program for making the benefits of our scientific advances and industrial progress available to more than half the people of the world. Their food is inadequate. They are the victims of disease. Their poverty is a handicap and a threat both to them and to more prosperous areas." This, too, could be one of Newton's "prettier shells."

The Basic Researchers

The practicality of chemistry characterizes its basic research as well as the analysis and synthesis with which it seeks new products for the market. This materialism has a drawback. It can overlook the fact that times change and what was once satisfactory theory is now out-dated dogma. But by and large, the chemist's preference for ex-periment rather than theory is his strength. He wastes less time with dialectics. This may explain why industrial chemistry's labs of the better kind are willing to underwrite truly basic research.

Nor is the end goal always a profitable new product. It can also be prestige, or simply a desire to keep its people from straying back to the campus. An outstanding example is Jersey Standard's affiliate, Esso Research and Engineering Company. Naturally enough, its projects concern anti-knock fuels and the like, but petroleum is a versatile raw material that can lead to many products. In the very practical direction, for example, are detergents. Halfway in the family of alkanes, the characteristic hydrocarbons in petroleum, is dodecane, a kerosene whose molecule is based on 12 carbon atoms. Down one side road it serves as a liquid fuel. Down another, the industry con-verts it or a related hydrocarbon into ABS, an aklyl benzene sulfonate that the Nazis invented as a soap substitute because they lacked natural fats, and which American housewives began buying eagerly after the war because it was so sudsy even in hard water. Then, of course, came trouble. Defying the bacteria that should break down the molecule, ABS bubbled right through sewage plants, put a head on tap water in the next town, went downriver to kill fish, and was excoriated in Congress. So Esso's labs switched to bacteriology—to gamma radiation, one of the ways expected to change ABS enough to make it quickly palatable for ordinary bacteria . . . *if* sewage is being treated adequately.

Meanwhile, in a direction that would sell neither gasoline nor soap, alkane chemistry was taking Esso out into Space and its Warren Meinschein into a fascinating argument. Previous research had led him to believe that some alkanes are products of ancient forms of life on earth. Now, with collaborators from Fordham, he had tested a speck of the famed Orgueil meteorite. Mass spectrometry showed that some of its molecules resembled hydrocarbons found in butter and other earthly products of known biological origin. Ergo, was this evidence of life forms out in Space? Or, skeptics retorted, were they molecules from something else, perhaps even contaminants that the meteorite gathered while flashing down through earth's atmosphere?

If meteorites offer the simplest proof of extraterrestrial life, however primitive, chemistry can bask in a bit of badly needed glamour. The coal tars had their heyday. Then the petrochemicals, and so on. Today, one plastic is just another plastic, one antibiotic just another antibiotic; and after aluminum's success story, even the panegyrists of Wall Street couldn't turn magnesium, titanium, and zirconium into truly "wonder" metals. But though its image has lost luster, chemistry is far from torpid. And to catalyze it, basic research offers challenge far beyond merely synthesizing a molecule that nature overlooked.

This challenge takes many forms and nowhere does it titillate curiosity more than within a new kind of chemistry that has no formal name yet. It is a chemical geometry that relates the structural shape of a molecule to its function.

Take something so basic as the sense of smell. The nose could write a history of chemistry. Sir Humphry Davy, for instance, was one of early chemistry's victims. He survived laboratory explosions only to pay for sniffing too much nitrous oxide—the same "laughing gas" that went on to supply antic fun for sniffing parties in the early 1800s, before dentists took it over as an anesthetic. Later came industry and the "stink chemistry" pillorized by Dr. Gottlieb in Sinclair Lewis's *Arrowsmith*. And science is now exploring a stereochemical version of the pronouncement by poet-philosopher Lucretius twenty centuries ago: "You cannot suppose that atoms of the same shape are entering our nostrils when stinking corpses are roasting as when the stage is freshly sprinkled with saffron of Cilicia." Some of today's chemists say that Lucretius's guess about different-shaped "pores" in the nose might be surprisingly accurate. From their experiments they have catalogued different primary odors and offer this explanation for the sensory talent of the nose: the "pores" are receptor cells of different shape, each accepting a volatile molecule of a specific configuration, then notifying the brain that it has arrived. So, by analogy, the cell becomes a socket that takes a plug of a certain shape. This has evolved into a theory based on perhaps seven primary odors. A molecule with roughly the shape of a disk registers as a musky odor. When it is altered chemically by adding atoms that give it a tail appendage, it registers as a floral odor, and so on. This would explain why a chemist can so easily change the odor of a compound. It also warns against taking an analogy too seriously. The same molecule that fits broadside into one receptor "socket" may fit end-on into another, and the brain registers the two primary odors as a complex one. Whether or not this will sell more perfumes or provide synthetic sex attractants in the war against insects, it does offer another clue toward solving the yawning mystery of the nervous system.

Here, of course, is a variation of the "site" chemistry that we have already met with other molecules. For instance, it is another version of the "lock and key" concept that pictures the enzyme as having a bosom that accommodates a "substrate" passenger molecule of the right kind; a lock that can be tampered with in the sense that an interloper molecule—a poison perhaps—can attach itself barnacle-like at this site.

This kind of research certainly goes beyond ordinary chemical cookery, which combines atoms to form molecules. It investigates phenomena for which even physical chemistry has lacked sufficient answers. The child interested in reality can no longer be brushed off when he asks: "What is dust?" "What is smoke?" "What is sticky?" "What is elastic?" Or, for that matter, why the shape of a snowflake, and, equally exquisite, the geometry of some viruses?

Such phenomena have not been explained well enough by surface tension, ionization, van der Waals forces, and the like. Reality takes complex forms and science now seeks simple explanations. These are possible with gases, whose molecules are relatively independent of each other, and to some extent with liquids, but solids are more troublesome. Our knowledge is too scanty about "surface chemistry," "texture chemistry," and other evidence that reality depends on the geometry of molecules and the force fields around them.

This opens avenues of basic research. Some have very practical possibilities. For example, why does a crystal grow? Presumably because the attracting forces among the atoms inside are balanced but atoms at the crystal surface are reaching out with forces that are unsatisfied. So metallurgy, heavily dependent upon metal crystals, hopes that research will learn how to grow a practical form of the crystals called "whiskers." Because these abnormally elongated crystals lack structural defects they theoretically offer strength far beyond that of crystals in the best superalloys.

Similarly, Department of Agriculture chemists work for better detergents, made of natural fat and therefore palatable to bacteria. Otherwise, the principle is that of the typical petroleum-based detergent. The molecule stands on end. The "acid" end buries itself in the water. The sudsy end is hydrophobic. Avoiding the water, it reaches out to gather dirt and greases. This, in turn, strongly resembles the project at Naval Research Laboratory to find the perfect lubricant—a long, thin molecule, "sticky" on one end so that it will adhere to a metal surface; "slippery" on the other and closely packed to form a solid layer of lubricant only one molecule thick.

In still another direction, of course, are the biochemists seeking the active sites on hormones and enzymes; and their associates who study the structure of DNA so that they can better locate the gene sites and understand the zipping and unzipping process with which the molecule performs its vital functions. But not all is the glamour of DNA and new drugs. Chemistry is also trying to understand other kinds of molecular geometry. At the University of Southern California, for example, Paul Saltman has been probing how iron and other vital metals are delivered to the bloodstream. The iron atom cannot cross the intestinal wall unless it is seized and carried through by a clawlike "chelating" compound. Somewhat similar are the clathrates; here guest atoms are caged in the lattice of a crystal.

Such is the variety of projects with which chemistry seeks to demonstrate that its successes have not stifled its curiosity. But it is significant that most of the basic research has been supported either by industry or by such other sciences as biology that need help from chemists. Faculty researchers at the universities have done little to brighten chemistry's image.

They have had their troubles, of course. Too many bright graduates have been attracted elsewhere: to nuclear physics, to molecular biology and similar glamour fields. "They find chemistry is still hard work," a department head sighed. "Maybe we can get some of them back with the electron microscope and nuclear magnetic resonance techniques. As it is, we badly lack postdoctoral students—that's why the country is importing so many from abroad."

Meanwhile, in contrast to industrial chemistry, the university men overlook their own lean record of accomplishment in past years and blame their troubles on Washington, which, they feel, has been too partial to their basic-research competitors in other fields. Comparing $500 million for Space in one year with $38 million for chemistry, they cry foul. Their favorite target is the NSF, patron of pure research. Like a runaway grand jury, the chemistry advisory panel to NSF prepared an "independent" report showing that NSF should have contributed $35 million in 1963 but gave only $9.5 million—far below the amount received by every other science, including astronomy and mathematics. The panel called this "an appalling state of affairs," "ruthless," and "callous insensitivity to needs." This was a bit shrill. It also came soon after xenon's embarrassing reminder that the academicians had not been performing their homework very well.

The Trouble with Dogma

There was no hint that xenon would cause so much commotion. Of the six so-called "rare gases" in our planet's atmosphere, this middleweight element is the rarest: only 1 part in 20 million. With the other five—argon, helium, neon, krypton, and radon—it was discovered in the 1890s and soon acquired a reputation for unsociability as well as scarcity. They refused to form chemical compounds. Science resigned itself to this inertness; occasionally found use for it. Because helium doesn't explode, it replaced dangerous hydrogen as a filler for dirigibles and balloons. Xenon eventually became one of the nonreactive fillers for electronic tubes.

Even in 1962, the year that made xenon famous, its behavior was not greeted with jubilation, except by foes of scientific dogma. This was the year when xenon exploded a myth, shook atomic theory, abruptly outdated the standard textbooks, made the arty ones look ridiculous, and, in general, displayed the dangers of firmly believing what is not necessarily so.

Academicians had been assuring three generations of students that xenon is totally inert, and for half that time had been explaining exactly why. Now, xenon was forming compounds practically at the beck of a finger. How could research have blundered so badly, so positively? And how, specifically, could chemistry, with its reputation for believing only the provable, have been so remiss? A quick answer: it was seduced by theory into neglecting work at the laboratory bench. This shifts the onus to physics, the main architect of atomic theory. But the indictment is too tightly drawn. It overlooks the distinction between seduction and rape. Seduction requires consent.

There is a simpler answer, no more complicated than the alert experiment, outside the mainstream of massive science, that exploded the inert-gas myth. This explanation doubts that science, materialistic or not, remains free of dogma. It was not free when science was youthful. It is less so today when science has grown too elephantine to move with agility, too busy with team effort and paperwork to experiment in the venturesome sense of the word.

At any rate, chemistry should have known better. It had received sound advice. Among its ancestral portraits is that of Robert Boyle, who did what his countryman Francis Bacon had only preached. Boyle experimented, and thereby produced his basic law of gases. But he could also preach. Scoffing at the cabalistic nonsense that passed for theory in his day, stressing the need to know the difference between a mixture and a compound, and between a compound and its elements, he set up guidelines for practical chemistry. In 1661, his demand for investigation appeared in a germinal book. He called it *The Sceptical Chymist.*

The word "chymist" changed harmlessly to "chemist." But did the skeptic's warning against dogma become dulled after three centuries? To be sure, chemistry acquired a reputation for keeping its feet on the ground when others soared into the dialectics of nature-

versus-nurture or wave-light versus corpuscular light. Chemistry found
the elements, classified them, combined them in multitudinous ways,
waxed great. And theorized about them too. But in their handling
of the inert gases, experiment and theory infected each other with
stagnation.

The trouble started with experiment. Argon, the first of these gases
discovered, did not react chemically. In itself, this oddity should
have been more challenging. Why wasn't it? Perhaps research chemists
were too busy elsewhere. And certainly, industry at the turn of the
century saw no need for argon compounds.

Meanwhile, something had to be done for chemistry's very useful
periodic table of the elements. It showed no vacancy for an element
of argon's atomic weight. To rescue the chart, theorists enlarged it
with an extra column and assigned argon to it. The position of this
column fitted the facts; any element in it would have a valence—a
combining power—of zero. Argon's valence obviously was zero. And
when, within a few years, the five other unreactive gases were discovered, the new column awaited them. Their atomic weights were
such as to place them neatly in vacancies above and below argon.
So the wisdom of creating the zero-valence column was confirmed and
all six occupants became known as the noble gases—"noble" in the
old, aloof sense of the word. They disdained chemical behavior. And
they were treated with suitable respect through the years when the
electron picture of the outer atom was being drawn and redrawn
to explain radiation and chemical action. At first, the electrons were
arrayed in various orbits around the nucleus, then in the Lewis-
Langmuir "shells," eventually in subshells and overlapping shells.
At first, the electron itself was a planet; eventually quantum mechanics inspired model-makers to think of a cloud—a smear of
the probable places where the same electron might be found.

This smeared the planetary analogy, but the image of the inviolable
noble gases remained inviolate. Each new theory had to account for
their lack of any chemical behavior. Accordingly, whatever the model
or the terminology, the idea remained essentially the one that I have
used before for simplicity. The electrons are arrayed in concentric
shells around the nucleus. Each shell can accommodate a specific
number of electrons. If the outermost shell is completely filled, the
atom is "stable." In most elements, this shell is not filled to capacity.

But a chemical reaction can fill it—atoms that need electrons combine with atoms that have them to spare.

Such was the theory that made science so positive about xenon and its companions. Each was chemically inert because the outer shell was already full—no electrons to spare, none wanted. It was the poker-player's pat hand. It was also what chemists called "closed-shell, closed-mind dogma." But that was not until many years passed.

Occasionally, to be sure, a chemist would try his hand with the noble gases. There was a minor flurry in the 1930s, for instance, after Linus Pauling of Caltech calculated that the noble gases could conceivably combine with the very active element fluorine. But experimenters who reported results were quickly refuted, some were ridiculed, and thereafter nobody in his right mind allowed the noble gases to divert him from the mainstreams of research.

Nobody, that is, until Neil Bartlett ran an experiment at the University of British Columbia in 1962. He had found that oxygen, normally greedy for electrons, lost them easily when combining with the very reactive gas platinum hexafluoride. This meant, of course, that the hexafluoride attracted electrons strongly. How strongly? Thanks to other plodding researchers, the energy needed to remove an electron—the "ionization potential"—was known for most elements. Consulting the list, Bartlett noticed that the ionization potential for an oxygen molecule and for xenon were almost the same. So he wondered. Could xenon's grip on an electron be overcome the same way, and would the xenon, now a positively charged ion, combine with the hexafluoride, now a negative ion?

But the oxygen experiment had been ridiculously simple: at room temperature, without elaborate paraphernalia. Could the impossible xenon be that easy? Bartlett tried. A glass diaphragm separated the two gases. When the diaphragm was broken, the colorless xenon and deep-red hexafluoride mixed, and promptly combined to give a yellow powder—the first genuine compound of a noble gas.

Bartlett's published report that he had made xenon hexafluoroplatinate brought other researchers rushing in. After confirming that he had not blundered, they pushed on. Soon they were making simpler compounds by heating xenon and fluorine. Soon, too, they were reporting compounds of radon and krypton. In April 1963, only ten months after Bartlett's report, came the first international conference on the new chemistry of noble gases. In an auditorium at the AEC's Argonne National Laboratory, scientists from thirty research centers gathered to discuss their progress.

Argonne, which has many programs and a $70-million annual operating budget, had become the big name in such research. Years earlier, it was the first to make platinum hexafluoride. This remained simply an afterproduct of nuclear-bomb research until Bartlett's galvanizing report. Argonne promptly wheeled its resources into a crash program and, two months later, reported it had made a second compound, xenon tetrafluoride. Thereafter it turned out one well-publicized report after another—one of them was signed by a team of seventeen authors. At first, Bartlett's discovery was given full credit: "The first true compound of xenon recently was reported by Bartlett." And such researchers as H. H. Hyman, Argonne's group leader in this field, punctiliously continued giving credit. Soon, however, a new image was forming; this may have been inevitable, but the image could have been redrawn with more finesse. Nor were Argonne's public-relations people entirely responsible.

For instance, two speeches by prominent members of chemistry's establishment: one by Paul M. Gross, retiring president of the AAAS; the other by AEC Chairman Seaborg. A few words were changed here and there, otherwise their two xenon stories were exactly alike and made the same propaganda. From the account by Seaborg, a Nobelist in chemistry:

". . . One of the best refutations of the chimera of bigness occurred in an AEC laboratory a little over a year ago. Under the Commission's education and research program, a young physicist from a small college came to carry on research for a time. He wanted to do something that leading scientists for nearly two-thirds of a century had believed impossible. . . . Doubts or not, the man had his chance. The result was a spectacular, unanticipated discovery in the field of chemistry. When a mixture of xenon and fluorine was heated . . . a deposit of white, colorless crystals of the compound xenon tetrafluoride was found, and the long-standing belief that rare gases are completely inert was shown to be a myth."

Here was a substitution of new mythology about the noble gases for the old. Oddly, though Bartlett didn't complain in print, the romantic "young scientist" did—but only because he had been cast as an eager beaver. Actually, he was a department head at Wheaton College, a consultant to Argonne, and a loyal member of its xenon team.

If history remembers to credit Canada's Bartlett, it may also record that the new myth was forming while science was excoriating the old. In England, the sound yet sprightly journal *New Scientist* headlined its article: "The Ignoble Gases: a Chemical Somersault." In the United States, the attack was more direct. From the editor of *Science*, physical chemist Philip H. Abelson: "For perhaps fifteen years, at least a million scientists all over the world have been blind. . . . All that was required to overthrow an entrenched dogma was a few hours of effort and a germ of skepticism."

That was a blow at the delinquency of experimenters. Others preferred to assail the theorists. A post-mortem by a university professor asked: "What have we learned from the Great Mistake?" and replied that chemistry had been victimized by quantum mechanics, whose theoreticians and computers have "produced not one firm prediction about even the simplest test-tube experiment." This was disputable. It was clear, however, that chemistry's creativity and good reputation had been injured by the delinquency of experimenters and theorists alike. But perhaps science would take this chemistry lesson to heart. Certainly the same mistake would not be repeated. That was all to be expected. In a neighboring field, dogma was already dictating the correct views about cancer, caries, cholesterol.

What other harm did neglect of the noble gases bring? It didn't cost industrial chemistry anything to speak of. Monsanto, Du Pont, Union Carbide, and the rest had gone on inventing and producing anyway, although now, naturally, industry pricked up its ears, as it does when it hears of any new tribe of chemicals. Several laboratory explosions at Argonne, for example, quickly showed possibilities in xenon trioxide. And the perxenates may become the most powerful of oxidizing agents.

It was education that took the serious drubbing. Teachers and their textbooks were left stranded with nonsense, and no newly certified truth to replace it. The best that academicians could offer now was a blurred idea about how already blurred electrons hook atoms together. There was the simple ionic-bond explanation, still sufficient for sodium chloride but not for xenon compounds; there was also the useful shared-electron concept, another tactic to leave both of two atoms with full outer shells. With sufficient imagination one could combine the two theories, and model-makers could then draw tortured pictures showing a molecule with ballooning electrons that make it look like a bunch of grapes.

The principle virtue of such explanations is that they are admittedly only stopgaps, consequently a warning to treat theory with reservations. This, too many of the newer textbooks had not done. Neglecting practical education, proclaiming that they had thrown away "the cookbook approach," joining the trend to favor graduate students, they ran riot with theory even in high-school texts, and tried to make it palatable with elegant drawings that turned science into an abstract art form. A Priestley Medalist worriedly foresaw the time when "the student who has never learned that one allotrope of phosphorus is red and the other white will nonetheless be able to describe the differences in atomic arrangement of the two." But the color difference is not trivial. It can be something so basic as the difference between striking an old-fashioned match and a safety match. Red phosphorus, used with the latter, is harmless. White phosphorus, in the former, is poisonous to the matchmakers and so combustible that, in pure form, it must be kept under water.

The attempt to force the abstract upon the ill-equipped or uninterested was not only overburdening the high-school chemistry course, it was penetrating physics and biology. And in a neighboring field, Max Beberman was disowning the extremism that engulfed the "new mathematics," which he had helped create. Blaming "charlatans who get a grant from the government," he found "teachers so frightened by the prospect of using esoteric mathematics that they have lost all common sense; and parents can't help the child at home because the symbolism is too forbidding." Mathematics, too, had become an art form.

In chemistry, the result was misty theory and bad art. And this practical science found itself the victim not only of old dogma about noble gases, but of new dogma in education. Like any dogma, this was originally a fresh new wind of change. Condemning authoritarianism and mere memorizing, it held that teaching should stimulate "self-discovery" by the students. When guided by a John Dewey, this made sense. Carried on by others, it entered a nonsense era of "science is essentially playful."

Science ignored the real Dewey when it began major curriculum reforms in 1956. The goal was reform in the high schools, specifically an attempt to bring text-writers of chemistry and physics together. But physicists and chemists couldn't cooperate, so the Physical Science Study Committee, led by physicist Jerrold Zacharias of MIT, focused on physics. With $5 million of NSF money it pioneered new teaching material and set up a "nonprofit" publishing company, which NSF later subsidized to move into college physics. The activities of PSSC stimulated chemistry, biology, and others to change their textbooks. By 1965, NSF had diverted over $65 million to such "course content improvement projects."

If Dewey was the inspiration for all this, he would have been astonished at the result. This pragmatist's revolt against abstract learning was entirely overlooked. Theory became rigid dogma. Ordinary students were lost. Only highly imaginative young minds reveled in a fairyland of geometry and atomic models that quantum physicists offered diffidently and teachers couldn't explain. I recall one chemistry textbook in the making. It had exhausted several writers and editors because it was impossible. The first twenty chapters, bristling with theory and imagined models of the atom, were the "core" of the book —whatever space remained would be a dump for "organic compounds, industrial applications, and such garbage." A year later, the noble-gas myth exploded.

Meanwhile, a White House advisory panel produced *Innovation and Experiment in Education*. This report didn't mention the noble gases. But one of its passages was remarkable because of two things: it touched on the need for more laymen to understand science; and the panel chairman was Zacharias, not noted for decrying his own accomplishments: ". . . A second deficiency lies in the fact that the programs attract the more talented students. The PSSC course, for example, appeals to those who cope best with the abstract. . . . Availability of a course which gave greater attention to the applications of physics might double the number of students who study physics and understand something of it when they leave school. It may well be that the time is ripe for attention to these considerations."

An amen came from those chemists who think both of the non-esoteric student joining their profession and of the student who simply needs an enlightening look into the world of chemistry around him.

The Water-Seekers

Air, food, water—these are very much in practical chemistry's province. Chemistry could clean our polluted air if a serious program received sufficient support. In America, at least, chemistry has been so bountiful that overeating has joined our list of problems. But what of water?

While chemical engineers were putting nuclear energy to peacetime work, they began developing another field of major importance for America and underdeveloped nations as well. It is called desalination. Though it has received nowhere near as much financial support as nuclear power, there is considerable kinship—economically, politically, even technically—between these two products of practical science.

. . . Economically, because neither nuclear power nor desalted water is a far-fetched hope any more. Neither stands entirely on its own feet, but the price gap has narrowed between them and rival ways to satisfy our soaring needs for electricity and water. In special cases, the gap has closed. The main difference is that nuclear power has been allowed some freedom to follow its own R & D pace; whereas the conversion of salt water to fresh has received orders to move at high speed. This is partly because water shortages, like such other chronic problems as transportation, were allowed to reach the crisis stage. So, to its embarrassment, desalination now finds itself a "crisis science."

. . . Politically, because private industry has preferred to let government pay for most of the research. Hence, as with nuclear power, desalting continually runs the risks of outright political interference as well as Washington's premature huzzas over "breakthroughs." As a result, the welter of interests and cacophony of voices send the R & D workers scurrying in different and often conflicting directions. Here, the difference is that Washington's laymen are restrained somewhat by their ignorance and downright awe of the atomic nucleus. Not so with desalted water. Though synthetic in a sense, it smacks of rainfall and what can be done with it politically. So, like reservoirs and irrigation projects, desalination inspires rolling out the congressional porkbarrel and the publicity drums.

. . . Technically, because the kinship is strong indeed. The two fields can be worked together; that is, a nuclear reactor can transfer its heat to boil the water out of salt water. But this is coincidence, albeit an important one. Desalination offers many other methods and combinations of methods; rivalry among them is healthy; they all help sweeten not only salt water but the reputation of science. For desalination need not be ambivalent like nuclear power; it is whole-heartedly for peace. Even in times of belligerence it is a noncombatant, although helpful. For instance, work done by one of the Interior Department's five demonstration plants, a $1.6-million evaporator type distilling over a million gallons of water daily. It started operation at San Diego in 1962 to test feasibility of the so-called "multi-flash stage" method, with its product helping supply the city's needs. Two years later came trouble for the United States naval base at Guantanamo Bay. Cuba's government had cut off its supply of fresh water. Since San Diego is another home base for Navy, it was simple enough to dismantle the equipment, ship it to Guantanamo, reinstall it, and start the still again.

There is another way in which desalting tones down the twentieth-century image of chemistry as a combatant. Thanks to its becoming a prosperous industry and potent profession, it seemed to be growing paunchy. Desalination gives it opportunity to play a youthful role again, and in character with its favorite traditions. Chemistry, which provided fertilizer and food, can again be a do-gooder of the practical kind. Man needs more fresh water, badly enough to get it from brackish supplies inland and, more dramatically, from the briny seas. Chemistry can make their water personally appetizing and in-dustrially useful.

Not that man has deep-seated loathing for the sea. Like his fellow mammal, the porpoise, he presumably originated in the sea, mother of all life. And he, too, likes to sport in the sea. Unlike the porpoise, however, he not only turned land-dweller but stayed that way. The food and frolic he found in the sea; the transportation and battle-fields it supplied—these were secondary to his landlubber life.

Chemically, too, he preferred what he could get on land, underground, and, in more recent times, from the air. His interest in seawater was incidental. For centuries, as an example, he augmented his supplies with "solar salt" made by bringing the briny water out to dry under the sun. When he tried scientific method, like adding dyes to the brine, that was to absorb more solar heat so the water would evaporate faster. Two other examples: in 1934, needing bromine for anti-knock gasolines, he began extracting it from seawater; and in 1941, his war needs for a light metal sent him to it again, now for magnesium. But all this was dabbling. It barely touched the 166 million tons of dissolved salts in a cubic mile of seawater, plus such other things as the gold in suspension; and it deliberately wasted the water.

Then came the second half of the twentieth century. With his tribe increasing, likewise his need for material comforts, modern man could no longer dismiss so blithely the treasures listed by scientists who go down in the sea. Most of the riches, of course, have had to go into inventory: hunger for food and chemicals has not yet driven us to farm and mine the oceans seriously; hunger for fusion power has not yet needed a crash program to harness their almost limitless deuterium. But the insufficiency of potable water, industrial water, irrigation water, becomes more acute yearly. Industry and agriculture complain lustily; so do housewife and gardener. True, chemistry can convert sewage to water better than the kind many of us now drink, unaware of the source; but our daintiness still demands "fresh" water. Where to find it?

Hindsight says that a big desalination program should have been one of the obvious answers. But man doesn't readily take quantum jumps. He prefers the gradual, plodding from emergency to emergency, trying to improve what he already has. Through the ages he has relied for fresh water on rainfall and increasingly complicated reservoir methods that first "nail the raindrop where it falls," then transport it where needed. This answer still has its defenders. Though our ignorance of earth science is such that nobody's figures mean much, the consensus at a National Academy conference was that clouds still form, still spill over, and the over-all supply of fresh water in the nation and world remains constant despite what we think when we pray for rain. But the problem becomes one of availability. As needs increase, and so does the pollution of streams and wells, we are driven farther and deeper for the rain moving down streams and through the soil. This increases cost. A congressional committee guesses that our needs would be met through the year 2000 by a $100-billion investment, plus an annual cost of several billion dollars. The money would finance a highly engineered system for storing, using, and reusing water from the nation's streams.

Then why not the other extreme, the alluring shortcut that provides rain where you want it? This is the method of the rainmaker, who "seeded" clouds at first with bits of dry ice (frozen carbon dioxide), then began injecting them with silver iodide. The art of rainmaking was high fashion in the early 1950s, was heavily supported by the United States Weather Bureau and Office of Naval Research, but quickly ran into stormy questions. Rain for whom? farmer or vacationist? Snow for whom? delighted skier or disgruntled trucker? The magnitude of such questions could grow. If clouds heading for one drought-stricken state were intercepted and dumped by an equally parched neighboring state, what would the governor of North Carolina then say to the governor of South Carolina? Not only did such squabbles arise but worriers looked ahead to a new cause for commotion among nations.

Soon enough, however, the specters banished themselves. Rainmaking, more sedately called weather modification, wasn't producing the claimed results. Nor did it succeed in the related field of flying aircraft to seed and "kill" hurricanes out at sea. So Project Stormfury lost its drama. The Weather Bureau found it easier to protect the public by finding and tracking hurricanes, from Abby through Winny, and concentrated on computer attempts to conquer the other great challenge—how to juggle a monstrous number of variables so that weather forecasts can be really accurate.

Now rainmaking certainly was not water-witching with a forked apple twig. Among scientists working on it were highly reputable ones. Why didn't it live up to expectations? The answer is familiar. It had been glamourized by writers, and meteorologists could not complain, because they oversold it. Now, some of them admitted how little they knew about how air moves in a cumulus cloud, much less about what electrifies a cloud and gives rain. And when they looked to physics for answers, they found none. A century ago,

Germany's great von Helmholtz had little doubt that he would add the thermodynamics of weather to his many trophies. But he found that it wasn't an equation or theory that could be tossed off in a year or two. Thereafter, physicists decided that weather was not in their field and sought something more rewarding.

I was discussing rainmaking with a foremost and certainly candid researcher. He was Bernard Vonnegut, a physical chemist whose work with smokes and fogs led to his joining Langmuir's rainmaking project at General Electric. Among other things, he developed the practical method of seeding clouds with silver iodide smoke. He later joined Arthur D. Little, Inc., the private research organization.

"One trouble has been meteorology's layer of dogma," he said. "Another is the grandiose claims. To say that we're on the threshold of killing hurricanes is preposterous. We're not even sure what a hurricane is, or a tornado. We stay with theories that became obsolete years ago. For instance, we now have evidence that rain forms a hundred times faster than theory said. And how does it form?"

He led me into his lab and opened his "cold box"—an ancient food freezer. "Now watch," he said. He breathed into the box. Then he shaved off a bit of dry ice and dropped it in. A cloudy multitude of ice crystals appeared in a flash.

"It always works," he said. "Provide the moisture, supercool it, seed it, and you get nucleation. But will a nucleated cloud rain? Maybe, maybe not. Certainly, nucleation gives ice crystals a chance to form. The theory is that they get bigger and when heavy enough they start falling. Falling, they melt. Thereby rain. But nature makes dandy rain regularly in Florida by a coalescing method, and she probably has several other ways. We've wasted time and millions of dollars asking the silly question: 'Does it make rain?' We should have asked: 'What does seeding really do—and how do clouds work naturally?' Those are the barriers facing us, and the weather forecasters as well."

On into the 1960s, Navy and the Weather Bureau continued seeding. But the excitement had departed, and eventually it was mainly NSF's chore to supply enthusiasm and funds for keeping the hope alive. However, the disappointment had accomplished one thing. It called attention to desalinators. At first, these were considered an answer only for special situations. Armies had used them for emergencies. There was already a scattering of peacetime ones throughout the world. None of these were very large or efficient. But they worked. Why not develop practical ones?

Congress had already put a tentative foot into this water. In 1952, it authorized $2 million for five years of R & D. Three years later, when rainmaking turned cloudy, Congress raised the fund to $10 million, to buy a breakthrough to cheap fresh water by 1963. By 1963, desalination had become crisis science and $75 million was added for a more massive effort. To do the job, Congress had created an Office of Saline Water and housed it in the Department of Interior, traditionally the chief custodian of the nation's natural resources and a busy builder of power dams and irrigation systems.

From the start, not surprisingly, there was trouble between layman and scientist. Congress repeatedly berated the desalters for dawdling: "The program cannot be allowed to drift without producing concrete results." The OSW fired back that it could not escape the need to do basic research first; that it just didn't know enough about the chemistry of water, rainy or otherwise. This was true; science had neglected something so prosaic. Eventually, OSW sponsored a report that warned against impetuosity ("Present processes do not supply the ultimate answer") and recommended "basic studies on the structure of water, aqueous solutions, ice and hydrates; on both living and synthetic membranes and the mechanism of transport of ions and water through them." The outcome was a somewhat one-sided compromise. The OSW proceeded with basic research. Meanwhile, accepting a special $10 million to start a separate budget, it built five prototype plants that Congress urged for a preview of desalination. Each of the five tried a different process and, though experimental, demonstrated that large-scale desalting could live up to hopes.

Dozens of other methods have been proposed or tried, in the United States and elsewhere. For example, OSW's list runs all the way from modern versions of the "solar still," in which the sun's energy evaporates water away from the salt, to the newest ideas for freezing seawater in a way that then allows separating the ice crystals cheaply from the salt and mother brine. In general, however, there are two main competitive types, each with many variations.

1—Ion Exchange

Its older versions grew out of the ordinary water-softener. The saline water filters through a bed of material that substitutes unobjectionable ions for those of the sodium chloride. The method works well—in emergency kits for liferafts, in the Sahara, for desalting brackish well water—but it needs more research to qualify it for big jobs. More important are the versions that use membranes to remove the salt. Postwar plastics made such membranes practical. Here, of course, the physical chemist faces mysteries similar to those confronting the biochemist, who is concerned with membranes and salt movements in the living body. In one OSW project, scientists at the University of Florida explored hundreds of chemical combinations before they developed a special membrane of cellulose acetate that allowed the escape of fresh water when a saline solution was put under pressure. In other words, the membrane is a sieve permeable to water but not salt. This escape is unlike ordinary osmosis, which merely moves water from the less salty side through to the more salty side of a membrane until salinity on both sides is equal. Hence the name "reverse osmosis" for this squeezing technique.

Meanwhile, a rival membrane method was developing. Called electrodialysis, it requires energy in the form of electric current rather than pressure. An OSW plant has demonstrated this method by converting 250,000 gallons of brackish water daily. Together with reverse osmosis, it is a leading candidate for converting such inland waters, but not so promising for saltier seawater.

2—Distillation

For seawater, and therefore the nation's populous coastal regions, the big hope is in the other main family of desalinators, the evaporators. These offspring of the old liquor-still evaporate the desired product away from its undesirable companions, then condense it back to liquid. This, of course, means wrenching water molecules out of the liquid into the gaseous state. To do it efficiently involves complicated thermodynamics, and on a large scale it requires considerable energy. Not surprisingly, then, the choice of heating method is important. It can easily account for much of the processing cost.

This is why the chemical engineer works with a sharp pencil. At Kuwait, on the Persian Gulf, the cost of fresh water badly needed by the oil companies there is reduced simply enough. They use their own cheap petroleum to convert seawater. But that is a special case. More typical of R & D ingenuity is the prototype built at San Diego and later transferred to Guantanamo. The OSW here tested feasibility of the "multistage flash" method. Distillation begins in a chamber where pressure is kept just below boiling point of the previously heated seawater. Part of this arriving brine immediately flashes—boils—into steam that goes to a cooling condenser and turns into distilled water. Remaining brine passes on through a total of thirty-six such stages, each at lower pressure to give another batch of steam. In the condensers the coolant is merely seawater. It starts out entirely cool but its temperature rises, thanks to heat surrendered by the condensing steam. By the time this preheated brine is itself ready to start through the flash stages it is almost boiling. It needs only 10 per cent more heat, supplied by a fuel-oil burner. Nevertheless, the oil bill accounted for a fourth of the desalination cost and, as expected, there were many technical problems. The expensive nuisance of scale deposits in the equipment is a drawback to any boiling method. To combat this, protective sulfuric acid accompanied the incoming seawater. Such other problems as severe corrosion had to await further research. In general, however, the plant gave eighteen months of technically rewarding service while adding its sizable trickle of fresh water to San Diego's supply system.

In all this, the situation contrasts with that in rainmaking, which would have been delighted with one commercial method. Desalination is already a fact and there is almost a surfeit of candidates for better ways to do the job. The distillation types have advanced farther technically for large-scale production, but only testing and competition will eventually decide the winners.

No gift of prophecy is needed, however, to see that the main deciding factor will be cost of the freshened water. As with nuclear power, the figures are shaky but give clues. In 1952, when the technology was young, the cost was estimated at $5 per 1000 gallons.

Ten years later, OSW calculated that a commercial version of its San Diego demonstrator would give water for $1.16. This would be a bargain for the California town that was paying $7 for potable water brought in by tank car, but was still discouragingly high for large cities.

How to bring costs down? A quick way is with a chart showing that conventional fresh water costs more every year, that desalinated water is getting cheaper, and the costs will meet around the year 1970. But this requires another chart indicating how the cost of de-salted water will be lowered. For instance, where natural gas is a cheap fuel and the plant is large enough—25 times bigger than the San Diego one—it might produce city water for 30 cents, competitive with other sources. There is also the lure of byproducts. Extracting the various chemicals in seawater would not only remove the cause of scale and similar evaporator troubles but give salable items like fertilizer and magnesium as well as ordinary salt.

In all predictions, however, it is electricity that now looms largest as a byproduct. Or, reversing the picture, desalted water could be the profitable byproduct of a mammoth, dual-purpose electric power plant. Either way, chemical engineer and power engineer would be working together, and each product would financially support the other. This explains the surging interest in combining nuclear power with desalination. Obviously, the method could be used with other fuels, but it is especially appealing as a spur to the nuclear-power program. In a favored concept the nuclear heat would conventionally turn ordinary water into high-energy steam for the turbogenerators. The difference is that all or part of this steam would then go on and heat the seawater evaporator. Ideally, of course, one should dispense with ordinary water as the intermediary and have the reactor produce steam directly from seawater. Then, after going through the generators, this steam would condense into fresh water. But this would introduce an assortment of highly difficult engineering problems.

The dual-purpose idea was urged as far back as 1955 by Senator Clinton Anderson of the Joint Committee on Atomic Energy. He foresaw this as a way to produce electricity for as low as 2 mills per kilowatt-hour and water for 15 cents per 1000 gallons. Hence, each product could easily compete with rivals. Since then, technology has advanced far enough in both fields to allow taking such ideas seriously. For example, a White House study group urged dual-purpose plants of a size able to supply enough water and electricity for a large city. It did remember to mention that other desalination methods might make the dual plants unnecessary, but its emphasis on the latter led President Johnson to promise more R & D money and call for a breakthrough, by 1969, that would lead to still bigger dual plants in the future.

A profusion of new R & D projects resulted and California, for one, looked ahead to a happy end for its water problems. But it was cautious, too, and joined the equally cautious AEC in a joint project of another kind. The AEC wanted a big power plant for demonstrating an advanced reactor of the Rickover "seed-and-blanket" type, and fueled with thorium plus uranium: not a true breeder but with semi-breeder capabilities. For its part, southern California wanted more of the water it is accustomed to—from the mountains. So California agreed to put up $80 million for the prototype, with AEC furnishing the rest. The plant might be tied in with a desalination experiment. But the main product would be 525,000 kilowatts. This power would run the large pumps of the State Water Project, pumps large enough to lift 100 million gallons of water per hour over the Tehachapi Mountains. This would please everybody but champions of desalination. California would get a sizable gush of water. The AEC would be trying out its new reactor while demonstrating that nuclear power could man the pumps.

This was one more indication that the future of desalination will not depend entirely on its technological merits. In this branch of science, practical politics will definitely have its say.

XV: *Out of This World*

From earthly chemistry to our space program is more than a leap into another dimension. It brings us to oddly assorted motives. One of them is militarily practical, America's drive to become the strongest spacefaring nation. Another is as visionary as sheer escapism—an interest in far-off places and the far-distant future that might just possibly make us forget the problems of our own place and time.

Between those extremes is the probe for evidence of extraterrestrial life. It claims to be purely scientific but cannot escape the purely personal. Science long ago lost its awe for the other heavenly bodies. It concedes that they are mysterious, and many are perhaps inscrutable, but it insists that they operate within some kind of universal system. And occupying his place in this system is man, ruler of a very ordinary planet swinging around a second-class sun.

As recently as two decades ago, this restless, brainy vertebrate could not think seriously of space voyaging. Today, after thousands of centuries, the time has ripened. He need no longer project only from what he can learn by peering upward. And from his calculations that there may be as many as a few hundred million planets in our galaxy, his common sense then doubts that only one—our planet, earth— would have bred intelligent life. This fascinates him. He realizes that he is not quite noble, but what about other peoples? He wants to know if, like his sun, he is a second-rater. And if so, what can he gain from the others? He realizes that he must proceed slowly. His engineering is such that the most he can expect in this century is to investigate suitable planets of his own solar system. He realizes, too, the odds against his finding on these planets any superiors, or peers, or even creatures that have evolved as far as he. But this is exploration. Even primitive plant or bacterial life will be evidence that he has counterparts elsewhere; that he has not been elevated—or condemned—to be alone in the ocean of Space.

Of course, this too has its element of escapism. But there is an inexorability that applies to all aspects of the space program. Just as the time became scientifically ripe to investigate the atomic nucleus, and soon afterward to investigate the molecule of heredity, the time has come to break the bonds of planet earth—the most daring of man's attempts to manipulate his environment. And being ever hopeful, he counts on this somehow improving his future. For proof, he produces what he has learned from paleontology, archeology, zoology, ecology, and other sciences that try to explain the ascent of man. They agree that, for one reason or another, in one fashion or another, nature demands change. They give it such names as evolution and progress. Whatever its name, and whether or not it has "purpose," we do know of the creatures that were outstripped by man and eventually became his prey—or his pets. This applies also to the waxing and waning of civilizations and nations. The virility of one generation may become the decadence of the next, but then a new robust horde hammers at the gates, and in Shelley's lone and level desert, boundless and bare, among the ruins of a colossal statue, a pedestal again proclaims proudly, "My name is Ozymandias, king of kings; look on my works, ye Mighty, and despair."

The only worthwhile debate, as we shall see, is over how to change. Increasingly, wisely or not, society turns the responsibility over to science. But there are many sciences, and the spectacular exploration of Space now makes all other research humdrum by comparison. To the realism of military science and of "pure science," it adds a dimension so free of customary bonds that, at first glance, it seems only for irresponsible utopians. Little wonder, then, that the space program has many and vociferous critics. The military aspect is accepted as necessity. The scientific part done with instruments is accepted too. But why the most expensive and inevitably hazardous part? Why this craving to be a Buck Rogers?

The answer is apparently in man's heritage. He can take no credit for what he is; evolution, working blindly or not, elevated him. But not beyond the inexorable. Driven by his acquired thrust of curiosity and thirst for knowledge, he cannot be satisfied. He may not soon find better worlds and, mayhap, learn from better peoples, but he expects to understand better whence he came and where he may be going. Without this goal the nonmilitary part of the space program would make no sense whatever.

It is unconvincing to picture the conventional treasures awaiting spacefarers; to dream this time not of the spices of the Indies or the gold of the Aztecs but of capturing the asteroid Ivar, with its possibly $30 trillion worth of platinum. Today's economists know that so much platinum would break the market. To them, the space program is a timely cushion against depression; it keeps our aerospace industry alive and prospering. Minerals or real estate on the moon are considered less important than the slice that California already has of the moon; the billions she receives from Project Apollo. But this, too, is strange arithmetic. We could prime our economic pumps as effectively by spending the same billions on the vast construction projects needed closer home. Nor need this be only the building of dams and new cities.

Our population figure is soaring. We demand more necessities, and new ones as well. For the year 1970 or so, our R & D timetable calls for genuine breakthroughs in nuclear power and desalination, in mass transit and 2000-mile-per-hour supersonic planes, in cancer cures and new hearts for faltering ones, and so on through an overwhelming list. Consequently, though the space program may not be the "moon madness" or "Simple Simon" adventure that critics call it, we do seem to have an acute case of imbalance when the same timetable includes such other-worldly, multibillion-dollar items as our first manned landing on the moon and first hunt for life on Mars. Already NASA, the civilian space agency, spends one-third of the research billions taken from taxpayers. To that add the space activities of our Defense Department, AEC, and others; the figure becomes almost half of Washington's R & D budget.

Meanwhile, budget-minded or not, the general public has doubts about all this. There is an undercurrent of "Is this next trip necessary?" Reacting to its Sputnik terror, the public demanded that Washington "do something." But that emergency passed; Space has become a blurred procession of Saturns and Centaurs, Rangers and Mariners.

The first American to land on the moon will be applauded, but the play lacks a pat final act. A population explosion is not yet pushing us off earth. Our planet and its sun may be doomed to cool and die, but nobody worries seriously about that timetable. Shall we build an empire in Space? We now associate colonies with bad-mannered peoples who agitate for independence. And we cannot overlook a new type of isolationism. Anthropologist Margaret Mead finds that "women want men to stay at home now probably more than at any other period in history." In London, theatergoers cheer the American comedian who says he has just returned from the moon, where he was greeted by the sign, "Go home, Yank." And in faraway *Pravda* a Russian writes: "Damn the moon and serve up better food."

Nor can the space explorers look to the world of science for united support. This arises from the rivalry for slices of the government's R & D pie. The announcement that NASA would race Russia to the moon merely formalized the split and gave opponents their argument that a spectacular staged by dolts was supplanting genuine science. Two years later, a random survey of two thousand scientists showed only 7 per cent approving the richness of NASA's budget, only 10 per cent agreeing that men-on-the-moon would produce new knowledge. Asked when the lunar landing should be made, 7 per cent bitterly replied "Never." Their only solace could be that the moon race had already fallen thirty-four months behind schedule.

Perhaps NASA is more to be pitied than blamed. It was unhealthily born, a child of the Sputnik fright. There was no carefully prepared mandate as for the nuclear program, and unlike the AEC it has not had a vigorous Joint Committee to protect it, and chastise it when necessary. Led by such congressmen as Minnesota's Joseph Karth, the House space committee eventually began asserting itself; the Senate space committee left matters to Senator Lyndon Johnson, who was succeeded to the chairmanship by his ally, Robert Kerr. So NASA's formative years were in the nature of a frantic counterthrust at Russia, combined with politics as usual. As a result, its technical programs stumbled. But yet it grew. And with money and power, it acquired the reputation of being an upstart among Washington's bureaucracies. Later, it strove to make more friends among laymen, among scientists and, through them, among members of Congress. Even this drew fire. For example, NASA agreed to give Columbia University's Graduate School of Journalism a $400,000 grant to study how NASA news was influencing the public. That was a gauche way to spend space money. It was also futility because NASA cannot be given a single image. For example:

... Though created as a civilian agency it swiftly grew para-military: the so-called "fourth arm of the Pentagon." This could hardly be otherwise. Satellites are potential bombing platforms. Meanwhile, they serve as splendid spies. "We're not going to the moon just to see its other side," a biochemist jeered.

... Though the moon-race announcement was eventually muffled, Project Apollo has been devouring three-fifths of NASA's $5-billion budgets. This infuriates those space researchers who want more money for such scientific spaceships as OSO, OAO, POGO, PAGEOS and, of course, for investigation of Mars—in accordance with NASA's stated objective, an orderly expansion of our knowledge about the atmosphere and Space.

... Though the name is National Aeronautics and Space Administration, grieving voices point out that the "aeronautics" part receives only 1 per cent of NASA's budget. They ask how this will develop supersonic transport planes or, at the other extreme, provide commercial aviation with the VTOL aircraft to meet Thomas Edison's prescription: "The aeroplane won't amount to a damn until they get a machine that will go straight up, go forward, go backward, come straight down and hover like a hummingbird."

In short, NASA becomes an example of overblown science and disheveled government wrapped into a chaotic package. But there is something else, though it requires the long view. The drive into Space, however it is directed and extravagant as it may become, is powerful enough to be inevitable. And if it succeeds even moderately well, the untidy details may become a footnote in spacefaring history, much as we now overlook the imperfections of Columbus, Magellan, Sir Walter Raleigh, and the underwriters of their seafaring voyages.

True, this time we are opening lanes through another kind of ocean. Physics warns not only of meteoroids but of the kind of weather the astronauts will face: the solar flares that send tongues of plasma twisting through interplanetary space; the cosmic-ray particles racing through our galaxy. But man has learned how to navigate new oceans before. And this time his hopes and his science can turn to engineers who have already done surprisingly well, considering the circumstances. Without their skill and imagination, there could be no exploration, either by the scientists' instrument-packed craft or by the vehicles that carry astronauts.

Consider a Mariner setting out for an unmanned fly-by past Mars. Each element of the mission requires finesse. The trajectory engineer, for instance, must plan a long, curving path that will bring the spaceship to Mars over 7 months and 300 million miles later. This means midcourse adjustments to correct for our guesswork about planetary distances and true velocity of the launching platform, which is earth; for the effect of solar-wind pressure and the gravitational tug from many directions—sun, earth, Mars, Mercury, Venus, Jupiter. Throughout, the solar cells must soak in solar radiation and convert it into electricity that will send the instrument reports back to earth. This means the craft must never be too far from the sun; and, on arrival, neither Mars nor its two moons should block off sight of the sun. Nor can they be allowed to come between the craft and its stabilizing guide, the star Canopus. The actual encounter with Mars must occur during the viewing period from a NASA tracking station in California's Mojave Desert. All this, and much else until the finale. The ship must not crash into Mars, contaminating it with our microorganisms, but cruise on and lose itself in an orbit around the sun. Throughout, no human hand has been aboard. The command given such an automated ship is more in the nature of a request.

That is one type of space engineering. Another deals more robustly with the new environment. It designs the great rockets and invents the fuels that tear them and their payloads, whether instrument packages or men, free from earth's atmosphere and gravitational clutch. Its biggest project, of course, has been Apollo, an extension of what we are already doing with nuclear-tipped missiles. This, then, is a burly business. It stems from aviation's pioneering, from the building of canals, railroads, power dams. It has a link, too, with the arctic explorers; with the men who conquered Mount Everest; with Auguste Piccard, first to soar into the stratosphere and first to search in the ocean depths. Because it deals with humans it is always survival-conscious. It experiments with a structure made of pressed cereals, which the moon visitor can use as either a shelter or emergency food. It busily investigates ways to boil water out of lunar rock, and from that, to get oxygen from the water molecules.

Already, it has supplied NASA with an argument against charges that it wastes money adventuring. Some byproducts it claims from the space program are trivial; for example, its expectation that the deodorants industry will be vitalized by the sweat pads developed for astronauts. More important is a long list of other things: better pumps, lubricants, ceramics, batteries, cameras, welding techniques, and the like. And these will be eclipsed if Space reveals what we have not yet learned on earth: how we are affected by radiation and what to do about it. The moon, nakedly unprotected against cosmic rays and other relentless bombardment, will teach us much.

Also, there will undoubtedly be colonies on the moon but not quite motels or ranch homes. Rather, these will be outposts taking advantage of conditions so inhospitable that few expect to find even the simplest forms of life. For instance, astronomers can man telescopes away from earth's interfering atmosphere and city lights. And the moon's low gravity can make it an ideal staging point for the odysseys ahead.

Barring terrestrial wars, the schedule calls for our lunar landing by 1970. This cannot be a fixed date. Even simpler programs have forced NASA to use what William Hines of the *Washington Star* calls "the rolling deadline and retroactive forecast." But of this we can be certain. It is axiomatic that there will be surprises, even on what we deprecate as our fossil moon.

The Spaceships

When Jules Verne wrote *From the Earth to the Moon* a century ago he was unusually prescient. He fired his spaceship from Florida. The French writer also showed himself to be alert, because propulsion came from the newly invented explosive called nitrocellulose. But the launching platform, sad to relate, was not very clever. It was merely a cannon 900 feet long.

Long before another century passes and, with it, the goal of merely reaching the moon, the brute rockets now rising from Florida will seem equally quaint, assuming that we fulfill Verne's faith in us: "The

Yankees are the world's foremost engineers, just as Italians are musicians and Germans are metaphysicians—by right of birth."

Verne looked ahead. So do we. In this matter of reaching the space places we talk about, it is too much, of course, to imagine exactly how imaginative our R & D will be in its search for better ways to propel a spaceship. That would require imagination to the second power. But although we can only project from what we see now, let us first take three glimpses very far ahead to provide perspective. They also show how unfettered our R & D must be if it is to overtake possibilities discussed by some of the bolder physicists.

1—Solar Power

If Space is the new ocean, then why not sailing ships? It is easy but erroneous to think that they have arrived. This is because strange-winged craft are already at work, and at important laboratories one can see newer ones being designed. The wing span of Pegasus, for example, is 96 feet. But this is not for sailing. It is a deliberately oversize target for meteoroids. Such wings complain electronically how badly they are being hit. Their reports have considerably reduced the fears of danger and raised hopes that equipping the manned spaceship with a "bumper" of some kind will protect it against punctures. More typical, however, are the unmanned craft that look like Dutch windmills, or dragonfly OGO (orbiting geophysical observatory). Their wings are simply panels glistening with solar cells that receive energy from the sun and convert it for the craft's electrical needs. Again, this is not propulsion by sunlight, but indirectly it shows the possibility. The fact is that photons of sunlight do exert pressure, much as a wind does. It is weak but not negligible. And like the auxiliary-powered sailing vessel that is first taken out of a harbor by its engine, and then proceeds under sail, the manned spaceship would be propelled by a rocket beyond interference from earth's atmosphere and gravity, and then be pushed on by a gentle wind of photons. Unlike the craft limited to orbiting, it could go anywhere in the solar system. It could use gravitational pull from various planets to "sail with the tide." Or, the steady push against negligible resistance might eventually accelerate the craft to an enormous velocity. A way to focus the sunlight would be better, but even without that, sunlight could be sufficient. Los Alamos Laboratory, for instance, speculates on a photon-propelled craft, shaped like a thin disk a quarter-mile wide, that would easily sail itself to Mars and back.

2—Antimatter

At the other extreme is the passenger spacecraft powered by a super-engine. The ultimate has already been indicated by this credo of the atom-smashing physicist: "For every object made of ordinary matter, a corresponding object of antimatter can exist. Elsewhere in the universe there may be entire galaxies composed of antimatter." The idea, originating in quantum physics, is supported by researchers who have found antiparticles that are "mirror images" of ordinary fundamental particles. The electron's counterpart, for example, is the positron—same mass and amount of electrical charge, but with this outstanding difference: the positron's charge is positive, not negative. The practical significance is this. There is evidence that when two opposite particles meet, they may vanish instantly, becoming energy. So, by extension, contact between a world of matter and one made of antimatter could annihilate both of them, with mass converted to energy. Be that as it may, this we know. Experimental physicists are making antiparticles. Why not, then, the super of all explosives—or rocket fuels? Theoretically, an engine powered by mixing matter and antimatter would send humans to other solar systems and do it with almost the speed of light. Of course, technical difficulties would have to be solved. How, for example, to shield our earth from the takeoff blast of that monstrous radiation?

3—Gravity Neutralizer

But need we use a stupendous fuel, particularly if the reach of imagination is brought down to voyaging among our neighbor planets? Here enters the intriguing possibility of canceling the force of gravity. This variation on a theme by Einstein is still too dreamy for most scientists, but a few dare share the idea of science fiction that we may some day neutralize the force that pulls us down to earth and makes today's space flight so ridiculously cumbersome. They say that the scoffing merely points up how primitive still is our knowledge of Space and earth alike. At any rate, the hope to insulate against gravity, or neutralize it some other efficient way, will not be crushed. Without this pull toward the center of the earth, we would not need to go on spending billions to launch brute-force rockets and planning even sturdier weightlifters of 20 million, 30 million, 50 million pounds' thrust. The spaceship could rise, as envisioned by Cyrano de Bergerac, like the morning dew. It could rise from earth. It could rise equally well from Mars, whose gravity is only a tenth of ours, or from great Jupiter, whose gravity is two and a half times ours. And the reverse would be as easy. "Coming down," the astronaut would work his throttle to allow enough gravitational pull for a soft landing.

It is understandable that NASA, forced by its need to produce quick, tangible results, is content that the force of gravity keeps earth orbiting around the sun and manmade satellites orbiting around earth. It also uses gravity for special jobs such as keeping a satellite correctly aligned with respect to earth. Otherwise, it considers the need to cooperate with gravity a nuisance. It worries constantly over how much weightlessness an astronaut can endure and, consequently, whether and how to create artificial gravity inside the spaceship. This may require tricky engineering but the problem is not insuperable. Many space labs already whirl humans with centrifuges, an object being to learn how much gravitational acceleration they can endure. Centrifugation inside the spaceship could generate the amount their well-being will need.

Meanwhile, the people of purer research have done as little as NASA's engineers about an antigravity device of some kind, and with less justification. They still say "Newton says . . ." The seventeenth-century theorist said truly but not sufficiently. Since then, factual science has moved on. Despite Thomas Jefferson, rocks have indeed fallen from the sky, and one meteorite actually struck a woman. Since then, though theoretically the bumblebee cannot fly, it has gone on flying. It may even be, in line with Einstein's fertile general theory of relativity, that the law of gravitation is the law of laws, governing electrons in their orbits around the nucleus as well as planets around their sun. Researchers have touched on gravity indirectly. For example, tiny experimental rotors have been spun at accelerations corresponding to a billion times that produced by earth's gravity. But science has grown timid about gravity itself. In attempts to classify

466 | SCIENCE: U.S.A.

nature's forces it lists "strong" ones in the atomic nucleus; a hundred times weaker are the electromagnetic forces; and so down to gravity, much the weakest and dismissed as too difficult to investigate thoroughly. Yet in large aggregates of matter, it does show its strength. It holds earth together. It also keeps the planets on course. Its pull toward the center is credited with firing the fusion of our sun and other stars, as well as explaining the astrophysicists' newly discovered delight, the big-bang explosion with which a quasar —whatever it is, galaxy or star—collapses cataclysmically under gravitational forces. But this is cosmology, which is highly theoretical. The earthier scientist confesses frustration because he does not know what gravitation is and cannot measure the gravitational attraction between atom and atom, or even between two of Newton's apples. The result is fantastic to the point of absurdity. Science leaves the idea of gravity control of some kind to the science fiction of an H. G. Wells or Hugo Gernsback; or to bizarre Roger W. Babson, the patriarchal business counselor, writer on religions, and onetime Prohibition Party candidate for President. Also, he was graduated from MIT in 1898, and there he heard professors doubt that a heavier-than-air machine would ever fly. Accordingly, his Gravity Research Foundation sponsors an annual conference where imaginative scientists may discuss their heresies. Organized science in the meantime goes on associating a gravity shield with such other oddities as perpetual motion, a scoffing that is itself odd because in superconductivity we already have a version of perpetual motion. Anyway, we do know that gravity exists—it makes us fall with every step that our legs take. Very well, we insulate against light, electricity, and magnetism; why not, then, against gravity? Now the spaceship would be practically weightless. Consequently, it would need only modest power to wrench itself free from earth's pull, and to send it from planet to planet. Today's brute booster rockets would become extinct.

Such is a sampling of far-out possibilities—how far, nobody knows. What of serious plans to make today's rockets extinct? There are many. How soon they bear fruit depends, as we have seen elsewhere, on how well R & D and Washington politics learn to walk together rather than on each other's toes. There is general agreement, however, about two things:

of a large satellite. Larger versions would use turbines and gene... enough current to propel a manned spaceship. Here, unlike Rov... method, the thrust would come not from hot hydrogen but indirec... from the electricity. In the ion version, for example, electromagne... fields accelerate charged particles to enormous speeds. Because t... thrust is small, such a rocket would need a boost. But then, pa... interference from our atmosphere and gravity, it would be an ide... bus for interplanetary travel as it goes on building up velocity... theoretically to hundreds of thousands of miles per hour. But, as wit... other exotic methods, the claims have far outstripped the development... "Right now," an advanced-propulsion physicist told me, "we're... trying to find out who is lying."

Meanwhile, the AEC's engineers have been working on various... nuclear ideas so they can be better prepared for one of Washington's... crisis demands. They have even supplied a shopping list—fifteen years... of R & D that would cost a billion dollars and include a SNAP whose... power would run into megawatts. But this could only be a hope:

. . . AEC had developed SNAP 10-A but could not get permission... to test-fly it. The Pentagon and the President's science adviser now... doubted that it was needed. Only rescue by the Joint Committee kept... the project alive, and eventually SNAP 10-A became history's first... reactor, albeit a small one, launched into Space. Meanwhile, the... Pentagon had dropped its option on SNAP 2; NASA was now merely... polite about SNAP 8, and so on. Here again, Washington was re-... quiring a "firm mission." This was partly punishing R & D for being... too profligate with dreams and money. Like any extreme, it was... also risky. There had been no firm mission for the transistor, the laser,... the airplane, and, centuries ago, the wheel. Nor was this cutting... budgets. The AEC went on pouring $100 million annually into the... vacuum of guesses about the future of SNAPs.

. . . The fate of something more terrestrial—ANP, the nuclear-... powered airplane—was more merciful. It was finally killed outright.... Here, AEC's involvement was with Air Force. General Electric got the... main contract for the propulsion system; Convair got the biggest... contract for the rest. GE estimated that $188 million and five years... would deliver the engine, ready for mounting in the plane. Ten years... later, GE's bill had reached $500 million and there was no engine

The lunar landing can be only the first, probing step. Even D. Brainerd Holmes, NASA's ardent organizer of the Apollo race to beat Russia, conceded "this program makes sense only if we go on from there." And Russia apparently feels likewise.

The rockets now blasting off, though spectacular, can only be a first step. Apollo's Saturn V, for example, is a multimillion-dollar version of a disposable paper napkin. Each stage soon runs out of its chemical fuel and is jettisoned. Such rockets would be especially inadequate for deep-space missions, even if built still larger and burning the better chemical fuels that are now being developed. They need too much fuel for too little payload.

Hence the work on new ideas. At least three types of efficient electric propulsion are under serious development. Then there is the strictly nuclear method. And here, as with power plants and desalination plants, the competing variations are many. In over-all terms of present R & D progress, however, the outstanding candidate for the moon and beyond is Rover.

This idea puts a shielded nuclear reactor into the rocket, as Admiral Rickover did in his submarine. Similarity ends there. Instead of providing steam for propellers, the heat from Rover's reactor is transformed into a direct push. This thrust is the same action-produces-a-reaction with which conventional rockets propel themselves by burning fuel and blasting the combustion gases out through one or more nozzles at the back—in other words, the principle of the commercial jetliner. But in Rover the thrust comes very differently. To be sure, it carries liquid hydrogen, which is a superb chemical fuel. But here the hydrogen is not for burning. Instead, it picks up heat while passing through tubes in the reactor. This builds up its pressure and it blasts out through the nozzle. Hydrogen is preferred because, of all elements, its molecular weight is the lowest. This directly affects its "specific impulse," which is a measure of efficiency—the amount of thrust that a pound of propellant gives in a second. Depending on the kind of reactor, the impulse from hydrogen is at least two and up to ten times the "miles per gallon" possible with chemical rockets. Furthermore, since the hydrogen is not being burned, there is no need to carry oxygen, which is sixteen times heavier. Balancing these and other factors, here is a way to increase payload and go far. One estimate: a Rover to Mars need be one-tenth the weight of a compara-